MW00700764

PSALMS AND HYMNS
TO THE LIVING GOD

Editorial Board
Scott Aniol, Senior Editor
Ryan J. Martin, Associate Editor
Matthew Sikes
Laramie Minga
Michael Riley

Typesetting and Layout
Dan Kreider, Hymnworks

Proofing
Caleb Aniol, Becky Aniol, Katelyn Aniol, Julie Carlyle, Joy Craft, Julie Carlyle, Judy Endean, Anna Magdalena Martin, Evangeline Martin, Jennifer Martin, Jonathan Martin, Cathy Wagner, Lindy Wagner

CONTENTS

PREFACE

The people of God sing. From the earliest days, in both Testaments, God's people sing as an expression of worship. Miriam and Moses, David and Asaph, Isaiah and Jeremiah, Jesus and Paul—they all sang their praise to God. Indeed, from cover to cover the Scriptures command such heartfelt responses of the affections of believing people: Sing to the LORD, for He has triumphed gloriously (Exod 15:21); Oh sing to the LORD a new song, for He has done marvelous things! (Psa 98:1); Sing praises to the LORD, for He has done gloriously (Isa 12:5); Let the word of Christ dwell in you richly . . . singing psalms and hymns and spiritual songs (Col 3:16). Singing praise to God is the natural response of those who adore their Maker. But singing is—thanks be to God—also the commanded duty of all God's people in all eras of His dealings with humankind. Singing is one of the ways we fulfill the chief end for which God made us: to glorify and enjoy Him.

Our singing to God is a most sacred thing. The words of the epistle of Hebrews surely apply as much to singing as they do to any other aspect of worship in Christ's assembly: Therefore let us be grateful for receiving a kingdom that cannot be shaken, and thus let us offer to God acceptable worship, with reverence and awe, for our God is a consuming fire (Heb 12:28–29). This command excludes from our worship any expression of song or prayer that is untrue, or unworthy, of the God who is over all and blessed forever. Paul took such a high and sober-minded view of preaching that when he commanded Timothy to preach the Word continually, he solemnly charged him in the presence of God and of Christ Jesus, who is to judge the living and the dead, and by His appearing and His kingdom (2 Tim 4:1). Likewise, we believe that the duty of holy singing by the saints of God in their weekly gatherings for worship is of such a nature that Paul's charge would be equally fitting for this aspect of divine worship.

We sing to God. We sing to the Father, thrice holy and forever blessed. We sing to our Savior, Jesus Christ, who shed His blood for us. We sing to the Holy Spirit whom God has given to us to dwell in our hearts, making us God's holy temple. This means that we dare not assume that the way we sing to God is a matter of "adiaphora" or indifference. We have an obligation to sing to God in a manner that is worthy of who He is and that exemplifies the expressions of reverence and joy found throughout Holy Scripture. This means that our singing must sound very different from popular music concerts and carnival tunes.

The careful inquirer can find saints in every age who felt the weight of this reverent obligation to sing to God in a manner worthy of Him. While Augustine believed church music a good way to raise the affections of worshippers, he warned in his Confessions, "When it happens to me that the music moves me more than the subject of the song, I confess myself to commit a sin deserving punishment." In his Preface to the Genevan Psalter, John Calvin said, "Touching the melody, it has seemed best that it be moderated in the manner which we have adopted, to carry gravity and majesty appropriate to the subject, and even to be suitable for singing in the church." John Wesley says in the Preface to his 1780 hymnbook that he sought to purge the hymnal of all "doggerel," "bombast," and "words without meaning." A. W. Tozer lamented the popular religious music of a generation ago: "Many of our popular songs and choruses in praise of Christ are hollow and unconvincing. Some are even shocking in their amorous endearments, and strike a reverent soul as being a kind of flattery offered to One with whom neither composer nor singer is acquainted. The whole thing is in the mood of the love ditty, the only difference being the substitution of the name of Christ for that of the earthly lover." Singing the truth (and we must sing only what is true) means we sing what is true doctrinally with expressions worthy of the eternal God who rides upon the thunderstorm.

This book of psalms and hymns is an attempt to collect some of the best congregational songs available in the English language. Herein are compiled texts and tunes from ancient Israel, North Africa, Syria, Greece, Italy, Germany, France, Spain, England, Scotland, Ireland, and America, covering a time period extending from the second century BC through the present. Translations into English come from sources originally written in Hebrew, Greek, Latin, German, French, Spanish, and more. This collection is truly catholic in its scope. In most cases, we have attempted to preserve each author's original text, particularly for hymns written in English. We have made some alterations for translations into English, especially updating archaic pronouns, as long as those changes did not sacrifice poetic integrity. In a few minor cases we have made changes for doctrinal reasons.

Our selection of hymns has been based on the central criterion of fidelity to biblical truth. What a church sings has often more impact upon the theology, devotion, and behavior of its members than the church's doctrinal confession or even what a pastor preaches. It is therefore important that a church sings only what is biblically true. This is the primary reason we have placed an emphasis on Scripture-based hymns in this collection.

With this expanded edition of Hymns to the Living God (2017), we have selected some of the best settings of English versified psalms and paired them with fitting tunes. We have attempted to include psalm settings that faithfully capture both the theological depth and poetic richness of the inspired psalms, while also prioritizing those that are intelligible and singable for modern Christians. Again, our sources for these translations range in both time and location, including historic settings from seventeenth-century English and Scottish Psalters and more recent contributions. Our LORD fulfilled the Psalms, sang the Psalms with his disciples, and through his apostles he clearly commanded us to sing psalms. We believe psalm singing is an important way to conserve biblical worship in Christian congregations.

We have assessed a hymn's truthfulness on at least three bases. First, we have endeavored to choose hymn texts that are theologically rich and sound. This is, without question, a biblical mandate for all Christian churches. When Paul told the Colossian church to sing psalms and hymns and spiritual songs, it is in the context of another command: Let the word of Christ dwell in you richly (Col 3:16). If the hymns we sing do not accurately articulate Biblical truth, we have disobeyed our LORD on a most basic level. We dare not suppress the truth or exchange the truth about God for a lie (Rom 1:18, 25). We do not want to teach any different doctrine (1 Tim 1:3). So we have aimed to include only hymns texts that are orthodox.

Second, we have chosen only those texts we believe correspond to Scripture on a poetic level. Poetry is not merely decorative—it is an essential part of the communication of truth. The poetry of hymns expresses not just the "what" of biblical doctrine, but also "how" God chose to aesthetically present His truth in Scripture. We have sought Christian poetry whose aesthetics represented both the beauty and holy affections of true evangelical belief. In this sense, we agree with John Wesley: "That which is of infinitely more moment than the spirit of poetry, is the spirit of piety." Therefore, we have worked to choose hymns whose poetry shapes the affections and imaginations of worshipers in ways similar to how Scripture does.

Third, we have chosen hymn tunes that we believe best communicate the kinds of sentiments and affections that are fitting for biblical truth. Tozer wisely cautioned, "Human emotions are curious and difficult to arouse, and there is always a danger that they may be aroused by the wrong means and for the wrong reasons." The church's battle against heresy defined Christian orthodoxy; there is a sense in which its battle against irreverent worship has attempted to define orthopathy: right affections. Orthopathy cannot be defined as precisely as the creeds and confessions have delineated Christian doctrine, but hymnbooks function similarly to those confessions. They are an attempt to represent instances of ordinate affection. We hope you find that deep love for Christ pulsing through the veins of our hymnal. As with poetry, musical form is not neutral; rather, melody, harmony, and rhythm combine to give expression to right affections.

The hymnal portion of Psalms and Hymns to the Living God is nearly identical to the previous edition. We moved some of the hymns based on Psalms to the Psalter section. We removed a few less useful hymns and added some well-loved classic hymns of the church that we had missed. We have also included some more recent examples of suitable hymnody that faithful churches have consistently enjoyed singing for many years. Since we included the best of other popular genres (like the gospel song), we concluded that a handful of more recent popular hymns with apparent longevity should also find a place in our book. Yet we still urge congregations to learn to enjoy the full spectrum of Christian hymnody, and not to allow their worship to descend into a myopic focus on what is contemporary and popular.

One may wonder if a new hymnal is necessary or relevant. Does not the use of electronic technology make a larger number of songs more accessible and inexpensive than producing a book of hymns? We are certainly aware of the benefits of technology, which is why most of the hymns in this collection and more are freely available at www.ClassicHymns.org. However, we believe there is great value in publishing and using good hymnals for several reasons.

First, when you hold a hymnal in your hands, you hold something of your Christian heritage. The physical nature of a hymnal has the effect of embodying a collection of the work of the church triumphant, and in using such a book, you identify with the entire church, and you sing her experience into yours.

Second, when you hold a good hymnal in your hands, you are holding the distilled affective responses of hundreds, if not thousands, of believers. A hymnal is a testimony of how Christians collectively have responded to the various truths of the Christian life. With hymnal in hand, one can peruse these responses and use them as a point of comparison for those of contemporary Christianity.

Third, a good hymnal remains the best devotional literature we have. Devotional literature is formative, and while it does not necessarily have to be printed, hymns in printed form provide a convenient and settled collection for personal and family devotion. Every Christian should have a hymnal (or several) at home for personal and family worship. Hymns ought to be contemplated, understood, and sung to the LORD outside church gatherings.

A printed hymnal offers saints a thoughtfully curated collection of some of the finest extra-Biblical expressions of God's truth in warm, devotional form. In this hymnbook you will find the great fundamental doctrines of Christian orthodoxy represented. As John Wesley said of his own hymnal, "This book is, in effect, a little body of experimental and practical divinity." In this volume, you will find words and music to give wings to the Christian's ordinate affections, whether they be of adoration to the Triune God, or of thanksgiving to Christ as Mediator, or of bittersweet tears at His atoning passion, or of steadfast hope in the goodness of God amidst days of trial. So, we trust that this volume contains nothing but songs which are, in the words of Calvin, "not only honest, but also holy," songs which are not just theologically strong, but devotionally warm.

Fourth, since producing printed hymnals is more time- and labor-intensive than producing electronic media, there is a greater likelihood that the editors of those hymnals have sifted through the chaff to find the very best of Christian hymnody. While any given hymnal contains some theological bias, it at least represents a kind of canon, a standard of Christian hymnody settled in the eyes of its editors.

A fifth reason for a printed hymnal is the importance of fostering a strong church culture of reading musical notation, particularly among the youth of the church. There is still great value in a congregation seeing musical notation, something not common when hymns are projected onto a screen. While musical education is not the sole goal of corporate worship, the more we understand what we are doing, the more meaningful the worship, and the better we can judge if what we are offering is appropriate. Further, since both the music and the lyrics contribute to a song's overall meaning, we believe that hymnals better serve Christ's church, for hymnals portray the two together.

Finally, singing is commanded by God. Singing is not simply a joyful expression of adoration and confession and praise to God, but it is also a most sacred duty. God wants us to sing by ourselves, sing in our families, and, most importantly, sing in fellowship with other believers. All Christians ought to sing heartily to the LORD (or "lustily and with a good courage," in the memorable words of John Wesley). This means they must learn to sing. They ought to seek to learn to sing the best they can, because God has bid them sing. Jonathan Edwards once said, "Those ... who neglect to learn to sing, live in sin, as they neglect what is necessary in order to their attending one of the ordinances of God's worship." We should not only learn to sing ourselves, but we should also teach our children to sing. This is reason enough for the publication of our hymnal, for hymnals help us keep this wonderful command of God.

If you are unfamiliar with using a hymnal and you have not participated in the singing of historic, classic hymnody, we challenge you to withhold initial judgment and comparison to "what you know." We are confident that if you will apply yourself to the study and singing of these hymns in the context of your church, family, and individual devotional life over a lengthy period of time, you will find that this collection will form your affections around proper responses to the Word of God and your worship of God will be increasingly enriched as you discipline yourself for godliness in this area.

No hymnal is perfect or adequate on its own. Yet it is our prayer that this revised and expanded collection of psalms and hymns will give honor to the living God and aid His people in singing His praises.

That Man Is Blest Who, Fearing God

1

Isaac Watts, 1707

ST. AGNES
CM

John B. Dykes, 1866

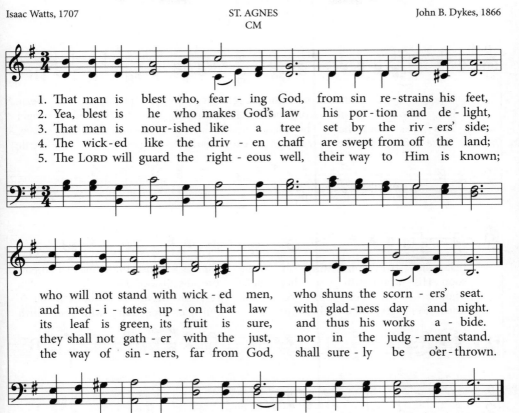

1. That man is blest who, fear - ing God, from sin re - strains his feet,
2. Yea, blest is he who makes God's law his por - tion and de - light,
3. That man is nour - ished like a tree set by the riv - ers' side;
4. The wick - ed like the driv - en chaff are swept from off the land;
5. The LORD will guard the right - eous well, their way to Him is known;

who will not stand with wick - ed men, who shuns the scorn - ers' seat.
and med - i - tates up - on that law with glad - ness day and night.
its leaf is green, its fruit is sure, and thus his works a - bide.
they shall not gath - er with the just, nor in the judg - ment stand.
the way of sin - ners, far from God, shall sure - ly be o'er - thrown.

O merciful and heavenly Father, Who has created us unto blessedness and sovereign joy, and has given unto us Thy holy Law, to be the only rule and measure, whereby we should live well and godly; make us by Thy good grace to renounce our own carnal and fleshly desires, and all evil company, shunning the way of sinners, that we may bring forth such fruits of the Spirit, that being always under Thy holy protection, we may have perfect assurance and confidence, that when Thy Son Jesus Christ shall appear to divide the goats from the sheep, we may be accounted among the number of them that are redeemed by His blood. Amen.

The Scottish Collects, 1595

2 Wherefore Do the Nations Rage?

The Psalter, 1912 · ABERYSTWYTH · 77 77 D · Joseph Parry, 1879

1. Where-fore do the na - tions rage and the peo - ple vain - ly dream
2. But the Lord will scorn them all, calm He sits en-throned on high;
3. This His word shall be made known, this Je - hov-ah's firm de - cree:
4. There-fore, kings, be wise, give ear; heark-en, judg - es of the earth;

that in tri - umph they can wage war a - gainst the King su - preme?
soon His wrath will on them fall, sore dis-pleased He will re - ply:
"Thou art My be - lov - ed Son, yea, I have be - got - ten Thee.
learn to serve the Lord with fear, min - gle trem-bling with your mirth.

Christ His Son a scoff they make, and the rul - ers plot - ting say:
"Yet ac - cord - ing to My will I have set My King to reign,
All the earth at Thy re - quest I will give Thee for Thy own;
Kiss the Son, lest o'er your way His con - sum - ing wrath should break;

"Their do - min - ion let us break, let us cast their yoke a - way."
and on Zi - on's ho - ly hill My A - noint - ed I main - tain."
then Thy might shall be con-fessed and Thy foes be o - ver - thrown."
but su - preme - ly blest are they who in Christ their ref - uge take.

O Lord, My Foes Are Multipled

3

The Book of Psalms for Worship © 2010
MARTYRDOM
CM
English Country Songs, 1893
arr. Ralph Vaughan Williams, 1906

1. O LORD, my foes are mul-ti-plied; a-gainst me man-y rise! They say of me, "He has no help, though he on God re-lies."

2. But You, my shield and glo-ry, LORD, my head You lift-ed high. And from His ho-ly hill the LORD gave an-swer to my cry.

3. I lay down, slept, and woke a-gain; the LORD sus-tains my life. I will not fear ten thou-sand strong sur-round-ing me with strife.

4. LORD, rise and save me, O my God; for You sub-due my foes! You strike the jaw of wick-ed men, and smash their teeth with blows.

5. De-liv-er-ance is of the LORD, to grant it as He will; O may the bless-ing that You give be on Your peo-ple still.

4 Give Ear, God of My Righteousness

Trinity Psalter Hymnal © 2018

BURFORD
CM

A. William's *Supplement to Psalmody*, c. 1780
harm. Edward Miller, 1790

1. Give ear, God of my right-ous-ness, my com-fort in dis - tress.
2. "The glo - ry of My name, O men, how long will you de - spise?
3. But know the LORD has set a - part the god - ly as His own;
4. Be an - gry, yet from sin de - part; con - sid - er and be still.
5. "O who can show us an - y good?" I hear so man - y say.
6. You filled my heart with great - er joy than oth - ers may have found,
7. In peace I will lie down and sleep; my heart will rest se - cure,

Dis - play Your mer - cy now to me, and an - swer my re - quest.
How long will you de - lude your-selves, still search-ing af - ter lies?"
the LORD will hear me when I call and my re - quest make known.
Pre - sent a right-eous sac - ri - fice, and wait up - on His will.
Now shine Your light up - on us, LORD; re - veal Your face, we pray.
as they re - joiced at har - vest time, when grain and wine a - bound.
for You a - lone, O gra-cious LORD, will keep me safe and sure.

Listen to My Words, O Lord

Book of Psalms for Worship © 2010

ABERYSTWYTH
77 77 D

Joseph Parry, 1879

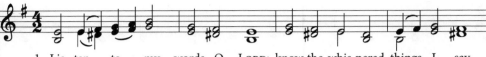

1. Lis-ten to my words, O Lord; know the whis-pered things I say.
2. For I know that You, O God, find in e-vil no de-light;
3. Yet in Your a-bound-ing love, to Your house will I draw near,
4. In their mouth there is no truth; all their heart de-struc-tion seeks,
5. Yet let all who trust in You sing for joy thro' all their days.

Heed my cry-ing out for help— God, my King, to You I pray.
e-vil can-not dwell with You, nor the proud stand in Your sight.
bow-ing to Your ho-ly place, wor-ship-ing in rev-'rent fear.
like an o-pen grave their throat, while their tongue with hon-ey speaks.
Guard all those who love Your name; let them give You joy-ful praise.

Hear me in the morn-ing, Lord, when I lift my voice on high,
You hate all who prac-tice sin. You de-stroy the one who lies;
Since, O Lord, my en-e-mies all a-round me lie in wait,
Make them bear their guilt, O God; snare them in the things they planned!
Bless-ing to the right-eous one, You, O Lord, will sure-ly bring;

set-ting forth my plea to You, look-ing out with watch-ful eye.
for the Lord a-bom-i-nates those who schemes of blood de-vise.
lead me in Your right-eous-ness; make Your way be-fore me straight.
Cast them out for all their sins: re-bels who a-gainst You stand.
with Your fa-vor like a shield, You will give him cov-er-ing.

6 Lord, Do Not Chasten Me in Wrath

Book of Psalms for Worship © 2010   OLIVE'S BROW   William B. Bradbury, 1853
LM

1. Lord, do not chas-ten me in wrath. Be gra-cious,
2. Now in Your stead-fast love, send help! Re - turn, O
3. I'm wea-ried from my moans and cries; I flood my
4. De - part from me, all e - vil men! The Lord has
5. My en - e - mies will come to shame, up - on them

Lord— I waste a - way! Lord, heal my bones and
Lord, to me and save! For none re - mem-bers
bed with tears each night. Be - cause of all my
heard my tear - ful cry, the Lord has heard my
great dis - may will fall; they are turned back the

trou - bled soul; O Lord, how long will You de - lay?
You in death, and who will praise You in the grave?
foes and grief, my eyes grow weak and lose their sight.
plead - ing voice, the Lord my prayer will not de - ny.
way they came, and shame will quick - ly seize them all.

O Lord, My God, in You I Refuge Take

Julie and Timothy Tennent © 2017   SONG 24   Orlando Gibbons, 1623
10 10 10 10

1. O Lord, my God, in You I re - fuge take; save me from those who would pur - sue my life. Like a strong li - on they would tear and shake, leav - ing no help in all my pain - ful strife.

2. If, Lord my God, I'm guilt - y in Your sight, if there is guilt and sin up - on my hand; if I've robbed friends, or e - vil done in spite, let my life be cast down at Your com - mand.

3. A - rise, O Lord, in an - ger that's re - plete; rise up a - gainst rage of my en - e - mies. A - wake, my God, rise to Your judg - ment seat; let the as - sem - bly know of Your de - crees.

4. The right-eous Lord, He judg - es all the earth. Judge me, O Lord, by my own right-eous-ness. Vin - di - cate my in - teg - ri - ty and worth, ac - cord - ing to my life of faith - ful - ness.

5. O God, You search the hearts and minds of men. You end the vi - o - lence of wick - ed ones. Bring all their sin to its ap - point - ed end, and keep se - cure - ly all Your right - eous ones.

6. My shield is God
    who saves those in the right;
The righteous judge
    who stands opposed to sin.
If we won't turn, His sword is raised to fight;
His bow is bent, and poised to strike again.

7. He has prepared His deadly weapons now;
He makes His arrows with their fiery shafts.
The wicked man conceives an evil vow,
Bringing to birth those sins and lies he crafts!

8. He digs a pit and makes it big and round;
But he falls in the pit that he has made.
His mischief turns,
    upon him does rebound;
Violence comes down on him
    and he's betrayed.

9. I will give thanks, which to the Lord is due;
His righteousness is over everything.
I'll sing praise to the Lord's name ever true;
The Lord Most High, His praises I will sing.

8A O LORD, Our Lord, in All the Earth

The Psalter, 1912   CLINTON   Joseph P. Holbrook, 1870
CM

1. O LORD, our Lord, in all the earth, how ex - cel - lent Thy name!
2. From lips of chil - dren, Thou, O LORD, hast might - y strength or - dained,
3. When I re - gard the won - drous heav'ns, Thy hand - i - work on high,
4. O what is man, in Thy re - gard to hold so large a place,
5. On man Thy wis - dom hath be - stowed a pow'r well nigh di - vine;
6. Thou hast sub - ject - ed all to him, and lord of all is he,
7. Thy might - y works and won - drous grace Thy glo - ry, LORD, pro - claim,

Thy glo - ry Thou hast spread a - far in all the star - ry frame.
that ad - ver - sar - ies should be stilled and venge - ful foes re - strained.
the moon and stars or - dained by Thee, "O what is man?" I cry.
and what the son of man, that Thou dost vis - it him in grace.
with hon - or Thou hast crowned his head with glo - ry like to Thine.
of flocks and herds, and beasts and birds, and all with - in the sea.
O LORD, our Lord, in all the earth, how ex - cel - lent Thy name.

O Lord, Our Lord, How Wondrous Great **8B**

Isaac Watts, 1719 DUNLAP'S CREEK Samuel McFarland, c. 1816
CM arr. Ryan J. Martin © 2023

1. O Lord, our Lord, how won-drous great is
2. When I be-hold Thy works on high, the
3. Lord, what is man, or all his race, who
4. That Thine e-ter - nal Son should bear to
5. Let him be crowned with maj - es - ty, who
6. Je - sus, our Lord, how won-drous great is

Thine ex-alt - ed name! The glo - ries of Thy
moon that rules the night, and stars that well a -
dwells so far be - low, that Thou shouldst vis - it
take a mor - tal form; made low - er than his
bowed His head in death; and be His hon - ors
Thine ex-alt - ed name! The glo - ries of Thy

heav'n - ly state let men and babes pro - claim.
dorn the sky, those mov - ing worlds of light;
him with grace, and love his na - ture so?
an - gels are, to save a dy - ing worm?
sound - ed high, by all things that have breath.
heav'n - ly state let the whole earth pro - claim.

9 O Lord, My Heart Will Praise You

Donald P. Owens © 2012   LANCASHIRE   Henry Smart, c. 1835
                                 76 76 D

1. O Lord, my heart will praise You; Your mar-vels I'll pro-claim.
2. You have re-buked the na-tions, the wick-ed are de-stroyed.
3. The Lord shall reign e-ter-nal; He set His judg-ment throne.
4. You win the full re-li-ance of those who know Your name.
5. O Lord, ex-tend Your mer-cy! Be-hold my wretch-ed-ness
6. The heath-en realms are sink-ing in pits their hands pre-pared.

I will be glad and praise You; Most High, I'll sing Your name.
You drained their rep-u-ta-tions; their names for-ev-er void.
He rules the world's tri-bu-nal, He makes His jus-tice known.
You nev-er fail the pi-ous, nor put their faith to shame.
from those who hate and curse me, You raise from gates of death
In nets they hid, un-think-ing, their foot is fast en-snared.

When my op-pon-ents wa-ver, Your face shall make them die.
De-struc-tion shows no pit-y; the foe is ter-ri-fied!
He gov-erns eve-ry na-tion with e-qual right-eous-ness.
Sing praise to God in Zi-on! Tell men His sav-ing deeds!
that I may praise, em-pha-tic, in Zi-on's cit-y gates.
The Lord is viewed with rap-ture for wise and just com-mands;

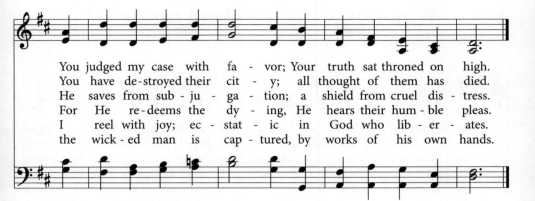

You judged my case with fa - vor; Your truth sat throned on high.
You have de-stroyed their cit - y; all thought of them has died.
He saves from sub - ju - ga - tion; a shield from cruel dis - tress.
For He re-deems the dy - ing, He hears their hum - ble pleas.
I reel with joy; ec - stat - ic in God who lib - er - ates.
the wick-ed man is cap - tured, by works of his own hands.

7. The wicked meet damnation to fester with the dead,
and likewise every nation oblivious to God.
The poor shall not continue in low oblivion;
their expectation in You, shall never be undone.

8. Arise, O LORD, with power, do not let man prevail;
judge every nation's tower, see earth's defenses fail.
O LORD, bring consternation to every citizen,
that every prideful nation may know themselves but men.

10   Why, Lord, Do You Stand Far Away?

Julie and Timothy Tennent © 2017   DUNDEE   *Scottish Psalter*, 1615
                              CM

1. Why, Lord, do You stand far a - way in times of trial and pain?
2. In pride they do not seek Him and they think, "There is no God!"
3. His mouth is full of lies and threats, and e - vil's on his tongue.
4. He crush - es help - less ones who sink and fall down hope - less - ly.
5. But You, God, see our woe and grief; You take it all to mind.
6. The Lord is King for ev - er - more, the na - tions will not stand.

The wick - ed ones in ar - ro - gance af - flict the weak for gain.
They pros - per and con - sid - er all God's judg - ments as a fraud.
He waits to am - bush in - no - cent, to mur - der old or young.
He says, "God has for - got - ten this, and He will nev - er see."
The help - less ones know You're their help; a Fa - ther or - phans find.
O Lord, You hear the cries of all af - flict - ed in the land.

Let them be caught in schemes they plan; the wick - ed boast in - deed!
They sneer at foes, and think these words: "For noth - ing can shake me.
For vic - tims he in se - cret waits, like li - ons wait for prey;
A - rise, O Lord, lift up Your hand; for - get not those in need!
O break the arm of e - vil ones; call them be - fore Your throne.
For You de - fend the fa - ther - less, and jus - tice You'll out - pour

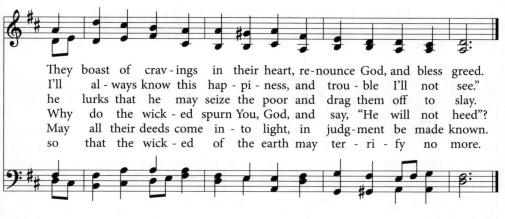

They boast of crav-ings in their heart, re-nounce God, and bless greed.
I'll al-ways know this hap-pi-ness, and trou-ble I'll not see."
he lurks that he may seize the poor and drag them off to slay.
Why do the wick-ed spurn You, God, and say, "He will not heed"?
May all their deeds come in-to light, in judg-ment be made known.
so that the wick-ed of the earth may ter-ri-fy no more.

I in the LORD Do Put My Trust 11

Scottish Psalter, 1650   SALISBURY   Thomas Ravenscroft, 1621
CM

1. I in the LORD do put my trust; how is it then that ye
2. For, lo, the wick-ed bend their bow, their shafts on string they fit,
3. If the foun-da-tions be de-stroyed, what hath the right-eous done?
4. His eyes do see, His eye-lids try men's sons. The just He proves;
5. Snares, fire and brim-stone, fur-ious storms, on sin-ners He shall rain;
6. Be-cause the LORD most right-eous doth in right-eous-ness de-light;

say to my soul, "Flee as a bird un - to your moun-tain high"?
that those who up-right are in heart they priv-i-ly may hit.
God in His ho-ly tem-ple is, in heav-en is His throne.
but His soul hates the wick-ed man, and Him that vio-lence loves.
this, as the por-tion of their cup, doth un-to them per-tain.
and with a pleas-ant coun-te-nance be - hold-eth the up-right.

12 Help, Lord, for Men of Virtue Fail

Isaac Watts, 1719   SASHA   Joan J. Pinkston © 1997
CMD

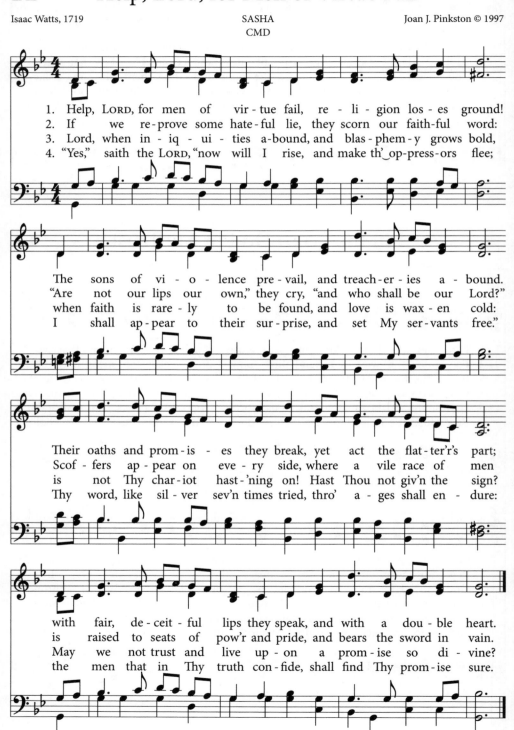

1. Help, LORD, for men of vir-tue fail, re-li-gion los-es ground!
2. If we re-prove some hate-ful lie, they scorn our faith-ful word:
3. Lord, when in-iq-ui-ties a-bound, and blas-phem-y grows bold,
4. "Yes," saith the LORD, "now will I rise, and make th' op-press-ors flee;

The sons of vi-o-lence pre-vail, and treach-er-ies a-bound.
"Are not our lips our own," they cry, "and who shall be our Lord?"
when faith is rare-ly to be found, and love is wax-en cold:
I shall ap-pear to their sur-prise, and set My ser-vants free."

Their oaths and prom-is-es they break, yet act the flat-ter'r's part;
Scof-fers ap-pear on eve-ry side, where a vile race of men
is not Thy char-iot hast-'ning on! Hast Thou not giv'n the sign?
Thy word, like sil-ver sev'n times tried, thro' a-ges shall en-dure:

with fair, de-ceit-ful lips they speak, and with a dou-ble heart.
is raised to seats of pow'r and pride, and bears the sword in vain.
May we not trust and live up-on a prom-ise so di-vine?
the men that in Thy truth con-fide, shall find Thy prom-ise sure.

How Long Will You Forget Me, Lord? **13**

The Book of Psalms for Worship © 2010   ST. BOTOLPH   Gordon Slater, 1929
CM

1. How long will You for - get me, Lord?
2. How long must I ad - vise my soul,
3. Con - sid - er me, O Lord, my God;
4. "See, I have o - ver - come him now!"
5. But Your un - fail - ing love I trust;

For - ev - er will it be? How long un - til You
and con - stant sad - ness know? How long must I be
give an - swer to my cry. Let me see light, or
my en - e - my will call; my ad - ver - sar - ies
Your sav - ing pow'r I praise. The Lord in boun - ty

show Your face which You've con - cealed from me?
sub - ject to the tri - umph of my foe?
I will sleep in death with those who die.
will re - joice when I be - gin to fall.
dealt with me; my songs to Him I raise.

14   Within His Heart the Fool Spoke

The Book of Psalms for Worship © 2010   PASSION CHORALE   Hans Leo Hassler, 1601
                                    76 76 D   adapt. Johann Sebastian Bach, 1729

1. With-in his heart the fool spoke, and said, "There is no God!"
2. To-geth-er they're cor-rupt-ed; they all have turned a-side.
3. There they will be in ter-ror, for God is with the just.

De-struc-tive in their vile deeds, not one of them does good.
Not one for good has la-bored, not e-ven one has tried.
Tho' you would shame the wretch-ed, the Lord re-mains his trust.

The Lord looks down from heav-en up-on the hu-man race:
Have all of them no knowl-edge whose deeds are so ab-horred?
From Zi-on, send sal-va-tion, and help to Is-rael bring!

has an-y-one shown wis-dom, does an-y seek God's face?
Like bread they eat My peo-ple, and call not on the Lord.
The Lord re-stores His cap-tives: let Ja-cob—Is-rael— sing!

Who, Lord, May Dwell Within Your Holy Place 15

Julie and Timothy Tennent © 2017

MORECAMBE
10 10 10 10

Frederick C. Arkinson, 1870

1. Who, Lord, may dwell with - in Your ho - ly place,
2. Who nev - er slan - der with an e - vil tongue,
3. The right - eous hon - or those who fear the Lord;
4. Who, Lord, may dwell with - in Your ho - ly place?

and live up - on Your ho - ly, right - eous hill?
nor do their neigh - bor an - y wrong - ful deed;
they keep their oath, de - spite the hurt or pain.
Who live up - on Your ho - ly, right - eous hill?

Those who walk blame - less - ly, and do what's right,
who cast no slur on eith - er friend or foe,
No wick - ed bribe they take for a re - ward.
Those who walk in this path and do these things,

and speak the truth from their heart ev - er still.
re - ject - ing those who walk by sin - ful creed.
Mon - ey is lent with - out dis - hon - est gain.
will not be moved or shak - en from Your will.

16 When in the Night I Meditate

The Psalter, 1912   ST. PETER   Alexander Robert Reinagle, 1836
CM

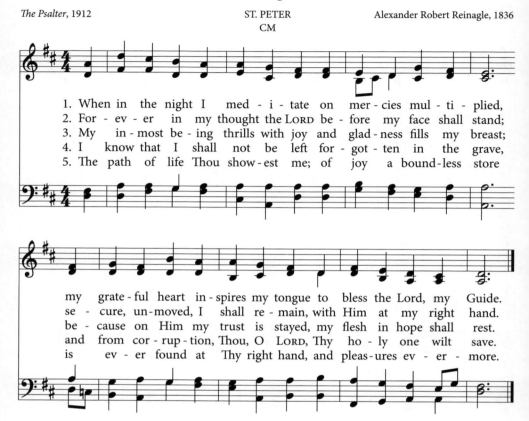

1. When in the night I med - i - tate on mer - cies mul - ti - plied,
2. For - ev - er in my thought the LORD be - fore my face shall stand;
3. My in - most be - ing thrills with joy and glad - ness fills my breast;
4. I know that I shall not be left for - got - ten in the grave,
5. The path of life Thou show - est me; of joy a bound - less store

my grate - ful heart in - spires my tongue to bless the Lord, my Guide.
se - cure, un - moved, I shall re - main, with Him at my right hand.
be - cause on Him my trust is stayed, my flesh in hope shall rest.
and from cor - rup - tion, Thou, O LORD, Thy ho - ly one wilt save.
is ev - er found at Thy right hand, and pleas - ures ev - er - more.

Hear, O My Lord, Regard My Cry

17

The Psalter, 1912

DZOVE BOSW
86 86 88 88

Armenian folk song

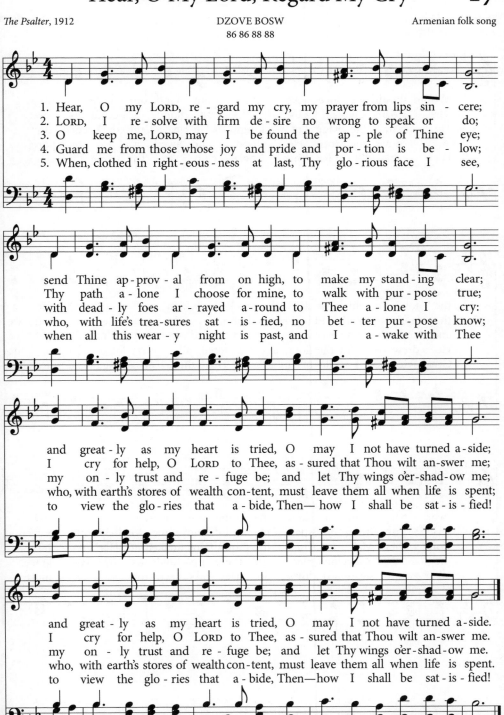

1. Hear, O my LORD, re - gard my cry, my prayer from lips sin - cere;
2. LORD, I re - solve with firm de - sire no wrong to speak or do;
3. O keep me, LORD, may I be found the ap - ple of Thine eye;
4. Guard me from those whose joy and pride and por - tion is be - low;
5. When, clothed in right - eous - ness at last, Thy glo - rious face I see,

send Thine ap - prov - al from on high, to make my stand - ing clear;
Thy path a - lone I choose for mine, to walk with pur - pose true;
with dead - ly foes ar - rayed a - round to Thee a - lone I cry:
who, with life's trea - sures sat - is - fied, no bet - ter pur - pose know;
when all this wear - y night is past, and I a - wake with Thee

and great - ly as my heart is tried, O may I not have turned a - side,
I cry for help, O LORD to Thee, as - sured that Thou wilt an - swer me;
my on - ly trust and re - fuge be; and let Thy wings o'er - shad - ow me;
who, with earth's stores of wealth con - tent, must leave them all when life is spent;
to view the glo - ries that a - bide, Then— how I shall be sat - is - fied!

and great - ly as my heart is tried, O may I not have turned a - side.
I cry for help, O LORD to Thee, as - sured that Thou wilt an - swer me.
my on - ly trust and re - fuge be; and let Thy wings o'er - shad - ow me.
who, with earth's stores of wealth con - tent, must leave them all when life is spent.
to view the glo - ries that a - bide, Then—how I shall be sat - is - fied!

18   Whom Should We Love Like Thee

st. 1–4 Henry Francis Lyte, 1834   LOVE UNKNOWN   John Ireland, 1918
st. 5 Scott Aniol © 2023   66 66 88

1. Whom should we love like Thee, our God, our Guide, our King,
   the tow'r to which we flee, the rock to which we cling? O for a
   wor - thy tongue to show the count - less mer - cies that we owe.

2. The storm up - on us fell, the floods a - round us rose;
   the depths of death and hell seemed on our souls to close; to God we
   cried in strong de - spair, He heard, and came to help our prayer.

3. He came, the King of kings, He cleaved the dark - ened sky;
   and on the temp - est's wings rode glo - rious down from high; the earth be -
   fore her Mak - er shook, the moun - tains quaked at His re - buke.

4. A - bove the storm He stood, and awed it to re - pose;
   He drew us from the flood, and scat - tered all our foes; He set us
   in a spa - cious place, and there up - holds us by His grace.

5. For this I'll praise Thee, LORD, un - to Thy name I'll sing!
   Great vic - to - ry He brings un - to His chos - en King, and shows Mes -
   si - ah stead - fast love, to Dav - id's seed for - ev - er - more.

The Heavens Declare Thy Glory, Lord   19A

Isaac Watts, 1719   UXBRIDGE   Lowell Mason, 1830
LM

1. The heav'ns de-clare Thy glo - ry, Lord; in eve - ry
2. The roll - ing sun, the chang - ing light, and nights and
3. Sun, moon, and stars con - vey Thy praise round the whole
4. Nor shall Thy spread-ing gos - pel rest till through the
5. Great Sun of right-eous - ness, a - rise, bless the dark
6. Thy no - blest won - ders here we view in souls re -

star Thy wis - dom shines; but when our eyes be -
days Thy pow'r con - fess; but the blest vol - ume
earth, and nev - er stand; so when Thy truth be -
world Thy truth has run; till Christ has all the
world with heav'n - ly light; Thy gos - pel makes the
newed and sins for - giv'n; Lord, cleanse my sins, my

hold Thy word, we read Thy name in fair - er lines.
Thou hast writ re - veals Thy jus - tice and Thy grace.
gan its race, it touched and glanced on eve - ry land.
na - tions blest that see the light, or feel the sun.
sim - ple wise; Thy laws are pure, Thy judg - ments right.
soul re - new, and make Thy word my guide to heav'n.

19B The Heavens Are Telling the Glories of God

Julie and Timothy Tennent © 2017

KREMSER
12 11 12 11

Neder-landtsch Gedenck-Clank, 1626
arr. Eduard Kremser, 1877

1. The heav - ens are tell - ing the glo - ries of
2. Their voice is not heard— there's no speech and no
3. It ris - es at one end of heav - en and
4. The law of the LORD is most per - fect and
5. The pre - cepts of God are right, giv - ing the
6. They are much more pre - cious than gold, and much

God, and the skies are de - clar - ing the work of His hands.
word, but their sound has gone forth to the earth's far - thest end.
trav - els; its cir - cuit ex - tends o - ver all of the earth.
ho - ly, re - viv - ing the soul and re - stor - ing the heart.
heart joy; com - mands of the LORD are pure, light - ing the eyes.
sweet - er than hon - ey and hon - ey - comb where hon - ey's stored;

For day af - ter day they speak, pour - ing forth know - ledge,
The sun in the heav - en comes forth like a bride - groom;
And noth - ing is hid - den from its heat or glo - ry,
The stat - utes of GOD can be trust - ed most sure - ly;
The fear of the LORD is en - dur - ing for - ev - er;
more - ov - er, by them is Your ser - vant in - struct - ed.

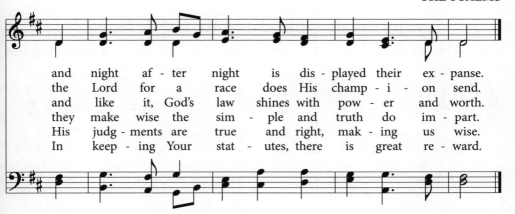

and	night	af - ter	night	is	dis - played	their	ex - panse.
the	Lord	for	a	race	does	His	champ - i - on	send.
and	like	it, God's	law	shines	with	pow - er	and	worth.
they	make	wise	the	sim - ple	and	truth	do	im - part.
His	judg - ments	are	true	and	right,	mak - ing	us	wise.
In	keep - ing	Your	stat - utes,	there	is	great	re - ward.

7. But who can discern his own faults and his errors?
   Forgive all my hidden sins—let them not rule!
   Then I will be blameless, complete, and acquitted of
   every transgression that besets the fool.

8. May all of the words of my mouth and the thoughts of
   my heart be accepted, O LORD, in Your sight;
   O LORD, my sure Rock and my precious Redeemer,
   may my life be pleasing and lived in Your light.

O God, Creator of all things; grant that we may acknowledge and magnify Thy great strength and power that declare themselves in the conserving and guiding of this world; suffer not that we wander any iota from Thy holy Law, which is pure and perfect, but that taking delight therein, we may wholly be so governed by it, that in the end we may be partakers of the heavenly salvation, through Jesus Christ. Amen.

The Scottish Collects, 1595

20 Jehovah Hear Thee in Thy Grief

The Psalter, 1912 OLIVE'S BROW William B. Bradbury, 1853
LM

1. Je - ho - vah hear thee in thy grief, our fa - thers'
2. Thy sac - ri - fice may He re - gard, and all thine
3. In thy sal - va - tion we re - joice, and in God's
4. Sal - va - tion will the LORD com - mand, and His a -
5. How vain their eve - ry con - fi - dence who on mere
6. Now we a - rise and up - right stand, while they, sub -

God de - fend thee still, send from His ho - ly place re -
of - f'rings bear in mind; thy heart's de - sire to thee ac -
name our ban - ners raise; Je - ho - vah heark - en to thy
noint - ed will de - fend; yea, with the strength of His right
hu - man help re - ly; but we rem - em - ber for de -
dued and help - less fall; Je - ho - vah, save us by Thy

lief, and strength - en thee from Zi - on's hill.
cord, ful - fill - ing all thou hast de - signed.
voice, ful - fill thy prayers through all thy days.
hand from heav'n He will an an - swer send.
fense the name of God, the LORD Most High.
hand, the King give an - swer when we call.

The King in Your Great Strength, O Lord **21**

Book of Psalms for Worship © 2010 HIGH OVER ALL
CMD Scottish air

1. The king in Your great strength, O Lord, has joy a - bun - dant - ly;
2. For You have wel - comed him with gifts, with bless - ings man - i - fold;
3. In Your sal - va - tion he is great, and glo - ri - fied is he;

in Your sal - va - tion he de - lights with joy ex - ceed - ing - ly,
and You have placed up - on his head a crown of pur - est gold.
and You up - on him have be - stowed most glo - rious maj - es - ty.

what he de - sired with - in his heart You ful - ly have sup - plied;
When he re - quest - ed life from You, You life to him did give;
For You will ev - er set on him the bless - ings of Your grace;

what he re - quest - ed with his lips, You nev - er have de - nied.
such length of days You gave to him: for - ev - er he will live.
and You will cause him to be filled with joy be - fore Your face.

22 My God, My God, O Why

The Book of Psalms for Singing © 1998

KINGSFOLD
CMD

English County Songs, 1893
harm. Ralph Vaughan Williams, 1906

1. My God, my God, O why have You for-sak-en me? O why
2. Our fa-thers put their trust in You; from You sal-va-tion came.
3. All those who look at me will laugh and cast re-proach at me.
4. You took me from my moth-er's womb to safe-ty at the breast.

are You so far from sav-ing me and from my groan-ing cry?
They begged You and You set them free; they were not put to shame.
Their mouths they o-pen wide: they wag their heads in mock-er-y.
Since birth, when I was cast on You, You've been my God, my rest.

By day and night, my God, I call; Your an-swer still de-lays.
But as for me, I am a worm and not a man at all.
"This man has trust-ed in the LORD; let God re-demp-tion send.
Be not far off, for grief is near, and none to help is found;

And yet You are the Ho-ly One who dwells in Is-rael's praise.
To men I am de-spised and base; their scorn-ings on me fall.
Now let his God de-liv-er him, for he de-lights in Him."
for bulls of Ba-shan cir-cle me, strong bulls do me sur-round.

5. Like lion jaws they open wide, and roar to tear their prey.
    My heart is wax, my bones unknit, my life is poured away.
    My strength is dried like shattered clay; my tongue sticks to my jaws;
    You bring me to the dust of death, and there You lay me down.

6. For see how dogs encircle me! On every side there stands
    a brotherhood of cruelty; they pierce my feet and hands.
    My bones are plain for me to count; men see me and they stare.
    My clothes among them they divide, and gamble for their share.

7. Now hurry, O my strength, to help! Be not far off, O Lord!
    But snatch my soul from raging dogs, and spare me from the sword.
    From lion's mouth and oxen horns O save me; hear my prayer!
    To all the church, my brethren dear, Your name I will declare.

8. Let those that fear the Lord sing praise! To Him give glory now,
    all Jacob's seed, all Israel's seed, in awe before Him bow.
    For He did not despise nor spurn the grief of one oppressed,
    not did He shun his cry for help, but heard and gave him rest.

9. When I proclaim my praise of You, then all the church will hear,
    and I will pay my vows in full where men hold Him in fear.
    The weak and poor will eat their fill and thus be satisfied.
    Those seeking Him will praise the Lord. So let your hearts abide.

10. All ends of earth will turn to Him, remembering the Lord,
    all families of the earth shall come and worship and adore.
    Dominion to the Lord belongs; He rules the nations well.
    The proud of all the earth will bow before Him where He dwells.

11. All those whose souls descend to dust will fall before His throne;
    they cannot keep themselves alive, they rest on Him alone.
    A seed shall serve Him; future sons will hear about the Lord.
    His righteousness they will declare to people yet unborn.

23A My Shepherd Will Supply My Need

Isaac Watts, 1719   RESIGNATION   William Walker's *Southern Harmony*, 1835
CMD

1. My Shep-herd will sup-ply my need, Je-ho-vah is His Name;
2. When I walk thro' the shades of death, Thy pres-ence is my stay;
3. The sure pro-vi-sions of my God at-tend me all my days;

in pas-tures fresh He makes me feed, be-side the liv-ing stream.
a word of Thy sup-port-ing breath drives all my fears a-way.
O may Thy house be mine a-bode, and all my work be praise!

He brings my wand-'ring spir-it back when I for-sake His ways;
Thy hand, in sight of all my foes, doth still my ta-ble spread,
There would I find a set-tled rest, while oth-ers go and come;

and leads me, for His mer-cy's sake, in paths of truth and grace.
my cup with bless-ings o-ver-flows, Thine oil a-noints my head.
no more a stran-ger or a guest, but like a child at home.

The King of Love My Shepherd Is   23B

Henry W. Baker, 1868   ST. COLUMBA   Irish melody
87 87   harm. *The English Hymnal*, 1906

1. The King of love my Shep - herd is, whose
2. Where streams of liv - ing wa - ter flow my
3. Per - verse and fool - ish oft I strayed, but
4. In death's dark vale I fear no ill with
5. Thou spread'st a ta - ble in my sight; Thy
6. And so through all the length of days Thy

good - ness fail - eth nev - er; I noth - ing lack if
ran - somed soul He lead - eth, and, where the ver - dant
yet in love He sought me. And on His shoul - der
Thee, dear LORD, be - side me; Thy rod and staff my
unc - tion grace be - stow - eth; and O what trans - port
good - ness fail - eth nev - er; Good Shep - herd, may I

I am His and He is mine for - ev - er.
pas - tures grow, with food ce - les - tial feed - eth.
gent - ly laid, and home re - joic - ing brought me.
com - fort still, Thy cross be - fore to guide me.
of de - light from Thy pure chal - ice flow - eth!
sing Thy praise with - in Thy house for - ev - er.

23C   The Lord Is My Shepherd

King James Version

David R. Erb © 2014

The Lord is my shep-herd; I shall not want. He

mak-eth me to lie down in green pas-tures: He lead-eth me be-side the

still wa-ters. He re-stor-eth my soul: He lead-eth me

in the paths of right-eous-ness for His name's sake.

Yea, tho' I walk thro' the val-ley of the shad-ow of death,

I will fear no e-vil: for Thou art with me; Thy rod and Thy

staff they com - fort me. Thou pre-par-est a ta-ble be-fore

me in the pre-sence of mine en - e - mies: Thou a-noint-est my head with oil;

my cup run - neth o - ver. Sure-ly good-ness and mer-cy shall

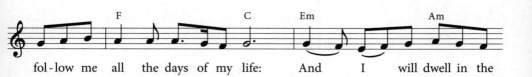

fol-low me all the days of my life: And I will dwell in the

house of the LORD for-ev - er. A - men, a - men.

E ternal and everlasting Father, Fountain of all joy; we render Thee praises and thanks that You have made known to us our Shepherd and Defender Who will deliver us from the power of our adversaries. Grant unto us, that we, casting away all fear and terror of death, may embrace and confess Thy truth, which it has pleased Thee to reveal to us by Thy Son, our Lord and sovereign Master, Christ Jesus. Amen.

The Scottish Collects, 1595

23D The Lord's My Shepherd

Scottish Psalter, 1650

CRIMOND
CM

Jessie Seymour Irvine, 1871
harm. David Grant, 1872

1. The Lord's my Shep-herd, I'll not want. He makes me down to lie
2. My soul He doth re-store a-gain; and me to walk doth make
3. Yea, though I walk thro' death's dark vale, yet will I fear no ill;
4. My ta-ble Thou hast fur-nish-éd in pres-ence of my foes;
5. Good-ness and mer-cy all my life shall sure-ly fol-low me;

in pas-tures green; He lead-eth me the qui-et wa-ters by.
with-in the paths of right-eous-ness, e'en for His own name's sake.
for Thou art with me, and Thy rod and staff me com-fort still.
my head Thou dost with oil a-noint, and my cup o-ver-flows.
and in God's house for ev-er-more my dwell-ing place shall be.

The Earth, with All That Dwell Therein   **24**

The Psalter, 1912   ST. ANNE   William Croft, 1708
                                          CM

1. The earth, with all that dwell there-in, with all its wealth un-told,
2. What man shall stand be-fore the LORD on Zi-on's ho-ly hill?
3. Lo, such are they that seek for God, and blest by Him they live;
4. Ye ev-er-last-ing doors, give way; lift up your heads, ye gates!
5. Who is this glo-rious King that comes to claim His sov-'reign right?
6. Ye ev-er-last-ing doors, give way; lift up your heads, ye gates!
7. Who is this glo-rious King that comes to claim His right-ful throne?

be-longs to GOD who found-ed it up-on the seas of old.
The clean of hand, the pure of heart, the just who do His will.
to them His per-fect right-eous-ness the GOD of grace will give.
For now, be-hold, to en-ter in the King of glo-ry waits.
It is the LORD om-nip-o-tent, all con-qu'ring in His might.
For now, be-hold, to en-ter in the King of glo-ry waits.
The LORD of hosts, He is the King of glo-ry, God a-lone.

25 As unto You I Lift My Soul

Julie and Timothy Tennent © 2017

AZMON
CM

Carl G. Gläser, 1828
arr. Lowell Mason, 1839

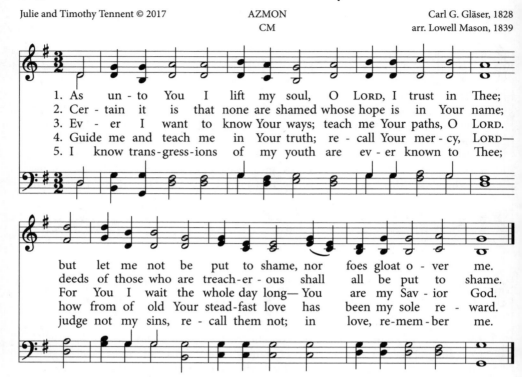

1. As un-to You I lift my soul, O LORD, I trust in Thee;
2. Cer-tain it is that none are shamed whose hope is in Your name;
3. Ev-er I want to know Your ways; teach me Your paths, O LORD.
4. Guide me and teach me in Your truth; re-call Your mer-cy, LORD—
5. I know trans-gress-ions of my youth are ev-er known to Thee;

but let me not be put to shame, nor foes gloat o-ver me.
deeds of those who are treach-er-ous shall all be put to shame.
For You I wait the whole day long— You are my Sav-ior God.
how from of old Your stead-fast love has been my sole re-ward.
judge not my sins, re-call them not; in love, re-mem-ber me.

6. Kind, good, and upright is the LORD;
He teaches those astray;
leading the humble in what's right,
and teaching them His way.

7. Moreover, all of the LORD's ways
are faithfulness and love;
neglecting not all those who keep
His cov'nant from above.

8. O LORD, for Your name's sake and grace,
have mercy all my years;
pardon my guilt, for it is great.
Who is the one who fears?

9. Quick is the LORD to know the one
who fears and longs to know.
Regarding him, He will instruct
the way that he should go.

10. Souls thus instructed by the Lord
will know prosperity;
their offspring shall receive the land,
a heritage from Thee.

11. The friendship of the LORD is giv'n
to those who fear Him still;
unto them He makes known His law,
His covenant and will.

12. My eyes are ever toward the LORD
who plucks me from the net.
Vexed though I am, Lord, turn to me;
be gracious to me yet.

13. When I'm afflicted and alone
with troubles of the heart,
bring me out of distress, O Lord;
forgiveness do impart.

14. Exulting foes all gather 'round;
they hate me with great hate.
Lord, guard my life and rescue me!
Let shame not be my fate.

15. You are my refuge and my hope;
let justice preserve me.
Zion has troubles—God redeem!
Our hope is all in Thee.

LORD, Vindicate Me

Book of Psalms for Worship © 2010   OESTREICH   Josh Bauder © 2017
CMD

1. LORD, vin-di-cate me; I have walked in my in-teg-ri-ty.
2. I will not be with worth-less men, nor with the hyp-o-crite.
3. O LORD, I love Your dwell-ing place; Your house is my de-light.
4. But I have set my-self to walk in my in-teg-ri-ty;

And I have trust-ed in the LORD; I've been un-wav-er-ing.
I hate the crowd of wick-ed men; with e-vil I'll not sit.
The place in which Your glo-ry dwells is love-ly in my sight.
O deal with me in gra-cious-ness, re-deem and set me free.

Ex-am-ine me and prove me, LORD; test heart and mind, I pray.
I'll guilt-less wash my hands and come be-fore Your al-tar, LORD.
With sin-ners do not take my soul, with men who blood have spilled.
My foot now stands on lev-el ground, a place of up-right-ness;

Since I be-hold Your stead-fast love; Your truth has led my way.
And I will shout with thank-ful voice; Your won-ders I'll re-cord.
Their hands per-form a wick-ed scheme; their hands with bribes are filled.
and where the con-gre-ga-tion meets, the LORD I there will bless.

27 The LORD, My Savior, Is My Light

Anne Steele, 1760

BOURBON
LM

Hesperian Harp, 1848
harm. Louise McAllister, 1958

1. The LORD, my Sav - ior, is my light; what ter - rors
can my soul af - fright? While GOD my strength, my
life is near, what po - tent arm shall make me fear?

2. The great - est joy my heart de - sires, and for which
all my soul as - pires, is in GOD's house to
spend my days, my life de - vot - ed to His praise.

3. This do I seek with cease - less prayer; and GOD at -
tends my ear - nest prayer; here may my soul His
beau - ties trace, and know the won - ders of His grace.

4. When trou - bles rise, my guard - ian GOD will hide me
safe in His a - bode! Firm as a rock my
hope shall stand, sus - tained by His al - might - y hand.

5. Should eve - ry earth - ly friend de - part, or should I
lose my par - ents' heart, then GOD on whom my
hopes de - pend will still be Fa - ther, Guide, and Friend.

To You I Call, O Lord, My Rock

28

Julie and Timothy Tennent © 2017   ESSLINGEN   Adam Krieger, 1667
CM

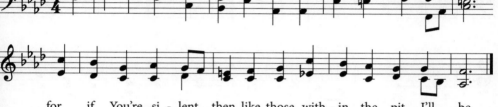

1. To You I call, O Lord my Rock; don't turn Your ear from me;
2. O, hear my cry for mer-cy, as to You for help I call;
3. Don't drag me off with wick-ed ones who e-vil do im-part,
4. Re-pay them for their e-vil work, for deeds their hands have done;
5. Since they do not re-gard the Lord, nor works His hands have done;
6. Praise to the Lord, for He has heard my cry for grace from Him.

for if You're si-lent, then like those with-in the pit I'll be.
as I lift up my hands to the Most Ho-ly Place of all.
who speak peace with their neigh-bors but hide mal-ice in their heart.
bring back on them what they de-serve, the e-vil of each one.
He'll tear them down, and nev-er build back up a sin-gle one.
The Lord's my strength and shield; I'm helped as my heart trusts in Him.

7. My heart does leap for joy, and I
   give thanks to Him in song.
   The Lord's His people's strength, and its
   salvation's fortress strong.

8. O save Your people, Lord, and bless
   Your own inheritance;
   and be their Shepherd, carry them—
   forever their defense.

29   Give to the LORD, Ye Sons of Fame

Isaac Watts, 1719   DUKE STREET   John Hatton, 1793
                            LM

1. Give to the LORD, ye sons of fame, give to the LORD re - nown and pow'r; a - scribe due hon - ors to His name, and His e - ter - nal might a - dore.

2. The LORD pro - claims His pow'r a - loud, o'er the vast o - cean and the land; His voice di - vides the wat - 'ry cloud, and light-nings blaze at His com - mand.

3. He speaks, and how - ling temp - ests rise, and lay the for - est bare a - round; the fierc - est beasts, with pit - eous cries, con - fess the ter - ror of the sound.

4. His thun - ders rend the vault - ed skies, and pal - ac - es and tem - ples shake. The moun - tains trem - ble at the noise, the val - leys roar, the des - erts quake.

5. The LORD sits sov - 'reign o'er the flood; the Thun - d'rer reigns for - ev - er King; but makes His tem - ple His a - bode, where we His aw - ful glo - ries sing.

6. We see no ter - rors in His name, but in our God a Fa - ther find. The voice that shakes all na - ture's frame, speaks com-fort to the pi - ous mind.

Sing to the LORD, Ye Saints of His

Isaac Watts, 1719

HERONGATE
LM

English folk melody
arr. Ralph Vaughan Williams, 1906

1. Sing to the LORD, ye saints of His, and tell how
2. His an - ger but a mo - ment stays; His love is
3. Firm was my health, my day was bright, and I pre -
4. But I for - got Thine arm was strong which made my
5. "Hear me, O GOD of grace," I said, "and bring me
6. My groans, and tears, and forms of woe, art turned to
7. My tongue, the glo - ry of my frame, shall ne'er be

large His good - ness is; let all your pow'rs re -
life and length of days. Tho' grief and tears the
sumed 'twould ne'er be night; fond - ly I said with -
moun - tain stand so long; soon as Thy face be -
from a - mong the dead!" Thy word re - buked the
joy and prais - es now; I throw my sack - cloth
si - lent of Thy name; Thy praise shall sound thro'

joice and bless, while you re - cord His ho - li - ness.
night em - ploy, the morn - ing star re - stores the joy.
in my heart, "Plea - sure and peace shall ne'er de - part."
gan to hide, my health was gone, my com - forts died.
pains I felt, Thy par - d'ning love re - moved my guilt.
on the ground, and ease and glad - ness gird me round.
earth and heav'n, for guilt re - moved and sins for - giv'n.

31   In Thee, O Lord, I Put My Trust

Scottish Psalter, 1650   OESTREICH   Josh Bauder © 2017
CMD

1. In Thee, O Lord, I put my trust, shamed let me nev-er be;
2. Be-cause Thou art my Rock, and Thee I for my for-tress take;
3. In - to Thine hands I do com-mit my spir't: for Thou art He,
4. I'll in Thy mer-cy glad-ly joy: for Thou my mis-er - ies
5. O Lord, up - on me mer-cy have, for trou-ble is on me:
6. I was a scorn to all my foes, and to my friends a fear;

ac - cord-ing to Thy right-eous-ness do Thou de-liv-er me.
there-fore do Thou me lead and guide, e'en for Thine own name's sake.
O Thou, Je - hov-ah, God of truth, Thou hast re-deem-ed me.
con - sid-ered hast; Thou hast my soul known in ad-ver-si - ties;
mine eye, my bel - ly, and my soul, with grief con-sum-ed be.
and spec - ial - ly re-proached of those that were my neigh-bors near:

Bow down Thine ear to me, with speed send me de-liv-er - ance:
And since Thou art my strength, there-fore pull me out of the net,
Those that do ly - ing van - i - ties re - gard, I have ab-horred:
and Thou hast not en - closed me with - in the en - e-my's hand;
Be - cause my life with grief is spent, my years with sighs and groans:
when they me saw they from me fled. E'en so I am for - got,

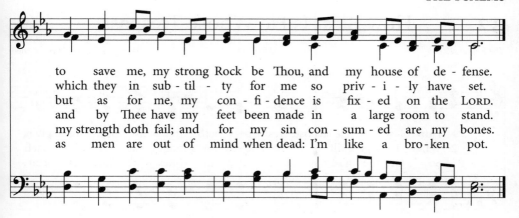

to	save me, my strong	Rock be Thou, and	my house of	de - fense.
which they	in sub - til - ty	for me so	priv - i - ly have	set.
but	as for me, my	con - fi - dence is	fix - ed on the	LORD.
and	by Thee have my	feet been made in	a large room to	stand.
my strength doth	fail; and for	my sin con - sum - ed	are my	bones.
as	men are out of	mind when dead: I'm	like a bro - ken	pot.

7. For slanders I of many heard; fear compassed me, while they
   against me did consult, and plot to take my life away.
   But as for me, O LORD, my trust upon Thee I did lay;
   and I to Thee, Thou art my God, did confidently say.

8. My times are wholly in Thine hand: do Thou deliver me
   from their hands that mine enemies and persecutors be.
   Thy countenance to shine do Thou upon Thy servant make:
   unto me give salvation, for Thy great mercies' sake.

9. Let me not be ashamed, O LORD, for on Thee called I have:
   let wicked men be shamed, let them be silent in the grave.
   To silence put the lying lips, that grievous things do say,
   and hard reports, in pride and scorn, on righteous men do lay.

10. How great's the goodness Thou for them that fear Thee keep'st in store,
    and wrought'st for them that trust in Thee the sons of men before!
    In secret of Thy presence Thou shalt hide them from man's pride:
    from strife of tongues Thou closely shalt, as in a tent, them hide.

11. All praise and thanks be to the LORD; for He hath magnified
    His wondrous love to me within a city fortified.
    For from Thine eyes cut off I am, I in my haste had said;
    my voice yet heard'st Thou, when to Thee with cries my moan I made.

12. O love the LORD, all ye His saints; because the LORD doth guard
    the faithful, and He plenteously proud doers doth reward.
    Be of good courage, and He strength unto your heart shall send,
    all ye whose hope and confidence doth on the LORD depend.

32 How Blest Is He Whose Trespass

The Psalter, 1912   AURELIA   Samuel Sebastian Wesley, 1864
76 76 D

1. How blest is He whose tres - pass hath free - ly been for - giv'n,
2. While I kept guilt - y si - lence, my strength was spent with grief;
3. So let the god - ly seek Thee in times when Thou art near;

whose sin is whol - ly cov - ered be - fore the sight of heav'n,
Thy hand was heav - y on me, my soul found no re - lief;
no whelm-ing floods shall reach them nor cause their hearts to fear.

to whom the LORD in mer - cy im - put - eth not his sin,
but when I owned my tres - pass, my sin hid not from Thee;
In Thee, O LORD, I hide me; Thou sav - est me from ill,

who hath a guile - less spir - it, whose heart is true with - in.
when I con-fessed trans - gres - sion, then Thou for - gav - est me.
and songs of Thy sal - va - tion my heart with rap - ture thrill.

Let All the Just to God, with Joy

33

Tate and Brady's *New Version*, 1696   LAND OF REST   Traditional American melody
CM   arr. Annabel M. Buchanan, 1938

1. Let all the just to God with joy their cheer - ful
2. Let harps, and psal - ter - ies, and lutes in joy - ful
3. For faith - ful is the word of God, His works with
4. By His al - might - y word at first heav'n's glo - rious
5. The swell - ing floods to - geth - er rolled He makes in
6. Let earth and all that dwell there - in be - fore Him
7. What - e'er the might - y Lord de - crees shall stand for -

voic - es raise; for well the right - eous
con - cert meet; and new made songs of
truth a - bound; He jus - tice loves, and
arch was reared, and all the beau - teous
heaps to lie; and lays, as in a
trem - bling stand; for when He spake the
ev - er sure; the set - tled pur - pose

it be - comes to sing glad songs of praise.
loud ap - plause the har - mo - ny com - plete.
all the earth is with His good - ness crowned.
hosts of light at His com - mand ap - peared.
store - house, safe, the wa - t'ry treas - ures by.
world, 'twas made, 'twas fixed at His com - mand.
of His heart to a - ges shall en - dure.

34 All of My Days I'll Bless and Praise the LORD

Julie and Timothy Tennent © 2017   MORECAMBE   Frederick C. Arkinson, 1870

10 10 10 10

1. All of my days I'll bless and praise the LORD;
2. Come, join with me to mag - ni - fy the LORD.
3. Each one who looks to Him is not a - shamed.
4. How good to taste the good - ness of the LORD;
5. Join not the li - ons hun - ger - ing for food,
6. Love you long life and want to see good days?

His praise will ev - er be with - in my mouth.
Let us to - geth - er praise His name on high!
For this poor man called; the LORD heard and saved.
blessed is the man who trusts in Him a - lone.
but trust the LORD in - stead, and have no want.
May your tongue keep from e - vil and all lies!

Boast, O my soul, ex - tol the liv - ing LORD;
Dai - ly I sought; the LORD has an - swered me,
God's right - eous an - gel con - stant - ly en - camps
In fear of God, you saints, for - ev - er dwell;
Know, all you chil - dren, lis - ten un - to me,
Now from all e - vil flee— in - stead do good;

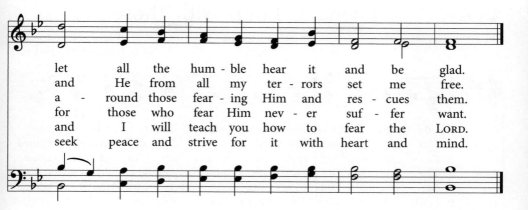

let all the hum - ble hear it and be glad.
and He from all my ter - rors set me free.
a - round those fear - ing Him and res - cues them.
for those who fear Him nev - er suf - fer want.
and I will teach you how to fear the LORD.
seek peace and strive for it with heart and mind.

7. Open are His eyes toward the righteous ones;
His ears attentive to their every cry.
Proud, evil men, the LORD God does oppose;
quickly He cuts their mem'ry from the earth.

8. Righteous cry out—the LORD will hear their cry;
saves them from all their troubles and distress.
The LORD is close to every broken heart,
and saves those who are crushed in heaviness.

9. Under His care, the righteous still have trials;
very sure is the LORD's deliverance.
Well He protects their bones and does assure
not one of them will ever broken be.

10. Expect the wicked to be slain by Him;
yes, foes of righteous ones will be condemned.
Zion's true servants, the LORD does redeem;
none who take refuge in Him stand condemned.

35A   Contend, O Lord, with Those

Julie and Timothy Tennent © 2017   TERRA BEATA   Traditional English melody
                                         SMD   adapt. Franklin L. Sheppard, 1915

1. Con - tend, O Lord, with those who do con - tend with me;
2. May those who seek my life now be dis - graced and shamed.
3. Be - cause they hid their net, dug pits with - out a cause,
4. The ruth - less tes - ti - fy; pose ques - tions filled with scorn;
5. But when I fell, they came, at - tacked with sland-'rous glee;
6. Lord, I will give You thanks; Your prais - es I will sing,

and fight a - gainst all those who fight a - gainst me con - stant - ly.
May those who plot my ru - in, Lord, be turned back and dis - mayed.
may nets they hid en - tan - gle them; in their pits let them fall.
they re - pay e - vil for my good and leave my soul for - lorn.
like wick - ed, they with mal - ice mocked, and gnashed their teeth at me.
and in the con - gre - ga - tion great, ex - alt - ing praise I'll bring.

Take up Your shield and sword; a - rise, come to my aid;
Like chaff be - fore the wind, may an - gels drive them out;
Then my soul will re - joice in the Lord's sal - va - tion,
And yet when they were ill, I fast - ed and I prayed;
How long will You look on? O Lord, come res - cue me!
Don't let my foes re - joice, who hate me with - out cause;

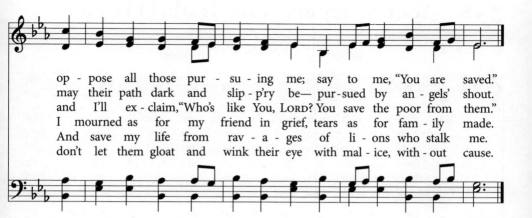

op - pose all those pur - su - ing me; say to me, "You are saved."
may their path dark and slip - p'ry be— pur - sued by an - gels' shout.
and I'll ex - claim, "Who's like You, LORD? You save the poor from them."
I mourned as for my friend in grief, tears as for fam - ily made.
And save my life from rav - a - ges of li - ons who stalk me.
don't let them gloat and wink their eye with mal - ice, with - out cause.

7. They do not speak in peace, but plan their wicked lies;
   against the peaceful, they say, "Ha! We've seen with our own eyes!"
   But You, O LORD, have seen; don't be far off, O Lord.
   Awake and rise to my defense; contend for me, my God.

8. LORD, in Your righteousness, don't let them gloat o'er me;
   don't let them think, "Aha, we won! We've conquered him wholly."
   May those who gloat o'er me and the distress I face,
   who lift themselves o'er me be clothed with shame and with disgrace.

9. May all who take delight that vindication's mine;
   may they with joy and gladness shout, and say, "The glory's Thine!"
   The LORD delights as those, His servants, are made strong;
   my tongue will sing Your righteousness and praises all day long.

35B Your Mercy and Your Truth, O Lord

Trinity Psalter Hymnal © 2018   WINCHESTER OLD   Este's *Psalmes*, 1592
CM

1. Your mer - cy and Your truth, O Lord, tran - scends the loft - y sky;
2. Lord, You pre - serve both man and beast. Your love is great and kind!
3. With great a - bun - dance in Your house, they feast till sat - is - fied;
4. The foun - tain of e - ter - nal life with You a - lone a - bides.
5. From those who know You, may Your love and mer - cy ne'er de - part.
6. Let not the proud raise foot or hand to drive me from Your side.

Your right - eous - ness, like moun - tains high; Your judg - ments, deep and wide.
Be - neath the shad - ow of Your wings man - kind may ref - uge find.
from streams of Your un - fail - ing joy their thirst shall be sup - plied.
With - in the bright - ness of Your light we see the light of life.
And may Your right - eous - ness pro - tect and bless the up - right heart.
The e - vil - do - ers are thrown down and nev - er shall a - rise.

My Heart Proclaims the One Who Sins   36

st. 1–2 by Michael E. Owens © 2016   CONTRITION   Christian Knorr von Rosenroth, 1684
st. 3–7 by Isaac Watts, 1719   LM

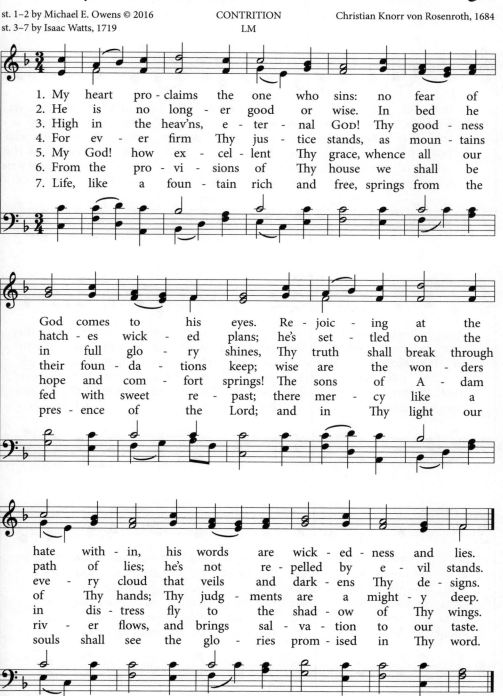

1. My heart pro-claims the one who sins: no fear of
2. He is no long-er good or wise. In bed he
3. High in the heav'ns, e-ter-nal GOD! Thy good-ness
4. For ev-er firm Thy jus-tice stands, as moun-tains
5. My God! how ex-cel-lent Thy grace, whence all our
6. From the pro-vi-sions of Thy house we shall be
7. Life, like a foun-tain rich and free, springs from the

God comes to his eyes. Re-joic-ing at the
hatch-es wick-ed plans; he's set-tled on the
in full glo-ry shines, Thy truth shall break through
their foun-da-tions keep; wise are the won-ders
hope and com-fort springs! The sons of A-dam
fed with sweet re-past; there mer-cy like a
pres-ence of the Lord; and in Thy light our

hate with-in, his words are wick-ed-ness and lies.
path of lies; he's not re-pelled by e-vil stands.
eve-ry cloud that veils and dark-ens Thy de-signs.
of Thy hands; Thy judg-ments are a might-y deep.
in dis-tress fly to the shad-ow of Thy wings.
riv-er flows, and brings sal-va-tion to our taste.
souls shall see the glo-ries prom-ised in Thy word.

37

Fret Not Thyself

The Psalter, 1912

ARIEL
88 6 88 6

Wolfgang Amadeus Mozart, 1756–1791
arr. Lowell Mason, 1836

1. Fret not thy - self, nor en - vious be, when wick - ed work-ers thou shalt see, who pros-per in their way; for like the grass they per - ish soon, and, like the herb cut down at noon, they

2. Trust in the LORD and still do well, with - in the land se - cure - ly dwell, feed on His faith - ful - ness; de - light thee al - so in the LORD, and to thy heart He will ac - cord the

3. Yea, to the LORD thy way is known; con - fide in Him who on the throne a - bides in pow'r di - vine; thy right-eous-ness He shall dis - play; re - splen-dent as the light of day, it

4. Rest in the Lord and be thou still, with pa - tience wait His ho - ly will, en - dur - ing to the end. Fret not tho' sin - ners' wont to dwell, and it shall not be found; but saints shall all the gains in - crease; for - sake thy wrath, from an - ger cease; it

5. Yea, thou shalt soon con - sid - er well the place where they were tage will give which ev - er shall a - bide; in e - vil times no land pos - sess, and find de - light and hap - pi - ness where

6. He knows the days the per - fect live, to them a her - i - shame they know, and in the days of fam - ine's woe they

with - er in a day, they with - er in a day.
good it would pos - sess, the good it would pos - sess.
shall un - cloud - ed shine, it shall un - cloud - ed shine.
will to e - vil tend, it will to e - vil tend.
fruits of peace a - bound, where fruits of peace a - bound.
shall be sat - is - fied, they shall be sat - is - fied.

7. The good man's steps are led aright,
    his way is pleasing in GOD's sight,
    established it shall stand;
    he shall not perish though he fall,
    the mighty LORD who rules o'er all
    upholds him with His hand, upholds him with His hand.

8. Though I am old who young have been,
    no saint have I forsaken seen,
    nor yet his home in need;
    he ever lends in gracious ways,
    his life true charity displays,
    his sons are blest indeed, his sons are blest indeed.

9. Depart from evil, do thou well,
    and evermore securely dwell;
    Jehovah loves the right.
    His faithfulness His saints have proved,
    forever they shall stand unmoved,
    but sinners God will smite, but sinners God will smite.

10. The righteous, through His favoring hand,
    shall yet inherit all the land,
    and dwell therein for aye;
    he talks of wisdom and of right,
    in God's pure law is his delight,
    his steps go not astray, his steps go not astray.

38 Amidst Thy Wrath, Remember Love

Isaac Watts, 1719   CRIMOND   Jessie Seymour Irvine, 1871
                                    CM   harm. David Grant, 1872

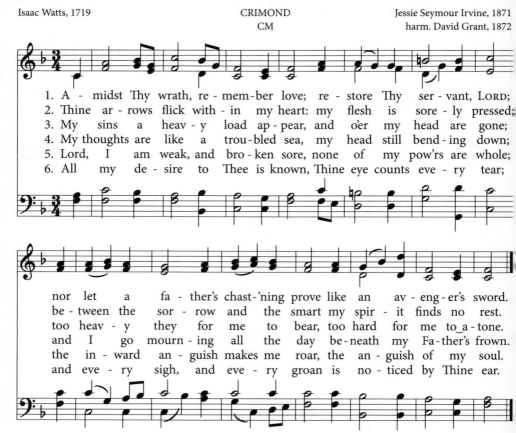

1. A - midst Thy wrath, re - mem-ber love; re - store Thy ser - vant, LORD;
2. Thine ar - rows flick with - in my heart: my flesh is sore - ly pressed;
3. My sins a heav - y load ap - pear, and o'er my head are gone;
4. My thoughts are like a trou-bled sea, my head still bend - ing down;
5. Lord, I am weak, and bro - ken sore, none of my pow'rs are whole;
6. All my de - sire to Thee is known, Thine eye counts eve - ry tear;

nor let a fa - ther's chast-'ning prove like an av - eng - er's sword.
be - tween the sor - row and the smart my spir - it finds no rest.
too heav - y they for me to bear, too hard for me to_a - tone.
and I go mourn - ing all the day be-neath my Fa-ther's frown.
the in - ward an - guish makes me roar, the an - guish of my soul.
and eve - ry sigh, and eve - ry groan is no - ticed by Thine ear.

7. Thou art my God, my only hope;
   my God will hear me cry,
   my God will bear my spirit up,
   when Satan bids me die.

8. My foot is ever apt to slide,
   my foes rejoice to see't;
   they raise their pleasure and their pride
   when they supplant my feet.

9. But I'll confess my guilt to Thee,
   and grieve for all my sin;
   I'll mourn how weak my graces be,
   and beg support divine.

10. My God, forgive my follies past,
    and be for ever nigh;
    O Lord of my salvation, haste,
    before Thy servant die!

Thus I Resolved Before the Lord

39A

Isaac Watts, 1719   SALISBURY   Thomas Ravenscroft, 1621

CM

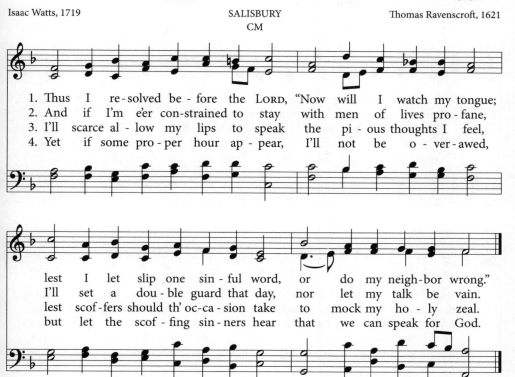

1. Thus I re-solved be - fore the LORD, "Now will I watch my tongue;
2. And if I'm e'er con-strained to stay with men of lives pro - fane,
3. I'll scarce al - low my lips to speak the pi - ous thoughts I feel,
4. Yet if some pro - per hour ap - pear, I'll not be o - ver-awed,

lest I let slip one sin - ful word, or do my neigh-bor wrong."
I'll set a dou - ble guard that day, nor let my talk be vain.
lest scof-fers should th' oc-ca - sion take to mock my ho - ly zeal.
but let the scof - fing sin - ners hear that we can speak for God.

A lmighty God, from whom proceeds all our sufficiency; assist us by Thy Holy Spirit, that we neither think nor do anything that is against Thy holy will; hear our prayers, defeat our enemies, and comfort us by the self-same Spirit, that we may continually feel Thy fatherly favor and good will, which You show to Thy own children; through Jesus Christ Thy Son. Amen.

The Scottish Collects, 1595

39B Behold, O Lord, My Days Are Made

Charles. H. Spurgeon, 1866   ARLINGTON   Thomas Arne, 1762
CM

1. Be - hold, O Lord, my days are made a hand-breadth at the most;
2. Then teach me, Lord, to know mine end, and know that I am frail;
3. What is there here that I should wait, my hope's in Thee a - lone;
4. A stran - ger in this land am I, a so - journ - er with Thee;
5. Though I'm ex - iled from glo - ry's land, yet not from glo - ry's King;

ere yet 'tis noon my flow'r must fade, and I give up the ghost.
to heav'n let all my thoughts as-cend, and let not earth pre - vail.
when wilt Thou o - pen glo - ry's gate and call me to Thy throne?
oh be not si - lent at my cry, but show Thy - self to me.
my God is ev - er near at hand, and there-fore I will sing.

I Waited for the Lord

40

The Book of Psalms for Singing © 1973

FINGAL
66 66 D

Irish traditional melody
arr. Leopold L. Dix, 1933

1. I wait - ed for the Lord; He stooped and heard my cry.
2. Man - y will see with awe, and so will trust the Lord.
3. You want no of - fer - ing, nor ask a sac - ri - fice,
4. "To do Your will, O God, to me is my de - light.

He brought me from the pit, out of the dun - geon mire,
Blessed he who trusts in God, and turns not to false men.
but You have giv - en me a read - y ear to hear.
Your law is part of me, deep in my heart, O God."

my feet set on a rock, my foot - steps made se - cure.
You have worked won - ders, Lord; no one com - pares to You!
You ask no of - f'rings burnt nor sac - ri - fice for sin.
In con - gre - ga - tion great I told Your right - eous - ness.

My lips He gave a song, a song to praise our God.
Should I de - clare each one, their num - ber is too great.
So I say, "Here I come, as in the scroll in - scribed."
You know, Lord, I spoke out; I did not close my lips.

41 How Blest the Man

The Psalter, 1912   HIGH OVER ALL   Scottish air
                                           CMD

1. How blest the man who thought-ful - ly the poor and weak be - friends;
2. Up - on the bed of suf - fer - ing Je - ho - vah will sus - tain,
3. My en - e - mies a - gainst me speak, and they my life have scorned
4. My foes, to - geth - er whis - per - ing, their e - vil plans de - vise;
5. Do Thou, Je - ho - vah, show me grace, and raise me up a - gain,
6. And as for me, in up - right-ness Thou dost up - hold me well,

de - liv - 'rance in the e - vil day to him Je - ho - vah sends.
and in his sick-ness GOD will soothe the wea - ri - ness and pain.
they wish my name to pass a - way, un - hon - ored and un-mourned
dis - ease, they say, cleaves fast to him, laid low, he shall not rise.
that I with jus - tice may re - quite these base and wick - ed men.
and set - test me be - fore Thy face for ev - er - more to dwell.

The LORD will keep him, guard his life, on earth he shall be blest;
O LORD, to Thee my cry as - cends, let me Thy mer - cy see;
My foe, de - ceit - ful, vis - its me, by seem-ing kind-ness led,
Yea, he who was my chos - en friend, in whom I put my trust,
By this I know as - sur - ed - ly that I am loved by Thee,
Blest be Je - ho - vah, Is - rael's God for ev - er - more. A - men.

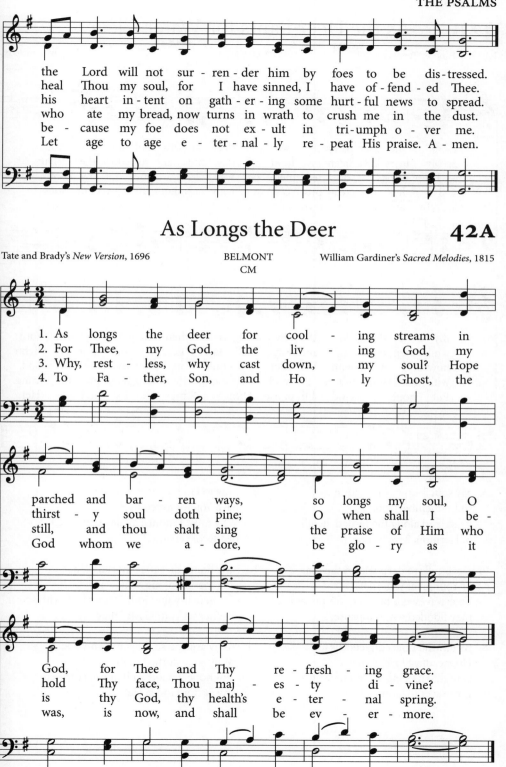

the Lord will not sur - ren - der him by foes to be dis - tressed.
heal Thou my soul, for I have sinned, I have of - fend - ed Thee.
his heart in - tent on gath - er - ing some hurt - ful news to spread.
who ate my bread, now turns in wrath to crush me in the dust.
be - cause my foe does not ex - ult in tri - umph o - ver me.
Let age to age e - ter - nal - ly re - peat His praise. A - men.

As Longs the Deer

42A

Tate and Brady's *New Version*, 1696

BELMONT
CM

William Gardiner's *Sacred Melodies*, 1815

1. As longs the deer for cool - ing streams in
2. For Thee, my God, the liv - ing God, my
3. Why, rest - less, why cast down, my soul? Hope
4. To Fa - ther, Son, and Ho - ly Ghost, the

parched and bar - ren ways, so longs my soul, O
thirst - y soul doth pine; O when shall I be -
still, and thou shalt sing the praise of Him who
God whom we a - dore, be glo - ry as it

God, for Thee and Thy re - fresh - ing grace.
hold Thy face, Thou maj - es - ty di - vine?
is thy God, thy health's e - ter - nal spring.
was, is now, and shall be ev - er - more.

42B   As the Deer Pants for Water Clear

Julie and Timothy Tennent © 2017   ST. COLUMBA   Irish melody

CM   harm. *The English Hymnal*, 1906

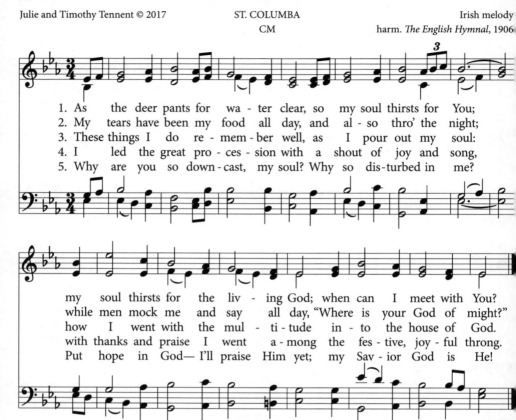

1. As the deer pants for wa - ter clear, so my soul thirsts for You;
2. My tears have been my food all day, and al - so thro' the night;
3. These things I do re - mem - ber well, as I pour out my soul:
4. I led the great pro - ces - sion with a shout of joy and song,
5. Why are you so down - cast, my soul? Why so dis - turbed in me?

my soul thirsts for the liv - ing God; when can I meet with You?
while men mock me and say all day, "Where is your God of might?"
how I went with the mul - ti - tude in - to the house of God.
with thanks and praise I went a - mong the fes - tive, joy - ful throng.
Put hope in God— I'll praise Him yet; my Sav - ior God is He!

6. My soul is downcast within me,
   so I remember You,
   from land along the Jordan, heights
   of Hermon, Mizar, too.

7. Deep calls to deep within the roar
   of Your great waterfalls;
   Your waves and breakers swept o'er me;
   they flooded without pause.

8. By day the LORD directs His love,
   His steadfast love to me;
   at night His song is with me still—
   my prayer to God will be.

9. I say to God my Rock, "O why
   have You forgotten me?
   Why must I mourn all day oppressed
   by the vile enemy?"

10. My bones do suffer mortal pain;
    my foes taunt me all day.
    "Where is your God?" they mock with scorn,
    "Where is your God?" they say.

11. Why are you so downcast, my soul?
    Why so disturbed in me?
    Put hope in God—I'll praise Him yet;
    my Savior God is He!

O Vindicate and Plead My Cause

43

Julie and Timothy Tennent © 2017

ST. COLUMBA
CM

Irish melody
harm. *The English Hymnal*, 1906

1. O vin - di - cate and plead my cause, O
2. You are my strong - hold and my God; why
3. Send forth Your light and send Your truth, and
4. Then I'll go to God's al - tar— God, my
5. Why are you so down - cast, my soul? Why

God, a - gainst my foe; come res - cue me
do you re - ject me? Why must I mourn
let them guide me well. O let them bring
joy and my de - light; and I will praise
so dis - turbed in me? Put hope in God—

from wick - ed men, a na - tion vile and low.
all day op - pressed by the vile en - e - my?
me to Your mount, the place where You do dwell.
You with the harp, O God, my God and light.
I'll praise Him yet; my Sav - ior God is He!

44   O God, We Have Heard of Your Works

Book of Psalms for Worship © 2010   FOUNDATION   *A Compilation of Genuine Church Music,* 1832
                                             11 11 11 11

1. O God, we have heard of Your works with our ears; our fathers have told what You did in past years: how nations were crushed and cast out by Your hand; You planted our fathers to live in the land.

2. Success did not come from the sword in their hand, nor by their arm's strength did they conquer the land. But rather it was by the light of Your face, Your right hand and arm, for You showed them Your grace.

3. O God, You alone are forever my King; command, and for Jacob deliverance bring. Through You we will surely push back all our foes, through Your name we'll trample on those who oppose.

4. No trust will I place in my sword or my bow. We'll boast in the God who saved us from the foe; all those hating us You have brought down in shame, and so we will ever give thanks to Your name.

My Heart Doth Overflow

The Psalter, 1912   FESTAL SONG   William Henry Walter, 1894
SM

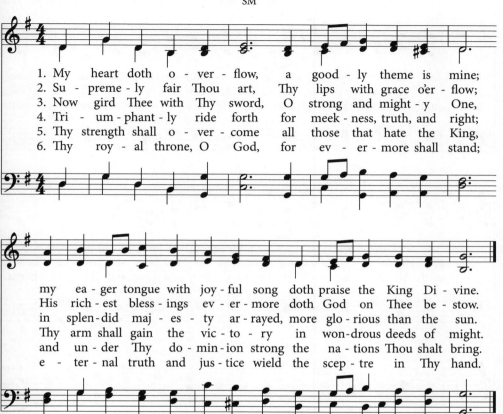

1. My heart doth o - ver - flow, a good - ly theme is mine;
2. Su - preme - ly fair Thou art, Thy lips with grace o'er - flow;
3. Now gird Thee with Thy sword, O strong and might - y One,
4. Tri - um - phant - ly ride forth for meek - ness, truth, and right;
5. Thy strength shall o - ver - come all those that hate the King,
6. Thy roy - al throne, O God, for ev - er - more shall stand;

my ea - ger tongue with joy - ful song doth praise the King Di - vine.
His rich - est bless - ings ev - er - more doth God on Thee be - stow.
in splen - did maj - es - ty ar - rayed, more glo - rious than the sun.
Thy arm shall gain the vic - to - ry in won - drous deeds of might.
and un - der Thy do - min - ion strong the na - tions Thou shalt bring.
e - ter - nal truth and jus - tice wield the scep - tre in Thy hand.

7. Since Thou art sinless found,
the Lord, Thy God confessed,
anointeth Thee with perfect joy,
Thou art supremely blest.

8. Thy garments breathe of myrrh
and spices sweet and rare;
glad strains of heavenly music ring
throughout Thy palace fair.

9. Amid Thy glorious train
kings' daughters waiting stand,
and fairest jewels bedeck Thy bride,
the queen at Thy right hand.

10. O King of royal race,
Thy sons of heavenly birth
Thou wilt endow with kingly gifts
As princes in the earth.

11. Thy name shall be proclaimed
Through all succeeding days,
And all the nations of the earth
Shall give Thee endless praise.

46A God Is Our Refuge and Our Strength

The Book of Psalms for Worship   EIN' FESTE BURG   Martin Luther, 1529
                                          88 88 66 66 8   harm. Charles Winfred Douglas, 1916

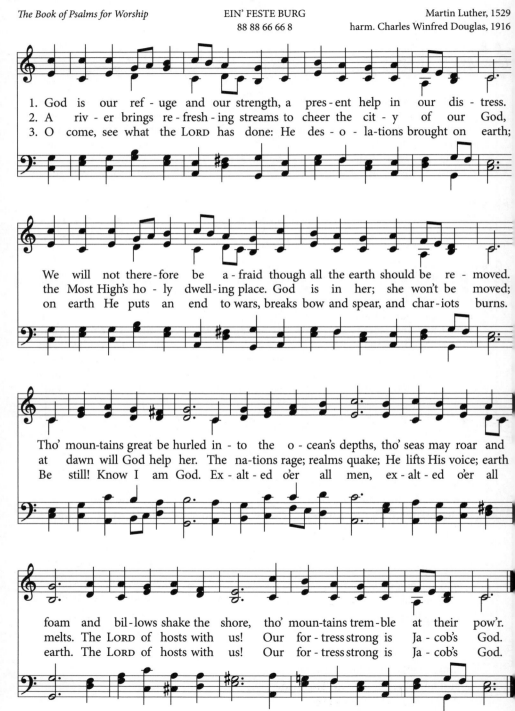

1. God is our ref - uge and our strength, a pres - ent help in our dis - tress.
2. A riv - er brings re - fresh - ing streams to cheer the cit - y of our God,
3. O come, see what the LORD has done: He des - o - la - tions brought on earth;

We will not there - fore be a - fraid though all the earth should be re - moved.
the Most High's ho - ly dwell - ing place. God is in her; she won't be moved;
on earth He puts an end to wars, breaks bow and spear, and char - iots burns.

Tho' moun - tains great be hurled in - to the o - cean's depths, tho' seas may roar and
at dawn will God help her. The na - tions rage; realms quake; He lifts His voice; earth
Be still! Know I am God. Ex - alt - ed o'er all men, ex - alt - ed o'er all

foam and bil - lows shake the shore, tho' moun - tains trem - ble at their pow'r.
melts. The LORD of hosts with us! Our for - tress strong is Ja - cob's God.
earth. The LORD of hosts with us! Our for - tress strong is Ja - cob's God.

God Is the Refuge of His Saints

46B

Isaac Watts, 1719

TRURO
LM

Thomas Williams's
Psalmodia Evangelica, 1789

1. God is the ref - uge of His saints, when storms of sharp dis -
2. Let moun-tains from their seats be hurled down to the deep, and
3. Loud may the trou - bled o - cean roar; in sac - red peace our
4. There is a stream whose gen - tle flow sup - plies the cit - y
5. That sa - cred stream, Thy ho - ly Word, our grief al - lays, our
6. Zi - on en - joys her Mon-arch's love, se - cure a - gainst a

tress in - vade; ere we can of - fer our com -
bur - ied there, con - vul - sions shake the sol - id
souls a - bide, while eve - ry na - tion, eve - ry
of our God; life, love, and joy, still glid - ing
fear con - trols; sweet peace Thy prom - is - es af -
threat - 'ning hour; nor can her firm foun - da - tions

plaints, be - hold Him pres - ent with His aid.
world, our faith shall nev - er yield to fear.
shore, trem - bles, and dreads the swell - ing tide.
through, and wat - 'ring our di - vine a - bode.
ford, and give new strength to faint - ing souls.
move, built on His truth, and armed with pow'r.

47 All Peoples, Clap Your Hands for Joy

The Book of Psalms for Singing © 1973

FOREST GREEN
CMD

English folk tune
harm. Ralph Vaughan Williams, 1906

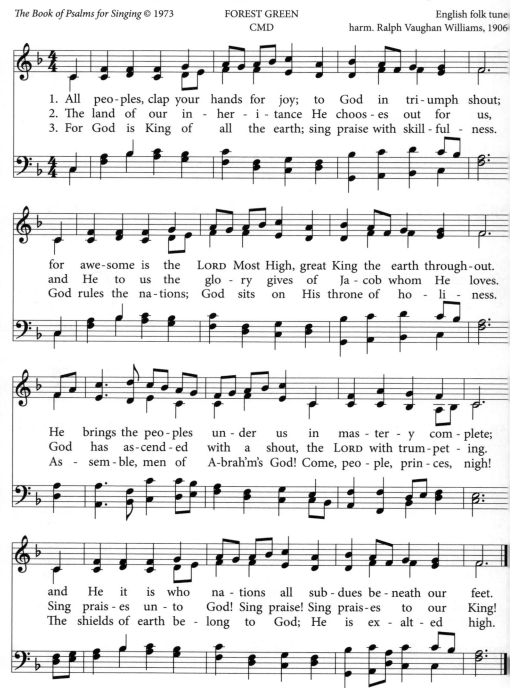

1. All peo-ples, clap your hands for joy; to God in tri-umph shout;
2. The land of our in-her-i-tance He choos-es out for us,
3. For God is King of all the earth; sing praise with skill-ful-ness.

for awe-some is the LORD Most High, great King the earth through-out.
and He to us the glo-ry gives of Ja-cob whom He loves.
God rules the na-tions; God sits on His throne of ho-li-ness.

He brings the peo-ples un-der us in mas-ter-y com-plete;
God has as-cend-ed with a shout, the LORD with trum-pet-ing.
As-sem-ble, men of A-brah'm's God! Come, peo-ple, prin-ces, nigh!

and He it is who na-tions all sub-dues be-neath our feet.
Sing prais-es un-to God! Sing praise! Sing prais-es to our King!
The shields of earth be-long to God; He is ex-alt-ed high.

The LORD Is Great, with Worthy Praise   **48**

The Psalter, 1912

JERUSALEM
LMD

Hubert Parry, 1916
adapt. Ryan J. Martin © 2016

1. The LORD is great; with worth-y praise pro-claim His pow'r, His name con-
2. With-in her dwell - ings for de - fense our God has made His pres - ence

fess, with - in the cit - y of our God, up - on His mount of ho - li -
known, and hos-tile kings, in sud-den fear, have fled as ships by temp - ests

ness. Mount Zi - on, glo - ri - ous and fair, gives joy to peo - ple in all
blown. With our own eyes we have be - held what oft our fa - thers told be -

lands; the cit - y of the might-y King in maj-es - ty se-cure-ly stands.
fore, that God who in His Zi - on dwells will keep her safe-ly ev - er - more.

49 Hear This, All Ye People, Hear

The Psalter, 1912 CANTERBURY Orlando Gibbons, 1623
77 77

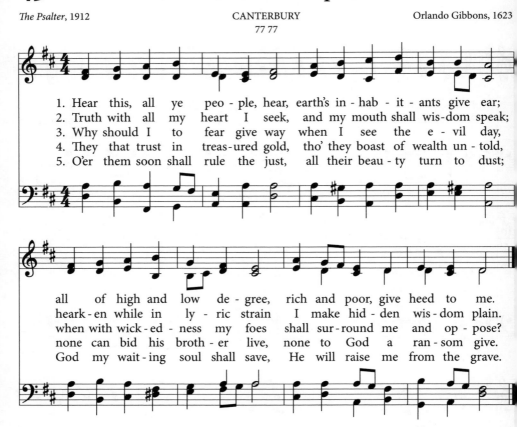

1. Hear this, all ye peo-ple, hear, earth's in-hab-it-ants give ear;
2. Truth with all my heart I seek, and my mouth shall wis-dom speak;
3. Why should I to fear give way when I see the e-vil day,
4. They that trust in treas-ured gold, tho' they boast of wealth un-told,
5. O'er them soon shall rule the just, all their beau-ty turn to dust,

all of high and low de-gree, rich and poor, give heed to me.
heark-en while in ly-ric strain I make hid-den wis-dom plain.
when with wick-ed-ness my foes shall sur-round me and op-pose?
none can bid his broth-er live, none to God a ran-som give.
God my wait-ing soul shall save, He will raise me from the grave.

H eavenly Father, conserver of all mankind; suffer us never to be so entangled with earthly and corruptible things, wherein the children of this world put their whole trust and assurance, but that we acknowledge at all times our own weakness and miseries, lest through our unthankfulness we be justly spoiled of the fruit of that hope which Thy children have in Thee only; through Jesus Christ. Amen.

The Scottish Collects, 1595

The Mighty God, the LORD

50A

Scottish Psalter, 1650   DIADEMATA   George Elvey, 1868
SMD

1. The might-y God, the LORD, hath spo-ken un-to all;
2. Our God shall sure-ly come, and si-lence shall not keep;
3. "To-geth-er let My saints un-to Me gath-ered be,

from ris-ing to the set-ting sun, He un-to earth doth call.
be-fore Him fire shall waste, and storms tem-pes-tuous round Him sweep.
those that by sac-ri-fice have made a cov-e-nant with Me."

From Zi-on, His own hill, where per-fect beau-ty dwells,
He to the heav'ns a-bove shall then send forth His call,
Then shall the heav'ns de-clare His right-eous-ness a-broad;

Je-ho-vah hath His glo-ry shown, in bright-ness that ex-cels.
and like-wise to the earth, that He may judge His peo-ple all:
be-cause the Lord Him-self is Judge, yea, none is Judge, but God.

50B   Hear, O My People, I Will Speak

The Psalter, 1912   MELITA   John B. Dykes, 1861
                              88 88 88

1. Hear, O My peo - ple, I will speak, a - gainst thee I will
2. I will re - ceive from out thy fold no of - f'ring for My
3. Be - hold, if I should hun - gry grow, I would not tell My
4. Bring thou to God the gift of thanks, and pay thy vows to
5. Thus speaks the Lord to wick - ed men: My stat - utes why do
6. Ye have con - sent - ed with the thief, ye have par - tak - en

tes - ti - fy; give ear to Me, O Is - ra - el, for
ho - ly shrine; the cat - tle on a thou - sand hills and
need to thee, for all the world it - self is Mine. And
God Most High; call ye up - on My ho - ly Name in
ye de - clare? Why take My cov - enant in your mouth, since
with the vile, your mouths to e - vil words ye give, your

God, thy cov - 'nant God, am I; I do not spurn thy
all the for - est beasts are Mine; each moun - tain bird to
all its wealth be - longs to Me; why should I aught of
days when sore dis - tress is nigh; de - liv - 'rance I will
ye for wis - dom do not care? For ye My ho - ly
tongues pro - claim de - ceit and guile, ye glo - ry in your

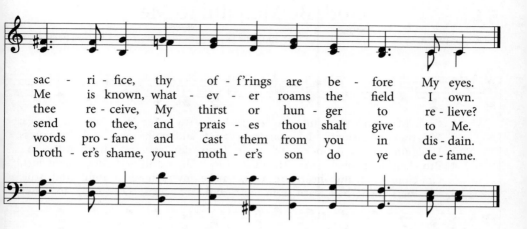

sac	-	ri	-	fice,	thy	of - f'rings	are	be	- fore	My	eyes.
Me		is	known,	what	- ev	- er	roams	the	field	I	own.
thee		re	- ceive,	My	thirst	or	hun	- ger	to	re	- lieve?
send		to	thee,	and	prais	- es	thou	shalt	give	to	Me.
words		pro	- fane	and	cast	them	from	you	in	dis	- dain.
broth	-	er's	shame,	your	moth	- er's	son	do	ye	de	- fame.

7. Thus have ye done; I silence kept,
   and this has been your secret thought,
   that I was wholly as yourselves,
   to take your evil deeds as nought;
   I will reprove you and array
   your deeds before your eyes this day.

8. Consider this, who God forget,
   lest I destroy with none to free;
   who offers sacrifice of thanks,
   he glorifies and honors Me;
   to him who orders well his way
   salvation free I will display.

51 God, Be Merciful to Me

The Psalter, 1912   REDHEAD   Richard Redhead, 1853
77 77 77

1. God, be mer - ci - ful to me, on Thy grace I rest my plea;
2. My trans-gres-sions I con-fess, grief and guilt my soul op - press;
3. I am e - vil, born in sin; Thou de - sir - est truth with - in.
4. Bro - ken, hum-bled to the dust by Thy wrath and judg-ment just,
5. Gra-cious God, my heart re - new, make my spir - it right and true;
6. Sin - ners then shall learn from me and re - turn, O God, to Thee;

plen-teous in com - pas - sion Thou, blot out my trans - gres-sions now;
I have sinned a - gainst Thy grace and pro-voked Thee to Thy face;
Thou a - lone my Sav - ior art, teach Thy wis - dom to my heart;
let my con - trite heart re - joice and in glad - ness hear Thy voice;
cast me not a - way from Thee, let Thy Spir - it dwell in me;
Sav - ior, all my guilt re - move, and my tongue shall sing Thy love;

wash me, make me pure with - in, cleanse, O cleanse me from my sin.
I con - fess Thy judg-ment just, speech-less, I Thy mer - cy trust.
make me pure, Thy grace be - stow, wash me whit - er than the snow.
from my sins O hide Thy face, blot them out in bound-less grace.
Thy sal - va - tion's joy im - part, stead - fast make my will - ing heart.
touch my si - lent lips, O Lord, and my mouth shall praise ac - cord.

7. Not the formal sacrifice
hath acceptance in Thy eyes;
broken hearts are in Thy sight
more than sacrificial rite;
contrite spirit, pleading cries,
Thou, O God, wilt not despise.

8. Prosper Zion in Thy grace
and her broken walls replace;
then our righteous sacrifice
shall delight Thy holy eyes;
free-will offerings, gladly made,
on Thy altar shall be laid.

Why Boast in Evil, Mighty Man?

52

Donald P. Owens © 2012

AUS TIEFER NOT
87 87 88 7

Martin Luther, 1524

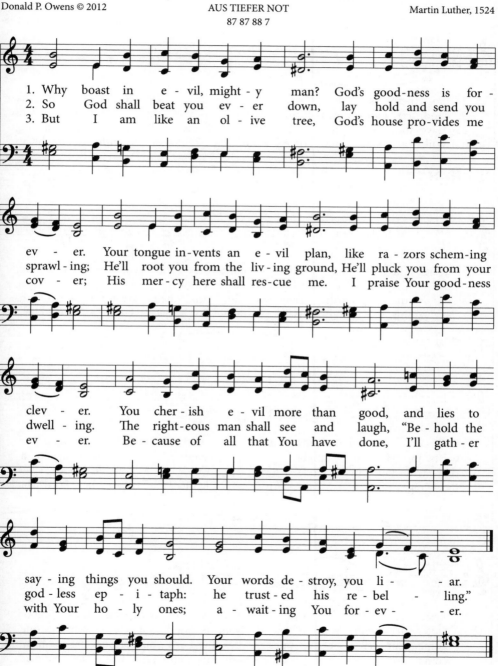

1. Why boast in e - vil, might - y man? God's good-ness is for -
ev - er. Your tongue in-vents an e - vil plan, like ra - zors schem-ing
clev - er. You cher - ish e - vil more than good, and lies to
say - ing things you should. Your words de - stroy, you li - - ar.

2. So God shall beat you ev - er down, lay hold and send you
sprawl - ing; He'll root you from the liv - ing ground, He'll pluck you from your
dwell - ing. The right-eous man shall see and laugh, "Be - hold the
god - less ep - i - taph: he trust - ed his re - bel - ling."

3. But I am like an ol - ive tree, God's house pro-vides me
cov - er; His mer - cy here shall res-cue me. I praise Your good-ness
ev - er. Be - cause of all that You have done, I'll gath - er
with Your ho - ly ones; a - wait - ing You for - ev - - er.

53   "Lo, There Is No God in Heaven"

David P. Regier © 2020

PICARDY
87 87 87

French melody, 17th cent
arr. Ralph Vaughan Williams, 1906

Unison

1. "Lo, there is no God in heav - en," says with - in his heart the fool. Full of dark - ness and cor - rup - tion, full of e - vil deeds, and cruel; full of wick - ed - ness, in - jus - tice, there is no one who does good.

2. God, He looks down from His heav - en; is there one who un - der - stands? Is there ev - en one who seeks Him, trusts in His al - might - y hand? All have turned a - side to - geth - er. None is good, not e - ven one.

3. Have the e - vil ones no know - ledge, nev - er call - ing on the Lord? They will fall in their great ter - ror; they will fall by God's own word. You shall ov - er - come your en - e - mies, for the Lord your prayers has heard.

4. Will a Sav - ior come from Zi - on, with a might - y sav - ing hand? Will He come to save His peo - ple, liv - ing in a cap - tive land? When the Lord shall come to free us, all His peo - ple will be glad.

O Save Me by Thy Name

54

The Psalter, 1912

SOUTHWELL
SM

William Daman
The Psalmes of David, 1579

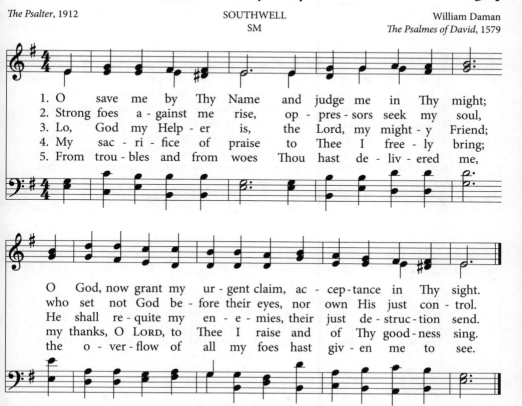

1. O save me by Thy Name and judge me in Thy might;
2. Strong foes a - gainst me rise, op - pres - sors seek my soul,
3. Lo, God my Help - er is, the Lord, my might - y Friend;
4. My sac - ri - fice of praise to Thee I free - ly bring;
5. From trou - bles and from woes Thou hast de - liv - ered me,

O God, now grant my ur - gent claim, ac - cep-tance in Thy sight.
who set not God be - fore their eyes, nor own His just con - trol.
He shall re - quite my en - e - mies, their just de - struc-tion send.
my thanks, O LORD, to Thee I raise and of Thy good-ness sing.
the o - ver-flow of all my foes hast giv - en me to see.

Almighty God and Heavenly Father, who never leaves destitute those that put their trust and confidence in Thee; take our cause into Your own hand against all our enemies, who are so terrible and so fearful, that they may understand that it is against Thee that they make their scheme; declare also Thy mercies toward them that help us, to the intent that we continually have occasion to offer up to Thee sacrifices of thanksgiving, through Jesus Christ, our Lord and Savior. Amen.

The Scottish Collects, 1595

55 Jehovah, to My Prayer Give Ear

The Psalter, 1912

BURFORD
CM

A. Williams's *Supplement to Psalmody*, c. 1780
harm. Edward Miller, 1790

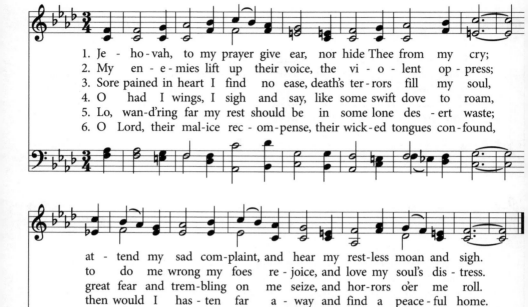

1. Je - ho - vah, to my prayer give ear, nor hide Thee from my cry;
2. My en - e - mies lift up their voice, the vi - o - lent op - press;
3. Sore pained in heart I find no ease, death's ter - rors fill my soul,
4. O had I wings, I sigh and say, like some swift dove to roam,
5. Lo, wan-d'ring far my rest should be in some lone des - ert waste;
6. O Lord, their mal-ice rec - om-pense, their wick-ed tongues con-found,

at - tend my sad com-plaint, and hear my rest-less moan and sigh.
to do me wrong my foes re - joice, and love my soul's dis - tress.
great fear and trem-bling on me seize, and hor-rors o'er me roll.
then would I has - ten far a - way and find a peace-ful home.
I from the storm - y wind would flee, and to a shel - ter haste.
for in the cit - y vi - o - lence and bit - ter strife a - bound.

7. They walk her walls both night and day,
   within all vices meet;
   opppression, fraud, and crime hold sway,
   nor leave the crowded street.

8. No foreign foe provokes alarm,
   but enemies within;
   may God destroy their power to harm
   and recompense their sin.

9. On God alone my soul relies,
   and He will soon relieve;
   the LORD will hear my plaintive cries
   at morning, noon, and eve.

10. He has redeemed my soul in peace,
    from conflict set me free;
    my many foes are made to cease,
    and strive no more with me.

11. The living God in righteousness
    will recompense with shame
    the men who, hardened by success,
    forget to fear His Name.

12. All treach'rous friends who overreach
    and break their plighted troth,
    who hide their hate with honeyed speech,
    with such the Lord is wroth.

13. Upon the LORD thy burden cast,
    to Him bring all thy care;
    He will sustain and hold thee fast,
    and give thee strength to bear.

14. God will not let His saints be moved;
    protected, they shall see
    their foes cut off and sin reproved;
    O God, I trust in Thee.

Be Gracious unto Me, O God

56

The Book of Psalms for Singing © 1973

MORNING SONG
86 86 86

Traditional American melody
Kentucky Harmony, 1813

1. Be gra-cious un-to me, O God, for man would me de-vour;
2. Be-cause a-gainst me man-y are who fight from plac-es high,
3. All day they wrest my words; their thoughts toward me are filled with hate.
4. In an-ger, God, cast peo-ples down in what they un-der-took.
5. My foes shall, when I cry, turn back, I know; God is for me.
6. My vows to Thee I'll pay, O God; thank-of-f'rings bring to Thee.

he fights a-gainst me all day long, op-press-ing by his pow'r.
the day I fear I'll trust in Thee. God's Word I'll mag-ni-fy.
They meet, they lurk, they mark my steps, as for my soul they wait.
Thou num-ber-est my wan-der-ings, not one dost o-ver-look.
In God— I'll praise His Word; the LORD— His Word my praise shall be!
For Thou from death didst save my soul, my feet from fall-ing free;

My foes are watch-ing day and night that they may me de-vour.
In God I trust. What can flesh do? Of that no fear have I.
Is there in-deed es-cape for them with wick-ed-ness so great?
With-in Thy bot-tle put my tears; are they not in Thy book?
In God I've trust-ed, I'll not fear what man can do to me.
I'll walk be-fore God in the light of those that liv-ing be.

57 Show Your Mercies, Lord, to Me

David P. Regier © 2018

HENDON
77 77 7

Henri A. Malan, 1837
harm. Lowell Mason, 1841

1. Show Your mer - cies, Lord to me; for my soul to
2. I call out to God Most High, who works all His
3. In the li - on's den I wait; they would slay me
4. Let Your glo - ry and Your worth, Lord, be praised in
5. Let my heart, un - wav - 'ring, sing prais - es to my
6. With the na - tions, these the cries: "Lord, Your mer - cies

You would flee. From my trou - ble, re - fuge bring in the shad - ow
wise de - sign. He, from heav - en, hear - ing me, saves me from the
in their hate. They de - stroy me with their words, with their tongues as
all the earth. Dead - ly snares all meant for me have con - sumed my
God, my King! Rise, my glo - ry, harp and lyre, wake the dawn with
fill the skies!" Let this joy - ful song be raised from the earth in

of Your wing, in the shad - ow of Your wing.
en - e - my, saves me from the en - e - my.
sharp - ened swords, with their tongues as sharp - ened swords.
en - e - my, have con - sumed my en - e - my.
morn - ing fire, wake the dawn with morn - ing fire!
grate - ful praise, from the earth in grate - ful praise!

Do You Speak Right Decrees, You Mute? **58**

Donald P. Owens © 2012   AUS TIEFER NOT   Martin Luther, 1524
87 87 88 7

1. Do you speak right de - crees, you mute? Or rule for truth, you
2. The wick - ed stray from birth; they lie! They drip with ser - pent's
3. God, break the teeth with which they bite, as li - on fangs, LORD,
4. Like snails which melt a - way in slime, like still - born bab - ies,
5. The right - eous shall re - joice to see the wick - ed slain in

judg - es? Oh no, your crook - ed hearts pol - lute; your hands hold se - cret
poi - son. As co - bras turn a haught - y eye and deaf, they will not
break them! Let them be wa - ter, quick in flight; let run - ning pan - ic
blind them. In - ter their bones in graves of grime; the sun shall nev - er
venge - ance. His feet shall wade their blood with glee, when God ful - fills their

grudg - es! In - stead of weigh - ing truth and right, your ver - dicts
list - en. The charm - er plays his lur - ing flute; they will not
take them! And when he bends his bow to aim, let all his
find them. Be - fore your pots can feel the fire, He'll take them
sen - tence. So men will all be forced to say, "There is a

foul the earth with blight. For you were born cor - rupt - ed.
sway to his pur - suit. De - spite his skill - ful charm - ing.
ar - rows fall in shame, like kind - ling cut to splin - ters.
in His burn - ing ire; His liv - ing, an - gry whirl - wind.
God who wins the day, and He re - wards the right - eous!"

59 Deliver Me from Those, O God

Julie and Timothy Tennent © 2017   SASHA   Joan J. Pinkston © 1998
CMD

1. De - liv - er me from those, O God, who are my en - e - mies;
2. See how they lie in wait for me! They fierce - ly do com - bine
3. A - wake, Al - might - y Lord of hosts, O God of Is - ra - el,
4. See what they spew out from their mouths, for in their lips are swords;
5. My lov - ing God goes be - fore me; He'll let me gloat and see
6. And for the sins which their mouths speak, the words their lips let fly,

pro - tect me from all those who do rise up to threat - en me.
a - gainst me, Lord; they do con - spire for no of - fense of mine.
a - rouse Your - self to pun - ish all the trai - tors who re - bel.
and they say, "Who can pos - si - bly hear an - y of our words?"
the end of all those wick - ed ones, who mock and slan - der me.
let them be caught in their own pride, be - cause they curse and lie.

De - liv - er me from wick - ed ones and e - vil - do - ing men,
I've done no wrong, yet they in wait are read - y to seize me.
At eve - ning they go to and fro; they make great noise and sound;
But You, O Lord, will laugh at them, You at the na - tions scoff;
But do not kill them, Lord, our shield, or peo - ple will for - get;
Con - sume them in Your wrath, O Lord; con - sume till they're no more.

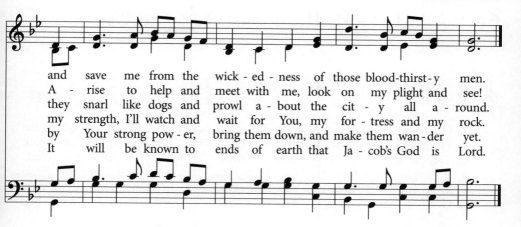

and	save	me from the	wick - ed - ness	of those blood-thirst-y	men.
A -	rise	to help and	meet with me, look on	my plight and	see!
they	snarl	like dogs and	prowl a - bout the	cit - y all a -	round.
my	strength,	I'll watch and	wait for You, my	for - tress and my	rock.
by	Your	strong pow - er,	bring them down, and	make them wan - der	yet.
It	will	be known to	ends of earth that	Ja - cob's God is	Lord.

7. At evening they go to and fro; they make great noise and sound;
   they snarl like dogs, and prowl about the city all around.
   They wander, searching for their food and if not satisfied,
   they howl like dogs and prowl around, and don't care how they've lied.

8. But I'll sing of Your strength, O God; at dawn Your love I'll praise;
   for You're my fortress, refuge, and my tow'r in troubled days.
   O God, You are my strength, and I sing praises unto You;
   O God, You are my fortress, full of lovingkindness true.

60   O God, Thou Hast Rejected Us

The Psalter, 1912   CLINTON   Joseph P. Holbrook, 1870
                          CM

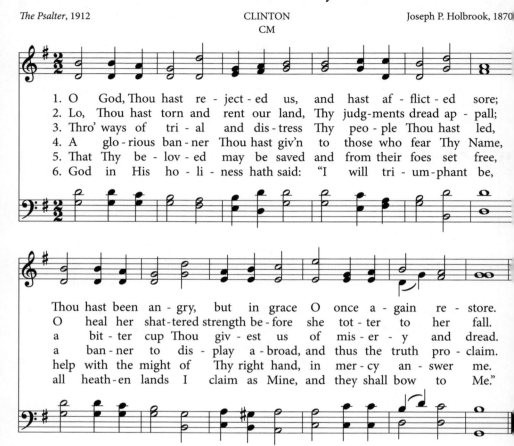

1. O God, Thou hast re-ject-ed us, and hast af-flict-ed sore;
Thou hast been an-gry, but in grace O once a-gain re-store.

2. Lo, Thou hast torn and rent our land, Thy judg-ments dread ap-pall;
O heal her shat-tered strength be-fore she tot-ter to her fall.

3. Thro' ways of tri-al and dis-tress Thy peo-ple Thou hast led,
a bit-ter cup Thou giv-est us of mis-er-y and dread.

4. A glo-rious ban-ner Thou hast giv'n to those who fear Thy Name,
a ban-ner to dis-play a-broad, and thus the truth pro-claim.

5. That Thy be-lov-ed may be saved and from their foes set free,
help with the might of Thy right hand, in mer-cy an-swer me.

6. God in His ho-li-ness hath said: "I will tri-um-phant be,
all heath-en lands I claim as Mine, and they shall bow to Me."

7. Now, therefore, who will lead us on
sin's strongholds to possess?
No longer cast us off, O God,
but give our hosts success.

8. Give Thou Thy help against the foe,
for help of man is vain;
through God we shall do valiantly,
the victory He shall gain.

O God, Regard My Humble Plea

The Psalter, 1912

INNSBRUCK
88 6 88 6

Heinrich Isaak, 1488
harm. Johann Sebastian Bach, 18th cent.

1. O God, re-gard my hum-ble plea; I can-not be so
2. In Thee my soul hath shel-ter found, and Thou hast been from
3. For Thou, O God, my vows hast heard, on me the her-i-
4. Be-fore Thy face shall I a-bide; O God, Thy truth and

far from Thee but Thou wilt hear my cry; when I by
foes a-round the tow'r to which I flee. With-in Thy
tage con-ferred of those that fear Thy Name; a blest a-
grace pro-vide to guard me in the way; so I will

trou-ble am dis-tressed, then lead me on the
house will I a-bide; my ref-uge sure, what-
noint-ing Thou dost give, and Thou wilt make me
make Thy prais-es known, and, hum-bly bend-ing

Rock to rest that high - - er is than I.
e'er be-tide, Thy shel - t'ring wings shall be.
ev - er live Thy prais - - es to pro-claim.
at Thy throne, my vows will dai-ly pay.

62 On God, on God My Soul Relies

Henry F. Lyte, 1793–1867

ROCKINGHAM
LM

A. Williams's *Supplement to Psalmody*, 1780
harm. Edward Miller, 1790

1. On God, on God my soul re - lies; from Him shall
2. My foes may rage, my foes may hate: on God, thy
3. Let all that live on God de - pend, and find Him
4. How poor are all in heav'n and earth, when matched with

my sal - va - tion rise; He is my Rock, my
God, my spir - it, wait! He is thy Rock, thy
an Al - might - y Friend; pour out their hearts be -
Him who gave them birth! Friends, yea, and foes a -

strong De - fense; what pow'r shall ev - er hurl me thence!
sure De - fense; be - lieve, and none shall hurl thee thence!
fore His throne, and rest for all on Him a - lone.
like must own, that might and love are God's a - lone.

O Lord, My God, Most Earnestly

The Psalter, 1912 RESIGNATION *Southern Harmony, 1835*
CMD

1. O Lord, my God, most ear-nest-ly my heart would seek Thy face,
2. The lov-ing-kind-ness of my God is more than life to me;
3. My Sav-ior, 'neath Thy shel-t'ring wings my soul de-lights to dwell;

with-in Thy ho-ly house once more to see Thy glo-rious grace.
so I will bless Thee while I live and lift my prayer to Thee.
still clos-er to Thy side I press, for near Thee all is well.

A-part from Thee I long and thirst, and naught can sat-is-fy;
In Thee my soul is sat-is-fied, my dark-ness turns to light,
My soul shall con-quer eve-ry foe, up-hold-en by Thy hand;

I wan-der in a des-ert land where all the streams are dry.
and joy-ful med-i-ta-tions fill the watch-es of the night.
Thy peo-ple shall re-joice in God, Thy saints in glo-ry stand.

63B   O God, You Are My God Alone

Trinity Psalter Hymnal © 2018   PUER NOBIS   Trier manuscript, 15th cent.
LM   adapt. Michael Praetorius, 1609

1. O God, You are my God a-lone, with ea-ger-
2. I've seen You in Your ho-ly place; Your pow'r and
3. I bless You, Lord, through-out my life, and raise my
4. I lie a-wake up-on my bed, re-mem-b'ring
5. For You have been my help, O God; I sing for
6. But those who seek to kill my soul to depths of
7. The king will then re-joice in God, and all who

ness I seek Your face. My soul and bod-y
glo-ry held my gaze. Your love is bet-ter
hands to You in prayer. My joy-ful lips will
You be-fore it's light; on You, my God, I
joy be-neath Your wings. Your right hand holds and
earth shall fall a-way; a sword of pow'r will
swear by Him ex-ult; but God will stop the

thirst for You, as in a dry and wea-ry place.
far than life, and thus my lips will sing Your praise.
sing Your praise; my soul is fed with rich-est fare.
med-i-tate, through-out the watch-es of the night.
strength-ens me; to You my soul for safe-ty clings.
bring them down, and they shall be the jack-al's prey.
li-ar's mouths, the ones who ut-ter what is false.

God, Hear My Voice

The Book of Psalms for Worship © 2010   BELMONT   William Gardiner's *Sacred Melodies*, 1815
CM

1. God, hear my voice, hear my com - plaint, pre -
2. Whose tongues are sharp - ened like a sword, with
3. They set their minds on e - vil plans, lay
4. But God will shoot a shaft at them and
5. Then all will fear and tell God's work, con -

serve me from my foe. Hide me from plots of
bit - ter speech like spears; to shoot in se - cret
traps, and say, "Who sees?"; with skill de - vise in -
wound them all with dread. So their own tongue will
sid - er - ing His deeds. The just find ref - uge

e - vil men, when sin - ners vio - lent grow.
at the just, they shock and do not fear.
jus - tic - es, man's heart and thoughts are deep.
trip them up; those see - ing shake their head.
in the LORD, in Him boast joy - ful - ly.

65 Praise Awaits You, God, in Zion

David P. Regier © 2020

ABBOT'S LEIGH
87 87 D

Cyril Taylor, 1941

1. Praise a-waits You, God, in Zi-on, and to You we
2. You de-clare to us Your good-ness by Your awe-some,
3. Lord, You give the earth its wa-ter, and You bless the

bring our vow. You have heard our prayer from heav-en;
might-y works. You have brought sal-va-tion's prom-ise
soil with rain, as You fill the hills with boun-ty,

let all flesh be-fore You bow. How trans-gres-sions rise a-
to the ends of all the earth. By Your pow'r, You set the
and the val-leys with their grain. With Your good-ness o-ver-

gainst me! You a-tone for all our sin. To Your right-eous,
moun-tains, si-lence o-ceans' roar-ing waves. All the na-tions
flow-ing, all the mead-ows lift their voice, as You crown her

ho - ly dwell - ing, You have drawn the bless - ed in.
bow in won - der; east and west shall give You praise.
days with boun - ty, let the earth sing and re - joice!

Come, All Ye People, Bless Our God 66A

he Psalter, 1912

ADOWA
88 6 88 6

Charles H. Gabriel, 1912

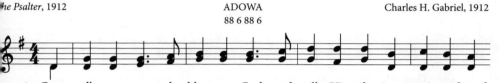

1. Come, all ye peo - ple, bless our God and tell His glo - rious praise a - broad,
2. We come with of - f'rings to His house, and here we pay the sol - emn vows
3. Come, hear, all ye who fear the Lord, while I with grate - ful heart re - cord
4. The Lord, who turns a - way the plea of those who love in - iq - ui - ty,

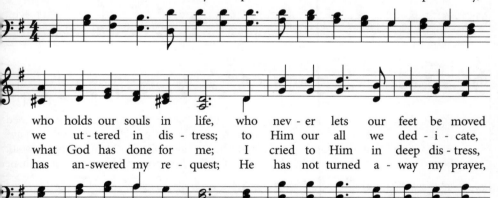

who holds our souls in life, who nev - er lets our feet be moved
we ut - tered in dis - tress; to Him our all we ded - i - cate,
what God has done for me; I cried to Him in deep dis - tress,
has an - swered my re - quest; He has not turned a - way my prayer,

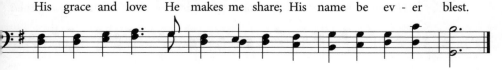

and, tho' our faith He oft has proved, up - holds us in the strife.
to Him we whol - ly con - se - crate the lives His mer - cies bless.
and now His won - drous grace I bless, for He has set me free.
His grace and love He makes me share; His name be ev - er blest.

66B O All You Peoples, Bless Our God

Book of Psalms for Worship © 2010
FOREST GREEN
CMD
English folk tune
harm. Ralph Vaughan Williams, 190

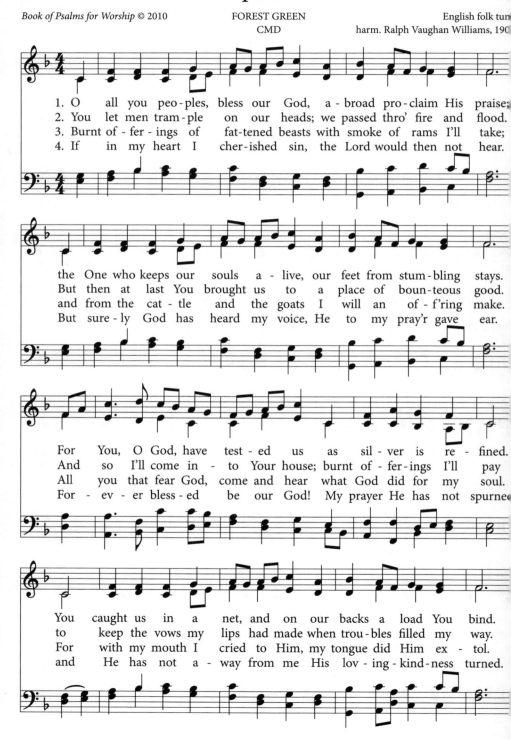

1. O all you peo-ples, bless our God, a-broad pro-claim His praise;
2. You let men tram-ple on our heads; we passed thro' fire and flood.
3. Burnt of-fer-ings of fat-tened beasts with smoke of rams I'll take;
4. If in my heart I cher-ished sin, the Lord would then not hear.

the One who keeps our souls a-live, our feet from stum-bling stays.
But then at last You brought us to a place of boun-teous good.
and from the cat-tle and the goats I will an of-f'ring make.
But sure-ly God has heard my voice, He to my pray'r gave ear.

For You, O God, have test-ed us as sil-ver is re-fined.
And so I'll come in-to Your house; burnt of-fer-ings I'll pay
All you that fear God, come and hear what God did for my soul.
For-ev-er bless-ed be our God! My prayer He has not spurned

You caught us in a net, and on our backs a load You bind.
to keep the vows my lips had made when trou-bles filled my way.
For with my mouth I cried to Him, my tongue did Him ex-tol.
and He has not a-way from me His lov-ing-kind-ness turned.

O God, to Show Us Mercy

67A

The Psalter, 1912, alt.

MEIRIONYDD
76 76 D

Welsh melody
ascribed to William Lloyd, 1840

1. O God, to us show mer - cy and bless us in Your grace;
2. O God, let all men praise You, let all the na - tions sing;
3. O God, let peo - ple praise You, let all the na - tions sing,

cause now to shine up - on us the bright-ness of Your face;
in eve - ry land let prais - es and songs of glad - ness ring;
for earth in rich a - bun - dance to us her fruit shall bring.

that so Your way most ho - ly on earth may soon be known,
for You shall judge the peo - ple in truth and right-eous - ness,
The Lord our God shall bless us, our God shall bless - ing send,

and un - to eve - ry peo - ple Your sav - ing grace be shown.
and through the earth the na - tions shall Your just rule con - fess.
and all the earth shall fear Him to its re - mot - est end.

67B   O God, Show Mercy to Us

Book of Psalms for Worship © 2010   THAXTED   Gustav Holst, 1918
13 13 13 13 13 13   arr. Brian E. Coombs, 2003

1. O God, show mer-cy to us, and bless us with Your grace;
2. For You will judge the peo-ples with per-fect eq-ui-ty;

and cause to shine up-on us the bright-ness of Your face;
to na-tions of the whole earth a gov-er-nor You'll be.

so that the whole world o-ver may tru-ly know Your way,
O God, let peo-ples praise You; let all the peo-ples praise.

and so that Your sal-va-tion all na-tions see dis-played.
The earth has brought its boun-ty through-out its har-vest days

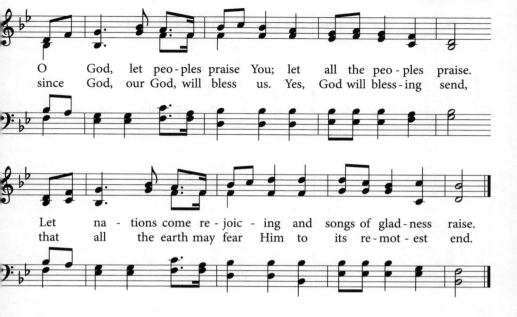

O   God,   let peo - ples praise You;   let   all the peo - ples   praise.
since   God,   our God, will bless   us.   Yes,   God will bless - ing   send,

Let   na - tions come re - joic - ing and songs of glad - ness raise.
that   all   the earth may fear   Him to   its re - mot - est end.

O Lord, Thou Hast Ascended 68A

he Psalter, 1912

LANCASHIRE (9)
76 76 D

1. O Lord, Thou hast ascended on high in might to reign;
   captivity Thou leadest a captive in Thy train.
   Rich gifts to Thee are offered by men who did rebel,
   who pray that now Jehovah, their God, with them may dwell.

2. Blest be the Lord who daily our heavy burden bears,
   the God of our salvation, who for His people cares.
   Our God is near to help us, our God is strong to save;
   the LORD alone is able to ransom from the grave.

3. Sing unto God, ye nations, ye kingdoms of the earth;
   sing unto God, all people, and praise His matchless worth.
   He rides in royal triumph upon the heav'ns abroad;
   He speaks, the mountains tremble before the voice of God.

4. All glory, might, and honor ascribe to God on high;
   His arm protects His people who on His pow'r rely.
   Forth from Thy holy dwelling Thine awful glories shine;
   Thou strengthenest Thy people; unending praise be Thine.

68B Let God Arise in All His Might

Isaac Watts, 1719

BOURBON
LM

Hesperian Harp, 184
harm. Louise McAllister, 195

1. Let God a - rise in all His might, and put the
2. He comes ar - rayed in burn - ing flames; jus - tice and
3. He rides and thun - ders thro' the sky; His name, Je
4. The wid - ow and the fa - ther - less fly to His
5. He breaks the cap - tive's heav - y chain, and pris - 'ners
6. King - doms and thrones to God be - long; crown Him, ye
7. Pro - claim His King, pro - nounce Him blest, He's your de

troops of hell to flight, as smoke, that sought to
ven - geance are His names: be - hold, His faint - ing
hov - ah, sounds on high; sing to His name, ye
aid in sharp dis - tress! In Him the poor and
see the light a - gain; but re - bels that dis -
na - tions, in your song; His won - drous names and
fense, your joy, your rest; when ter - rors rise, and

cloud the skies, be - fore the ris - ing tem - pest flies.
foes ex - pire like melt - ing wax be - fore the fire!
sons of grace; ye saints re - joice be - fore His face.
help - less find a judge that's just, a Fa - ther kind.
pute His will shall dwell in chains and dark - ness still.
pow'rs re - hearse; His hon - ors shall en - rich your verse.
na - tions faints, God is the strength of eve - ry saint.

Thy Lovingkindness, Lord

69A

The Psalter, 1912 — EVENTIDE — William Henry Monk, 1861
10 10 10 10

1. Thy lov - ing - kind - ness, Lord, is good and free,
2. Need - y and sor - row - ful, to Thee I cry;
3. With joy the meek shall see my soul re - stored;
4. Let heav'n a - bove His grace and glo - ry tell,

in ten - der mer - cy turn Thou un - to me;
let Thy sal - va - tion set my soul on high;
your heart shall live, ye saints that seek the Lord;
let earth and sea, and all that in them dwell;

hide not Thy face from me in my dis - tress,
then I will sing and praise Thy ho - ly name,
He helps the need - y and re - gards their cries,
sal - va - tion to His peo - ple God will give,

in mer - cy hear my prayer, Thy ser - vant bless.
my thank - ful song Thy mer - cy shall pro - claim.
those in dis - tress the LORD will not de - spise.
and they that love His name with Him shall live.

69B

Save Me, O God

Isaac Watts, 1719

KINGSFOLD
CMD

English County Songs, 189?

harm. Ralph Vaughan Williams, 190?

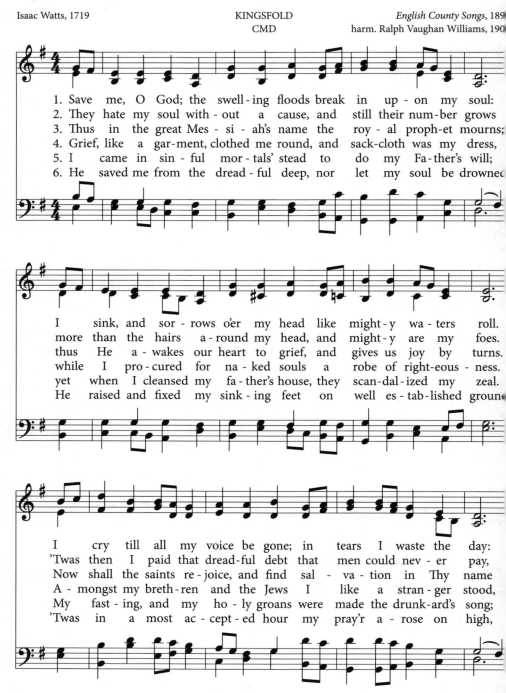

1. Save me, O God; the swell-ing floods break in up-on my soul:
2. They hate my soul with-out a cause, and still their num-ber grows
3. Thus in the great Mes-si-ah's name the roy-al proph-et mourns;
4. Grief, like a gar-ment, clothed me round, and sack-cloth was my dress,
5. I came in sin-ful mor-tals' stead to do my Fa-ther's will;
6. He saved me from the dread-ful deep, nor let my soul be drowned

I sink, and sor-rows o'er my head like might-y wa-ters roll.
more than the hairs a-round my head, and might-y are my foes.
thus He a-wakes our heart to grief, and gives us joy by turns.
while I pro-cured for na-ked souls a robe of right-eous-ness.
yet when I cleansed my fa-ther's house, they scan-dal-ized my zeal.
He raised and fixed my sink-ing feet on well es-tab-lished ground.

I cry till all my voice be gone; in tears I waste the day:
'Twas then I paid that dread-ful debt that men could nev-er pay,
Now shall the saints re-joice, and find sal-va-tion in Thy name
A-mongst my breth-ren and the Jews I like a stran-ger stood,
My fast-ing, and my ho-ly groans were made the drunk-ard's song;
'Twas in a most ac-cept-ed hour my pray'r a-rose on high,

my	God, be - hold my	long - ing	eyes,	and	short-en	Thy	de -	lay.
and	gave those hon - ors	to	Thy	law,	which	sin - ners	took a -	way.
for	I have borne their	heav - y	load	of	sor - row,	pain, and shame.
and	bore their vile	re - proach, to	bring	the	Gen-tiles	near to	God.
but	God from His	ce - les - tial	throne heard	my	com-plain-ing	tongue.
and	for my sake	my	God shall	hear	the	dy - ing	sin - ner's	cry.

In Haste, O God, Attend My Call   70A

Isaac Watts, 1719

KINGSFOLD (78)
CMD

1. In haste, O God, attend my call,
   nor hear my cries in vain;
   oh let Thy speed prevent my fall,
   and still my hope sustain.
   When foes insidious wound my name,
   and tempt my soul astray,
   then let them fall with lasting shame,
   to their own plots a prey.

2. While all that love Thy name rejoice,
   and glory in Thy word,
   in Thy salvation raise their voice,
   and magnify the Lord.
   O Thou my help in time of need,
   behold my sore dismay;
   in pity hasten to my aid,
   nor let Thy grace delay.

70B Make Haste, O God, My Soul to Bless!

Charles H. Spurgeon, 1866   KEDRON   attr. Elkanah Kelsay Dare, 179[?]

LM

1. Make haste, O God, my soul to bless! My help and my De - liv - 'rer Thou; make haste for I'm in deep dis - tress, my case is ur - gent; help me now.

2. Make haste, O God! make haste to save! For time is short, and death is nigh; make haste ere I am in my grave, and with the lost for - ev - er lie.

3. Make haste, for I am poor and low; and Sa - tan mocks my prayers and tears; O God, in mer - cy be not slow, but snatch me from my hor - rid fears.

4. Make haste, O God, and hear my cries; then with the souls who seek Thy face, and those who Thy sal - va - tion prize, I'll mag - ni - fy Thy match - less grace.

In Thee, O Lord, I Put My Trust

71

The Psalter, 1912

CRIMOND
CM

Jessie Seymour Irvine, 1871
harm. David Grant, 1872

1. In Thee, O LORD, I put my trust; shamed let me nev - er be;
2. Be Thou my rock, my dwell-ing - place, for - ev - er mine, as now;
3. De - liv - er me from wick - ed hands, save me from men un - just,
4. Thou hast up - held me in Thy grace from child-hood's ear - ly days;

O save me by Thy right - eous - ness, give ear, and res - cue me.
sal - va - tion Thou hast willed for me, my rock and fort - ress, Thou.
for Thou, Je - hov - ah, art my hope, from youth Thou art my trust.
to Thee from whom I life re - ceived will I give con-stant praise.

72   Hail to the Lord's Anointed

James Montgomery, 1822   ST. THEODULPH   Melchior Teschner, 161

76 76 D

1. Hail to the Lord's a - noint - ed, great Da - vid's great - er Son!
2. He comes with com - fort speed - y to those who suf - fer wrong;
3. He shall come down like show - ers up - on the fruit - ful earth;
4. A - ra - bia's de - sert ran - ger to Him shall bow the knee,
5. Kings shall fall down be - fore Him, and gold and in - cense bring,
6. For Him shall prayer un - ceas - ing, and dai - ly vows as - cend;
7. O'er eve - ry foe vic - to - rious, He on His throne shall rest,

Hail, in the time ap - point - ed, His reign on earth be - gun!
to help the poor and need - y, and bid the weak be strong;
and love, joy, hope, like flow - ers, spring in His path to birth;
the E - thi - o - pian stran - ger His glo - ry come to see;
all na - tions shall a - dore Him, His praise all peo - ple sing;
His king - dom still in - creas - ing, a king - dom with - out end;
from age to age more glo - rious, all - bless - ing and all - blessed;

He comes to break op - pres - sion, to set the cap - tive free,
to give them songs for sigh - ing, their dark - ness turn to light,
be - fore Him on the moun - tains shall peace, the her - ald, go;
with of - f'rings of de - vo - tion, ships from the isles shall meet,
for He shall have do - min - ion o'er riv - er, sea, and shore,
the moun - tain dews shall nour - ish a seed in weak - ness sown,
the tide of time shall nev - er His cov - e - nant re - move;

to take a - way trans - gres - sion, and rule in eq - ui - ty.
whose souls, con-demned and dy - ing, were pre - cious in His sight.
and right - eous - ness, in foun - tains, from hill to val - ley flow.
to pour the wealth of o - cean in trib - ute at His feet.
far as the ea - gle's pin - ion or dove's light wing can soar.
whose fruit shall spread and flour - ish, and shake like Leb - a - non.
His name shall stand for - ev - er— that name to us is Love.

O God, How Good Thou Art 73

The Psalter, 1912
OLIVET
66 4 66 64
Lowell Mason, 1832

1. O God, how good Thou art to all the pure of heart,
2. Ev - er, O Lord, with Thee, all shall be well with me,
3. In earth or heav'n a - bove who is there that I love
4. O it is good that I may still to God draw nigh,

though life seems vain; bur - dened with anx - ious care, I groped in
held by Thy hand; and Thou wilt guide my feet by Thy own
com - pared with Thee? My heart may faint with fears, but God my
as oft be - fore; the Lord Je - hov - ah blest, my ref - uge

dark de - spair, till in Thy house of prayer all was made plain.
coun - sel sweet, till I, for glo - ry meet, in glo - ry stand.
strength ap-pears, and will to end - less years my por - tion be.
and my rest, shall be in praise con-fessed for ev - er - more.

74 Why Have You Long Rejected Us, O God?

Julie and Timothy Tennent © 2017   EVENTIDE   William Henry. Monk, 1861
                                 10 10 10 10

1. Why have You long re - ject - ed us, O God?
2. Turn Your steps toward this dev - as - ta - tion great;
3. They've tak - en ax - es as men would chop trees;
4. They said with - in their hearts, "We'll crush them whole!"
5. How long, O God, will foes de - ride Your name?
6. But You, O God, are my King from of old;

Why does Your an - ger burn a - gainst Your sheep?
the en - e - my de - stroyed the ho - ly place.
they've smashed the carved work, brought un - ho - ly shame.
They burned each place where wor - ship was of Thee.
How long will en - e - mies their scorn de - ploy?
You bring sal - va - tion un - to all the earth.

You pur - chased us— Your own in - her - i - tance;
Your foes have roared in - to Your meet - ing place,
They burned Your sanc - tu - ar - y to the ground,
No might - y signs or proph - ets can be found,
Why do You hold Your hand back and de - lay?
You split the seas wide o - pen by Your pow'r;

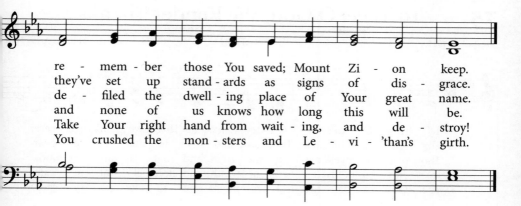

re	-	mem - ber	those	You	saved;	Mount	Zi	-	on		keep.
they've	set	up	stand - ards	as	signs	of	dis	-	grace.		
de	-	filed	the	dwell - ing	place	of	Your	great	name.		
and	none	of	us	knows	how	long	this	will	be.		
Take	Your	right	hand	from	wait - ing,	and	de	-	stroy!		
You	crushed	the	mon - sters	and	Le	-	vi -	'than's	girth.		

7. You opened springs and dried up rivers' flow;
    the day and night, sun, moon belong to You.
    You set earth's bound'ries—where they end, You know;
    You made the summer and the winter, too.

8. Now, LORD, remember how Your foes have mocked;
    how foolish people have reviled Your name.
    Don't hand Your dove to wild beasts to devour,
    and don't forget Your people, clothed in shame.

9. Keep Your own covenant, O Lord, in mind,
    for violence fills dark places in the land.
    Don't let oppressed ones tremble in disgrace,
    but may the needy praise Your name and stand.

10. Rise up, O God, and now defend Your cause;
    see how fools mock You all day scornfully.
    Do not ignore the clamor of Your foes;
    their uproar rises up continually.

75 To Thee, O God, We Render Thanks

The Psalter, 1912   ARLINGTON   Thomas Arne, 176

CM

1. To Thee, O God, we ren-der thanks, to Thee give thanks sin - cere,
2. Thy right-eous judg-ment, Thou hast said, shall in due time ap - pear,
3. Thou teach-est meek-ness to the proud, and mak-est sin - ners know
4. Je - hov-ah holds a cup of wrath, and holds it not in vain,
5. The God of Is - rael I will praise and all His glo - ry show;

be - cause Thy won-drous works de-clare that Thou art ev - er near.
and Thou who didst es - tab-lish it wilt fill the earth with fear.
that none is judge but God a - lone, to hon - or or bring low.
for all the wick - ed of the earth its bit - ter dregs shall drain.
the right-eous He will high ex - alt and bring the wick - ed low.

God Is Truly Known in Judah

76

Book of Psalms for Worship © 2010

REGENT SQUARE
87 87 87

Henry Smart, 1867

1. God is tru - ly known in Ju - dah; great His name in
2. You're more glo - rious and ma - jes - tic than the moun - tains
3. Horse and rid - er both lie sleep - ing, cast down in - to
4. You from heav - en spoke Your ver - dict, and the earth in
5. Give the LORD your God your prom - ise, and ful - fill your

Is - ra - el. He has pitched His tent in Sa - lem;
filled with prey. Brave and val - iant ones You plun - dered,
death's dark night. You re - buked them, God of Ja - cob—
fear was still. Sav - ing all the earth's af - flict - ed,
vows sin - cere. Let all those a - round bring trib - ute

His house stands on Zi - on's hill. There He broke the
now they slum - ber in the grave; though they once were
awe - in - spir - ing in Your might! Once Your an - ger
God a - rose to do His will. With what's left from
to the One to be re - vered. He brings low the

flam - ing ar - rows, there war's shield and sword made still.
might - y war - riors, none can lift his hands to save.
has been kin - dled, who can stand be - fore Your sight?
wrath You're gird - ed; hu - man wrath will praise You still.
pride of princ - es, and by kings of earth is feared.

77 I Cried Aloud for God to Help

Trinity Psalter Hymnal © 2018   RESIGNATION   William Walker's *Southern Harmony*, 183
CMD

1. I cried a - loud for God to help; I knew that God woul[c]
2. You kept my eye from rest - ful sleep— so great my pain and
3. "For - ev - er will the Lord re - ject and nev - er show His
4. Then I re - plied, "Such ques - tions show my own in - fir - mi
5. O God, most ho - ly are Your ways. What god is great like
6. The wa - ters saw You, O my God; they saw and were a -

hear.   When I was plunged in deep dis - tress, I
woe.   I thought a - bout the form - er days, the
grace?   Has He, His stead - fast love with - drawn, for -
ty,   the firm right hand of God Most High thro'
You?   You are the God by won - ders known, whose
fraid.   The ver - y depths be - came con - vulsed; the

sought the Lord in prayer.   At night I stretched un -
years of long a - go.   Through - out the night, the
e'er His mer - cy ceased?   For - ev - er has His
years must change - less be."   The LORD's deeds I re -
pow'r the na - tions view.   Your peo - ple You re -
clouds poured down their rain.   The thun - der rolled a -

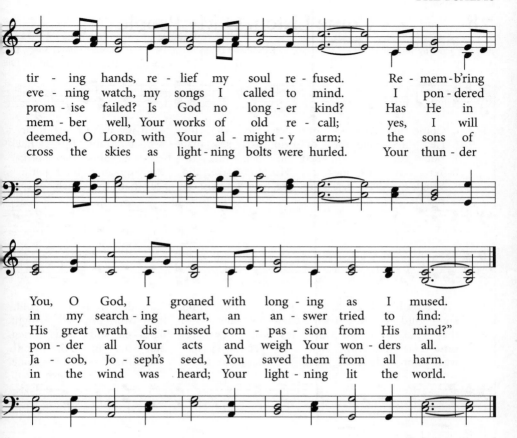

tir - ing hands, re - lief my soul re - fused. Re - mem - b'ring
eve - ning watch, my songs I called to mind. I pon - dered
prom - ise failed? Is God no long - er kind? Has He in
mem - ber well, Your works of old re - call; yes, I will
deemed, O LORD, with Your al - might - y arm; the sons of
cross the skies as light - ning bolts were hurled. Your thun - der

You, O God, I groaned with long - ing as I mused.
in my search - ing heart, an an - swer tried to find:
His great wrath dis - missed com - pas - sion from His mind?"
pon - der all Your acts and weigh Your won - ders all.
Ja - cob, Jo - seph's seed, You saved them from all harm.
in the wind was heard; Your light - ning lit the world.

7. The whole earth shook and trembled then,
   Your path was through the sea.
   Your way through mighty waters led;
   Your footprints none could see.
   Your people, like a flock of sheep,
   You guided every day;
   by Moses' and by Aaron's hand
   You led them on the way.

78 Come Listen, O My People

Julie and Timothy Tennent © 2017 KINGSFOLD *English County Songs*, 1893
CMD harm. Ralph Vaughan Williams, 1906

1. Come lis - ten, O my peo - ple, to the teach-ing we've been told.
2. He led them thro' di - vid - ed sea; made wa - ter stand up - right.
3. But they con - tin - ued in their sin; re - belled a - gainst the Lord;
4. Yet in His mer - cy, He for - gave; did not de - stroy their path;
5. What we have heard and we have known, our fa - thers told each one,

My mouth will speak in par - a - bles, things hid - den from of old.
He guid - ed them with cloud by day, with light from fire all night.
they put God to the test when they de - mand - ed food and cried.
time af - ter time, held an - ger back; did not stir up His wrath.
we'll not hide from our chil - dren, but will tell what God has done.

So that each gen - er - a - tion and the chil - dren yet un - born,
He split the rocks in des - ert land, gave wa - ter great as seas.
They spoke a - gainst Him as they said, "Can God pro - duce this feat?
For He re - mem - bered they were flesh, a breeze that does not stand.
The stat - utes giv'n to Ja - cob and the law which we were taught;

would know these things and in their turn, would tell of God the Lord.
He brought them streams out of the rock that flowed a - bun - dant - ly.
He struck the rock for wa - ter, but can He sup - ply us meat?"
How of - ten they re - belled a - gainst the Lord in des - ert land!
we'll tell the prais - es of the Lord, His pow'r and won-ders wrought

In Thy Heritage the Nations

79

The Psalter, 1912, alt.

BLAENWERN
87 87 D

William P. Rowlands, 1905

1. In Thy her - i - tage the na - tions now, O God, tri - um - phant stand;
2. O how long a - gainst Thy peo - ple shall Thy an - ger burn, O LORD?
3. O re - mem - ber not a - gainst us e - vil by our fa - thers wrought;
4. Let Thy foes no long - er scorn Thee, now a - venge Thy ser - vants slain;

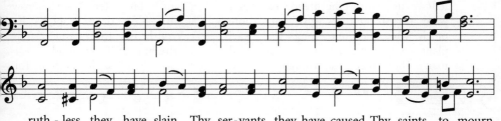

they de - file Thy ho - ly tem - ple, they de - stroy Thy cho - sen land;
On Thy en - e - mies, the heath - en, be Thy in - dig - na - tion poured;
haste to help us in Thy mer - cy, near to ru - in we are brought;
loose the pris - 'ner, save the dy - ing, all Thy en - e - mies re - strain;

ruth - less, they have slain Thy ser - vants, they have caused Thy saints to mourn,
smite the king - doms that de - fy Thee, call - ing not up - on Thy Name.
help us, God of our sal - va - tion, for the glo - ry of Thy Name;
then Thy flock, Thy cho - sen peo - ple, un - to Thee Thy thanks shall raise,

in the sight of all a - bout us we en - dure re - proach and scorn.
They have long de - voured Thy peo - ple and have swept Thy land with flame.
for Thy Name's sake come and save us, take a - way our sin and shame.
and to eve - ry gen - e - ra - tion, we will sing Thy glo - rious praise.

80 O Thou Great Shepherd of Thy Chosen Race

James Langran, 1912   FINLANDIA   Jean Sibelius 1899

10 10 10 10 10 10

1. O Thou great Shep-herd of Thy cho-sen race, who lead-est like a flock Thy Is-rael dear, from out the cher-u-bim re-veal Thy face, be-fore our host now let Thy might ap-

2. How long, O LORD, wilt Thou dis-dain our prayer? For Thou hast fed us with the bread of tears, and bit-ter sor-row Thou hast made us share; the na-tions round us mock with scorn-ful

3. A vine Thou brought-est forth from E-gypt's land; the na-tions were thrust out to give it room; it took deep root, it spread on eve-ry hand, the hills were cov-ered with its shade and

4. Why hast Thou bro-ken down its cir-cling wall that they may pluck who pass a-long the way? Wild beasts from out the wood de-stroy it all and feed up-on Thy vine by night and

5. Look down, be-hold and vis-it this Thy vine which Thou hast plant-ed with Thy own right hand, the branch Thou mad-est strong and owned it Thine, for it is burned with fire, no more to

6. O let Thy hand Thy cho-sen one sus-tain, the son of man Thou mad-est strong to be; so we shall faith-ful to Thy cause re-main; re-vive Thou us, and we will call on

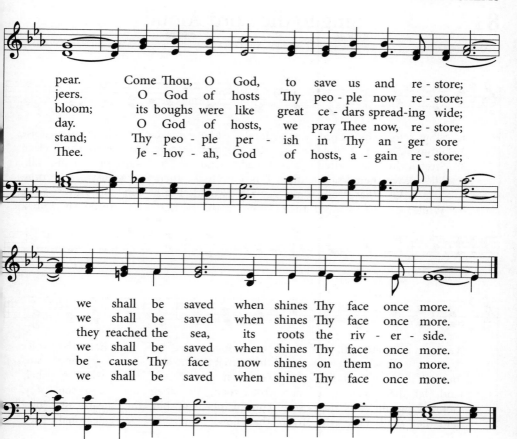

pear. Come Thou, O God, to save us and re - store;
jeers. O God of hosts Thy peo - ple now re - store;
bloom; its boughs were like great ce - dars spread-ing wide;
day. O God of hosts, we pray Thee now, re - store;
stand; Thy peo - ple per - ish in Thy an - ger sore
Thee. Je - hov - ah, God of hosts, a - gain re - store;

we shall be saved when shines Thy face once more.
we shall be saved when shines Thy face once more.
they reached the sea, its roots the riv - er - side.
we shall be saved when shines Thy face once more.
be - cause Thy face now shines on them no more.
we shall be saved when shines Thy face once more.

81 Sing to the Lord Aloud

Isaac Watts, 1719   FESTAL SONG   William Henry Walter, 1894
SM

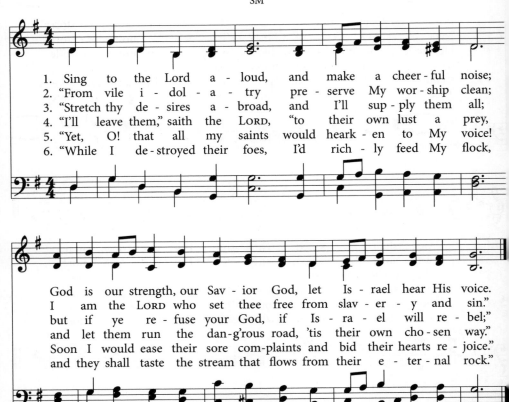

1. Sing to the Lord a - loud, and make a cheer - ful noise;
2. "From vile i - dol - a - try pre - serve My wor - ship clean;
3. "Stretch thy de - sires a - broad, and I'll sup - ply them all;
4. "I'll leave them," saith the LORD, "to their own lust a prey,
5. "Yet, O! that all my saints would heark - en to My voice!
6. "While I de - stroyed their foes, I'd rich - ly feed My flock,

God is our strength, our Sav - ior God, let Is - rael hear His voice.
I am the LORD who set thee free from slav - er - y and sin."
but if ye re - fuse your God, if Is - ra - el will re - bel;"
and let them run the dan - g'rous road, 'tis their own cho - sen way."
Soon I would ease their sore com - plaints and bid their hearts re - joice."
and they shall taste the stream that flows from their e - ter - nal rock."

Where'er His Creatures Gather

The Psalter, 1912 ANGEL'S STORY Arthur H. Mann, 1883
76 76 D

1. Wher-e'er His crea-tures gath - er the un - seen God is near;
2. Do jus-tice for the help-less, the or-phan's cause main-tain.
3. The Most High God has called you and set you up on high,

let ru-lers fear their Ru - ler, their Judge let judg-es fear.
De - fend the poor and need - y, op-pressed and wronged for gain.
but ye to Him must an - swer, for ye like men must die.

How long, ye earth - ly judg - es, will ye per-vert the right?
When ru - lers walk in dark - ness, when judg - es truth for - sake,
A - rise, O God E - ter - nal, Thou Judge of all the earth,

How long shall wick - ed per - sons have fa - vor in your sight?
the cor - ner-stones are crum - bled, the firm foun-da - tions shake.
through all Thy ran - somed na - tions send now Thy jus - tice forth.

83   O God, No Longer Hold Thy Peace

The Psalter, 1912   FOREST GREEN   English folk tune
              CMD   harm. Ralph Vaughan Williams, 1906

1. O God, no long-er hold Thy peace, no long-er si-lent be;
2. Thy an-cient foes, con-spir-ing still, with one con-sent a-gree,
3. Make them like dust and stub-ble blown be-fore the whirl-wind dire,

Thy en-e-mies lift up their head to fight Thy saints and Thee.
and they who with Thy peo-ple strive make war, O God, with Thee.
in ter-ror driv'n be-fore the storm of Thy con-sum-ing fire.

A-gainst Thy own, whom Thou dost love, their craft Thy foes em-ploy;
O God, who in our fa-thers' time didst smite our foes and Thine,
Con-found them in their sin till they to Thee for par-don fly,

they think to cut Thy peo-ple off, Thy peo-ple would de-stroy.
so smite Thy en-e-mies to-day who in their pride com-bine.
till in dis-may they trem-bling own that Thou art GOD Most High.

How Lovely, Lord of Hosts, to Me   **84**

Book of Psalms for Worship © 2010   MELITA   John B. Dykes, 1861
88 88 88

1. How love - ly, Lord of hosts, to me the tab - er - na - cles
2. The spar - row has her place of rest; the swal - low through Your
3. Blessed they who in Your house a - bide; to You they ev - er

of Your grace! O how I long, yes, faint to see the
kind - ly care has found where she may build her nest and
ren - der praise. Blessed they who in Your strength con - fide, and

Lord's own courts, His dwell - ing place! My heart and flesh with
brood her young in safe - ty there. Your al - tars as my
in whose heart are pil - grims' ways. They make the vale of

joy draw nigh; as to the liv - ing God I cry.
rest I sing, O Lord of hosts, my God, my King.
tears a spring, with show'rs of bless - ing cov - er - ing.

85
In Times of Old

Dan Kreider
and Dustin Battles © 2021

SINE NOMINE
10 10 10 with refrain

Ralph Vaughan Williams, 1906

1. In times of old You showed Your fa - vor, LORD,
2. Re - turn, O God! Re - store us once a - gain!
3. For grace out - poured, for lov - ing - kind - ness shown,
4. The paths of truth and lov - ing - kind - ness meet;

to Ja - cob's line whose for - tunes You re - stored,
Put off Your an - ger, par - don all our sin!
our list'n - ing ears will wait for You a - lone.
sweet the em - brace of right - eous - ness and peace.

for all their sins, for - give - ness free - ly poured:
Will You for - ev - er with our souls con - tend?
You speak of peace, You make sal - va - tion known;
You will re - store and give our land in - crease.

O LORD, have mer - cy on us for - ev - er.

Bow Down Thy Ear, O Lord

The Psalter, 1912

MARYTON
LM

H. Percy Smith, 1874

1. Bow down Thy ear, O LORD, and hear, for I am poor and great my need; pre - serve my soul, for Thee I fear; O God, Thy trust - ing ser - vant heed.
2. O Lord, be mer - ci - ful to me, for all the day to Thee I cry; re - joice Thy ser - vant, for to Thee I lift my soul, O Lord Most High.
3. For Thou, O Lord, art good and kind, and read - y to for - give Thou art; a - bun - dant mer - cy sup - pli - ca - tion heed; in trou - ble I will they shall find who call on Thee with all their heart.
4. O LORD, in - cline Thy ear to me, my voice of sup - pli - ca - tion heed; in trou - ble I will cry to Thee, for Thou wilt an - swer when I plead.
5. There is no God but Thee a - lone, no works like Thine, O Lord Most High; all na - tions shall sur - round Thy throne and their Cre - a - tor glo - ri - fy.
6. In all Thy deeds how great Thou art! Thou one true God, Thy way make clear; teach me with un - di - vi - ded heart to trust Thy truth, Thy Name to fear.

86B   Hear Me, O Lord, and Answer Me

Trinity Psalter Hymnal © 2018   BLOCKLEY   Thomas Blockley, 186
                                              LM

1. Hear me, O Lord, and an - swer me; for I am
need - y, I am poor. Safe - guard Your god - ly
ser - vant's life; save me, my God, I trust in You.

2. All day I cry to You, O Lord, show me Your
grace, be mer - ci - ful. Glad - den Your ser - vant's
soul, O Lord, for un - to You I lift my soul.

3. For You, O Lord, a - lone are good; read - y and
will - ing to for - give. All those who call up -
on Your name You will a - bun - dant mer - cy give.

4. Lis - ten, O Lord, and heed my prayer; hear now my
plea for grace, my cry. In my dis - tress I
call on You, for in Your mer - cy You re - ply.

5. Sure - ly a - mong the man - y gods, Lord, there is
none to ri - val You; deeds that the oth - ers
may per - form nev - er com - pare with works You do.

6. All of the na - tions You have made, Lord, they will
come and laud Your name. There is no God but
You a - lone; great are Your deeds and great Your fame.

7. Teach me, O Lord, Your way, that I
   from Your great truth may not depart;
   so I might always fear Your name,
   give me an undivided heart.

8. I will, O Lord, with all my heart
   give You my thanks unceasingly.
   Great is Your steadfast love to me;
   from Sheol's depths You rescue me.

9. Insolent men attack me, God,
   men strong and ruthless, men of strife;
   they do not seek Your face, O God,
   but seek to take away my life.

10. You, Lord, are merciful and kind,
    slow to show anger, rich in grace;
    You, God, abound in steadfast love;
    great is Your truth and faithfulness.

11. Turn now Your face to me, O Lord,
    and unto me Your mercy show;
    rescue Your lowly handmaid's son,
    unto Your servant strength bestow.

12. Grant me a sign of favor, Lord,
    which those who hate me now may see;
    surely they will be put to shame,
    for You have helped to comfort me.

87   Zion, Founded on the Mountains

The Psalter, 1912   CORONAE   William Henry Monk, 187
                                  87 87 47

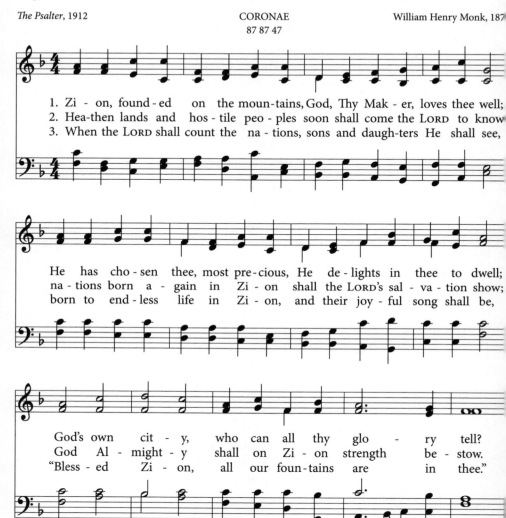

1. Zi - on, found - ed   on the moun-tains, God, Thy Mak - er, loves thee well;
2. Hea-then lands and   hos - tile peo - ples soon shall come the LORD to know
3. When the LORD shall count the   na - tions, sons and daugh-ters He   shall see,

He   has   cho - sen   thee, most pre-cious, He   de - lights in   thee   to   dwell;
na - tions born a - gain in   Zi - on   shall the LORD's sal - va - tion show;
born to   end - less   life in   Zi - on,   and their joy - ful   song shall be,

God's own   cit - y,   who   can   all   thy   glo -   ry   tell?
God   Al - might - y   shall   on   Zi - on   strength   be - stow.
"Bless - ed   Zi - on,   all   our   foun-tains   are   in   thee."

LORD, the God of My Salvation

...e Psalter, 1912   EBENEZER   Thomas J. Williams, 1897

87 87 D

1. LORD, the God of my sal - va - tion, day and night I cry to Thee;
2. Thou hast brought me down to dark-ness, 'neath Thy wrath I am op-pressed;
3. Un - to Thee with hands up - lift - ed dai - ly I di - rect my cry;

let my prayer now find ac - cept-ance, in Thy mer - cy an - swer me.
all the bil - lows of af - flic - tion o - ver - whelm my soul dis-tressed.
hear, O LORD, my sup - pli - ca - tion, hear and save me e'er I die.

Full of trou - bles and af - flic - tion, nigh to death my soul is brought,
Thou hast made my friends des - pise me, and com - pan - ion - less I go,
Wilt Thou wait to show Thy won - ders and Thy mer - cy to the dead?

help - less, like one cast for - ev - er from Thy care and from Thy thought.
bound, and help-less in my bond - age, pin - ing in my bit - ter woe.
Let me live to tell Thy prais - es, by Thy lov - ing - kind - ness led.

89 My Song Forever Shall Record

The Psalter, 1912

KEDRON
LM

attr. Elkanah Kelsay Dare, 17*

1. My song for - ev - er shall re - cord the
2. I sing of mer - cies that en - dure, for -
3. Be - hold God's truth and grace dis - played, for
4. The heav'ns shall join in glad ac - cord to
5. The heav'ns and earth, by right di - vine, the
6. In vi - sion to His saints God spake: "From

ten - der mer - cies of the LORD; Thy faith - ful - ness will
ev - er build - ed firm and sure, of faith - ful - ness that
He has faith - ful cov - 'nant made, and He has sworn that
praise Thy won - drous works, O LORD; Thy faith - ful - ness shall
world and all there - in, are Thine; the whole cre - a - tion's
out the peo - ple one I take, a might - y lead - er,

I pro - claim, and eve - ry age shall know Thy name.
nev - er dies, es - tab - lished change - less in the skies.
Da - vid's Son shall ev - er sit up - on His throne.
praise com - mand where ho - ly ones as - sem - bled stand.
won - drous frame pro - claims its Mak - er's glo - rious Name.
true and brave, or - dained, ex - alt - ed, strong to save."

7. "Yea, he shall triumph in My Name,
   and great shall be his pow'r and fame,
   from sea to sea his mighty hand
   shall hold dominion o'er the land."

8. "For him My mercy shall endure,
   My cov'nant made with him is sure,
   his throne and race I will maintain
   forever, while the heav'ns remain."

9. On Thy anointed wrath is poured
   as if Thy cov'nant were abhorred;
   Thou hast profaned his kingly crown,
   his matchless strength is broken down.

10. Where are Thy mercies which of old
    were in Thy promises foretold?
    Remember, Lord, the bitter shame
    heaped on Thy own anointed's name.

11. Blest be the LORD for evermore,
    whose promise stands from days of yore.
    His word is faithful now as then;
    blest be His Name. Amen. Amen.

90   O God, Our Help in Ages Past

Isaac Watts, 1719, alt.   ST. ANNE   William Croft, 170?
                   CM

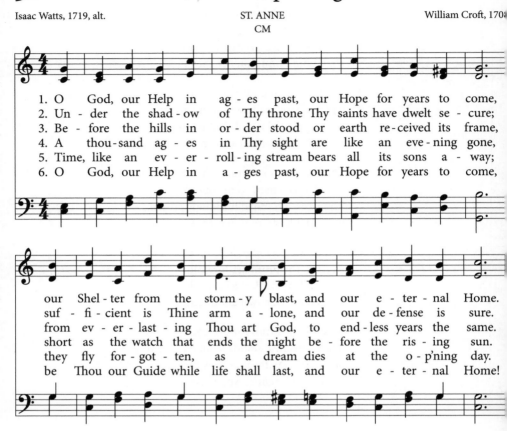

1. O God, our Help in ag - es past, our Hope for years to come,
2. Un - der the shad - ow of Thy throne Thy saints have dwelt se - cure;
3. Be - fore the hills in or - der stood or earth re - ceived its frame,
4. A thou - sand ag - es in Thy sight are like an eve - ning gone,
5. Time, like an ev - er - roll - ing stream bears all its sons a - way;
6. O God, our Help in a - ges past, our Hope for years to come,

our Shel - ter from the storm - y blast, and our e - ter - nal Home.
suf - fi - cient is Thine arm a - lone, and our de - fense is sure.
from ev - er - last - ing Thou art God, to end - less years the same.
short as the watch that ends the night be - fore the ris - ing sun.
they fly for - got - ten, as a dream dies at the o - p'ning day.
be Thou our Guide while life shall last, and our e - ter - nal Home!

E ternal God, the only refuge of the afflicted; seeing that the shortness of this present life admonishes us to turn ourselves away from earthly things and to have our meditation on heavenly matters, grant unto us that we may employ our whole life on the consideration of Thy mercy and goodness, and that Thy anger may be so turned from us that we may have continually whereby to rejoice in Thee, through Jesus Christ, our Lord. Amen.

The Scottish Collects, 1595

Call Jehovah Thy Salvation

mes Montgomery, 1822

HYFRYDOL
87 87 D

Rowland Prichard, 1844

1. Call Je - ho - vah thy sal - va - tion, rest be-neath th' Al - might - y's shade;
2. From the sword at noon-day wast - ing, from the noi - some pes - ti - lence,
3. On - ly with thine eyes the an - guish of the wick - ed thou shalt see,

in His se - cret hab - i - ta - tion dwell, and nev - er be dis-mayed.
in the depth of mid - night blast - ing, God shall be thy sure de - fense.
when by slow dis - ease they lan - guish, when they per - ish sud - den - ly.

There no tu - mult shall a - larm thee, thou shalt dread no hid - den snare;
Fear not thou the dead - ly quiv - er, when a thou - sand feel the blow;
Thee, tho' winds and waves be swell - ing, God, thine hope, shall bear thro' all;

guile nor vi - o - lence can harm thee in e - ter - nal safe-guard there.
mer - cy shall thy soul de - liv - er, tho' ten thou - sand be laid low.
plague shall not come nigh thy dwell - ing, thee no e - vil shall be - fall.

92 It Is Good to Sing Your Praises

The Psalter, 1912   ELLESDIE   attr. Wolfgang Amadeus Mozart, 1756–179
                                    87 87 D   in Leavitt's *The Christian Lyre*, 183
                                                 arr. Hubert P. Main, 1839–192

1. It is good to sing Your prais - es and to thank You, O Most High,
2. You have filled our hearts with glad - ness at the works Your hands have wrough
3. But the good shall live be - fore You, plant-ed in Your dwell - ing place,

show - ing forth Your lov - ing kind - ness when the morn - ing lights the sky.
You have made our lives vic - to - rious; great Your works and deep Your though
fruit - ful trees and ev - er ver - dant, nour-ished by Your bound-less grace

It is good when night is fall - ing of Your faith - ful - ness to tell,
You, O Lord, on high ex - alt - ed, reign for - ev - er - more in might;
In His good-ness to the right-eous, God His right-eous-ness dis - plays;

while with sweet, mel - o - dious prais - es songs of a - dor - a - tion swell.
all Your en - e - mies shall per - ish, sin be ban - ished from Your sight.
God, my Rock, my Strength and Ref - uge, just and true are all Your ways.

The Lord Reigns over All

93

Trinity Psalter Hymnal © 2018

FESTAL SONG
SM

William Henry Walter, 1894

1. The Lord reigns o - ver all; He's robed in maj - es - ty.
2. The world es - tab - lished stands un - moved, it shall en - dure.
3. The floods have lift - ed up, Lord, lift - ed up their voice;
4. The Lord, en - throned on high, more pow - er - ful is He
5. You stat - utes, Lord, stand firm; un - chang - ing is Your word.

The Lord is robed and wears His belt of strength and dig - ni - ty.
From ev - er - last - ing You are God, Your throne is ev - er sure.
the floods have lift - ed up their waves and made a might - y noise.
than thun - der of the o - cean's waves or break - ers of the sea.
And ho - li - ness a - dorns Your house for - ev - er - more, O Lord.

94   O Lord, Thou Judge of All the Earth

The Psalter, 1912   DISTRESS   William Walker's *Southern Harmony*, 1835
           LM

1. O Lord, Thou Judge of all the earth, to whom all
2. How long, O Lord, in boast-ful pride shall wick-ed
3. Be wise, ye fools and brut-ish men; shall not He
4. The Lord will judge in right-eous ness, from Him all
5. That man is blest whom Thou, O Lord, with chas-t'ning
6. Un-less the Lord had been my Help, my life had

ven-geance doth be-long, a-rise and show Thy
men tri-um-phant stand? How long shall they af-
see who formed the eye? Shall not He hear who
truth and know-ledge flow; the fool-ish thoughts of
hand dost teach Thy will, for in the day when
quick-ly passed a-way; but when my foot had

glo-ry forth, re-quite the proud, con-demn the wrong.
flict Thy saints and scorn Thy wrath, Thy dread-ful hand?
formed the ear, and judge, who reign-eth God most high?
wick-ed men, how vain they are the Lord doth know.
sin-ners fall that man in peace a-bid-eth still.
al-most slipped, O Lord, Thy mer-cy was my stay.

7. Amid the doubts that fill my mind
Thy comforts, Lord, bring joy to me;
can wickedness, though throned in might,
have fellowship, O Lord, with Thee?

8. The wicked, in their might arrayed,
against the righteous join their pow'r,
but to the Lord I flee for help;
He is my Refuge and my Tow'r.

Now with Joyful Exultation

95

...e Psalter, 1912

BEECHER
87 87 D

John Zundel, 1870

1. Now with joy - ful ex - ul - ta - tion let us sing to GOD our praise;
2. For how great a God, and glo - rious, is the LORD to whom we sing;
3. To the LORD such might re - veal - ing, let us come with rev-'rence meet,
4. While He of - fers peace and par - don, let us hear His voice to - day,

to the rock of our sal - va - tion loud ho - san - nas let us raise.
o - ver i - dol gods vic - to - rious, great is He, our God and King.
and, be - fore our ma - ker kneel - ing, let us wor - ship at His feet.
lest, if we our hearts should har - den, we should per - ish in the way;

Thank-ful trib - ute glad - ly bring-ing, let us come be - fore Him now,
In His hand are earth's deep pla - ces, al - so His are all the hills;
He is our own God who leads us, we the peo - ple of His care;
lest to us, so un - be - liev - ing, He in judg-ment shall de - clare:

and, with psalms His prais - es sing - ing, joy - ful in His pres-ence bow.
His the sea whose bounds He trac - es, His the land His boun - ty fills.
with a shep-herd's hand He feeds us as His flock in pas-tures fair.
"You, so long my Spir - it griev-ing, nev - er in my rest can share."

96 · O Sing a New Song to the Lord

The Psalter, 1912   TRURO   Thomas William
    LM   *Psalmodia Evangelica, 178*

1. O sing a new song to the LORD, sing all the earth and
2. Tell all the world His won-drous ways, tell heath-en na-tions
3. The heath-en gods are i-dols vain; the shin-ing heav'ns the
4. Let eve-ry tongue and eve-ry tribe give to the LORD due
5. O fear and bow, a-dorned with grace, and tell each land that
6. Let heav'n be glad, let earth re-joice, the teem-ing sea re-
7. So let them shout be-fore our God, for lo, He comes, He

bless His name; from day to day His praise re-
far and near; great is the LORD, and great His
Lord sup-ports; both light and hon-or lead His
praise and sing; all glo-ry un-to Him as
God is King; the earth He foun-ded in its
sound with praise; let wav-ing fields lift high their
comes with might, to wield the scep-ter and the

cord, the LORD's re-deem-ing grace pro-claim.
praise, and Him a-lone let na-tions fear.
train; while strength and beau-ty fill His courts.
cribe, come, throng His courts, and of-f'rings bring.
place, and jus-tice to the world will bring.
voice, and all the trees their an-them raise.
rod, to judge the world with truth and right.

Jehovah Reigns, Let Earth Be Glad

97

The Psalter, 1912, alt. ELY / LM Thomas Turton, 1844

1. Je - ho - vah reigns; let earth be glad and all the
2. Con - sum - ing fire de - stroys His foes, a - round the
3. The heav'ns His right - eous - ness pro - claim, through earth His
4. Zi - on re - joic - es to be - hold Thy judg - ments
5. All ye that tru - ly love the LORD, hate sin, for
6. For good men light and joy are sown to bless them

isles their joy make known; with clouds and dark - ness
world His light - nings blaze; the trem - bling earth His
glo - ry shines a - broad; from i - dol - wor - ship
in the earth, O LORD; Thy glo - ry to the
He is just and pure; to saints His help He
in the har - vest - time; ye saints, your joy in

He is clad, on truth and jus - tice rests His throne.
pres - ence knows, the moun - tains melt be - fore His gaze.
turn with shame and bow be - fore the liv - ing God.
world un - fold, su - preme o'er all be Thou a - dored.
will ac - cord and keep them in His love se - cure.
GOD make known and ev - er praise His Name sub - lime.

98   Sing a New Song to Jehovah

The Psalter, 1912   AUSTRIAN HYMN   Franz Joseph Haydn, 179
                         87 87 D

1. Sing a new song to Je-ho-vah for the won-ders He hath wroug
2. Truth and mer-cy toward His peo-ple He hath ev-er kept in mind
3. Seas with all your full-ness thun-der, all earth's peo-ples now re-joice;

His right hand and arm most ho-ly tri-umph to His cause have broug
and His full and free sal-va-tion He hath shown to all man-kind.
floods and hills in praise u-nit-ing to the LORD lift up your voice.

In His love and ten-der mer-cy He hath made sal-va-tion know
Sing, O earth, sing to Je-ho-vah, prais-es to Je-ho-vah sing;
For, be-hold, Je-ho-vah com-eth, robed in jus-tice and in might

in the sight of eve-ry na-tion He His right-eous-ness hath show
with the swell-ing notes of mu-sic shout be-fore the LORD, the King.
He a-lone will judge the na-tions, and His judg-ment shall be right.

God Is King Forever

99

...e Psalter, 1912

NICAEA
11 12 12 10

John B. Dykes, 1861

1. God is King for - ev - er: let the na - tions trem - ble;
2. Mer - ci - ful as might - y, He de - lights in jus - tice,
3. Ho - ly men of old in Him a - lone con - fid - ed;

throned a - bove the cher - u - bim, by all the earth a -
for He reigns in right - eous - ness and rules in e - qui -
He for - gave their sins, al - though they felt His chas - t'ning

dored; He is great in Zi - on, high a - bove all
ty; wor - ship and ex - alt Him, bow - ing down be -
rod; in His ho - ly tem - ple wor - ship and a -

peo - ples; praise Him with fear, for ho - ly is the Lord.
fore Him, per - fect in pow'r and ho - li - ness is He.
dore Him, faith - ful and ho - ly is the Lord our God.

100   All People That on Earth Do Dwell

st. 1–4, William Kethe, 1561
st. 5, Thomas Ken, 1674

OLD HUNDREDTH
LM

Louis Bourgeois
Genevan Psalter, 155

1. All peo - ple that on earth do dwell, sing
2. Know that the LORD is God in - deed; with
3. O en - ter then His gates with praise, ap -
4. Be - cause the LORD our God is good; His
5. Praise God, from whom all bless - ings flow; praise

to the LORD with cheer - ful voice; Him serve with mirth, His
out our aid He did us make; we are His flock, He
proach with joy His courts un - to; praise, laud, and bless His
mer - cy is for - ev - er sure; His truth at all times
Him, all crea - tures here be - low; praise Him a - bove, ye

praise forth - tell; come ye be - fore Him and re - joice!
doth us feed, and for His sheep He doth us take.
name al - ways, for it is seem - ly so to do.
firm - ly stood, and shall from age to age en - dure.
heav'n - ly host; praise Fa - ther, Son, and Ho - ly Ghost!

Of Justice and of Grace I Sing   **101**

Isaac Watts, 1719   NEW BRITAIN   *Columbian Harmony, 1829*
CM

1. Of jus - tice and of grace I sing, and pay my GOD my vows; Thy grace and jus - tice, heav'n - ly King, teach me to rule my house.
2. Now to my tent, O GOD, re - pair, and make Thy ser - vant wise; I'll suf - fer noth - ing near me there that shall of - fend Thine eyes.
3. The man that doth his neigh - bor wrong by false - hood or by force, the scorn - ful eye, the slan - d'rous tongue, I'll thrust them from my doors.
4. I'll seek the faith - ful and the just, and will their help en - joy; these are the friends that I shall trust, the ser - vants I'll em - ploy.
5. The wretch that deals in sly de - ceit I'll ev - er hate, and ban - ish from my sight.
6. I'll purge my fam - i - ly a - round, and make the wick - ed flee; so shall my house be ev - er found a dwell - ing fit for Thee.

102 Thou, O Lord, Art God Alone

The Psalter, 1912, alt. ST. GEORGE'S WINDSOR George Elvey, 185
77 77 D

1. Thou, O Lord, art God a-lone, ev-er-last-ing is Thy throne;
2. If with love com-pas-sion-ate we, Thy ser-vants, mourn her state,
3. This all a-ges shall re-cord for the glo-ry of the Lord;
4. As one lays a gar-ment by, Thou wilt change the star-ry sky

thro' the a-ges men shall sing praise to heav'n's e-ter-nal King.
wilt not Thou, O gra-cious Lord, help in Zi-on's need af-ford?
Thou dost hear the hum-ble prayer, for the help-less Thou dost care.
like a ves-ture worn and old; but Thy years shall ne'er be told.

You, en-throned a-bove the skies, wilt for Zi-on's help a-rise;
Lord, Thy glo-ry shall ap-pear, kings and na-tions then shall fear;
Thou e-ter-nal art, and great, heav'n and earth Thou didst cre-ate;
Thou wilt make Thy ser-vants' race ev-er live be-fore Thy face,

let Thy grace to her ap-pear, for the prom-ised time is near.
and Thy name shall be a-dored when Thy Zi-on is re-stored.
heav'n and earth shall pass a-way, change-less Thou shalt live for aye.
and for-ev-er at Thy side chil-dren's chil-dren shall a-bide.

O My Soul, Bless Your Redeemer   **103**

Sabbath-School Psalmodist, 1866   STUTTGART   Witt's *Psalmodia Sacra*, Gotha, 1715
                                          87 87

1. O   my soul, bless your Re - deem - er;   all with - in me, bless His Name;
2. He   for - gives all   your trans - gres - sions, all dis - eas - es   gen - tly heals;
3. Far   as   east from west is   dis - tant, He has put a - way our sin;
4. As   it   was with - out be - gin - ning, so it lasts with - out an end;
5. Un - to such as   keep His cov - 'nant and are stead - fast in His way;
6. Bless your Ma - ker,   all you crea - tures, ev - er un - der His con - trol,

bless the Fa - ther and for - get not all His mer - cies   to pro - claim.
God re - deems you from de - struc - tion, and with you so   kind - ly deals.
like the pi - ty of a   fa - ther has the LORD's com - pas - sion been.
to their chil - dren's chil - dren ev - er shall His right - eous - ness ex - tend.
un - to those who still re - mem - ber the com - mand - ments and o - bey.
all thro' - out His vast do - min - ion; bless the LORD of all, my soul!

104 Praise the LORD, My Soul, O Praise Him!

Sing Psalms © Free Church of Scotland   NETTLETON   J. Wyeth
87 87 D   *Repository of Sacred Music*, Part II, 181

1. Praise the LORD, my soul, O praise Him! LORD my God, you
2. He makes clouds of heav'n His char - iot; on the wings of
3. But when You re - buked the wa - ters, at Your thun - der
4. God makes springs pour down the val - leys. Streams that flow from
5. He makes grass grow for the cat - tle, plants for man to

are so great! Wrapped in light as with a gar - ment, clothed in
wind He rides. He makes flames of fire His ser - vants; winds o
they took flight; they re - ced - ed to the val - leys, flow - ing
eve - ry hill quench the thirst of all His crea - tures, and wild
cul - ti - vate— bring - ing from the earth its pro - duce, food for

maj - es - ty and state. Like a tent He spreads the
bey what He de - cides. He set earth on its foun
down the moun - tains' height to the place that You ap
don - keys drink their fill. Birds sing sweet - ly in the
all man - kind to eat: wine that to man's con - sti

heav - ens, and a - bove the wa - ters there sets the frame - work
da - tions, so that it should nev - er move; then the deep sub
poin - ted. You set bounds to their do - main, so that nev - er
branch - es, nest - ing by the riv - er - side. From a - bove, the
tu - tion joy and glad - ness will im - part, oil that makes the

of His dwell - ing, mak - ing it an up - per layer.
merged the moun - tains till the wa - ters stood a - bove.
will the wa - ters o - ver - whelm the land a - gain.
earth is wa - tered, by God's boun - ty sat - is - fied.
face re - splen - dent, bread that for - ti - fies the heart.

6. Blessed with water are the forests— trees which to the LORD belong,
   mighty cedars that He planted on the heights of Lebanon.
   Birds reside among the cedars; storks upon the pine trees nest.
   Wild goats live among high mountains; conies in the crags find rest.

7. See the moon that marks the seasons; to its setting moves the sun.
   You send darkness, night approaches; foraging has now begun.
   Lions roar throughout the forest, while from God they seek their prey;
   comes the sun, they slink back homewards. Man goes out to toil all day.

8. LORD, how many are Your wonders! Wisely You have made them all.
   Earth is full of all Your creatures, living things, both great and small.
   And the sea, so vast and spacious, brings forth life abundantly.
   There leviathan is playing; to and fro the ships go by.

9. All Your creatures look towards You for their food to be supplied.
   What You give to them they gather, with Your goodness satisfied.
   When You hide your face, they're troubled; lifeless, they return to earth.
   When new life comes from Your Spirit, to earth's face You give rebirth.

10. May the LORD's majestic glory always last and never fade;
    May the LORD rejoice and triumph in the works that He has made.
    When He gazes on creation, earth begins to shake in fear.
    At His touch the mountains tremble; smoke and flames of fire appear.

11. To the LORD throughout my lifetime, to my God I will sing praise.
    May my meditation please Him, as to Him my song I raise.
    But may sinners flee before Him, and the wicked be no more.
    Praise be to the LORD Almighty; O my soul, the LORD adore!

105   Give Thanks to the LORD God

Sing Psalms © Free Church of Scotland   ST. DENIO   Welsh melody
                         11 11 11 11   from John Roberts's *Caniadau y Cyssegr*, 183

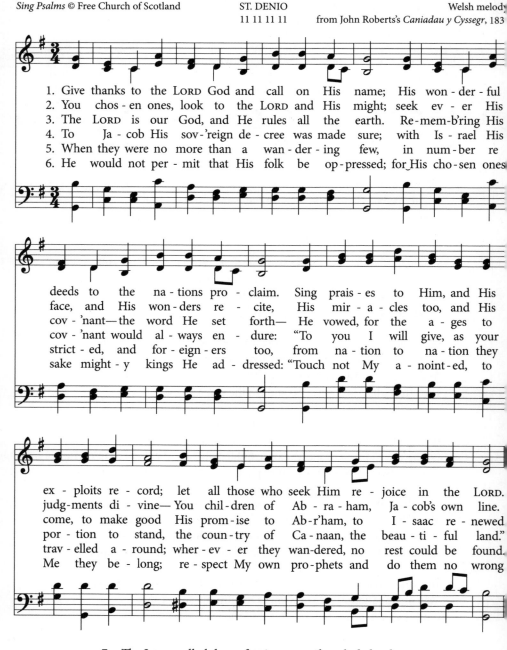

1. Give thanks to the LORD God and call on His name; His won-der-ful
2. You chos-en ones, look to the LORD and His might; seek ev-er His
3. The LORD is our God, and He rules all the earth. Re-mem-b'ring His
4. To Ja-cob His sov-'reign de-cree was made sure; with Is-rael His
5. When they were no more than a wan-der-ing few, in num-ber re
6. He would not per-mit that His folk be op-pressed; for His cho-sen ones

deeds to the na-tions pro-claim. Sing prais-es to Him, and His
face, and His won-ders re-cite, His mir-a-cles too, and His
cov-'nant—the word He set forth— He vowed, for the a-ges to
cov-'nant would al-ways en-dure: "To you I will give, as your
strict-ed, and for-eign-ers too, from na-tion to na-tion they
sake might-y kings He ad-dressed: "Touch not My a-noint-ed, to

ex-ploits re-cord; let all those who seek Him re-joice in the LORD.
judg-ments di-vine— You chil-dren of Ab-ra-ham, Ja-cob's own line.
come, to make good His prom-ise to Ab-r'ham, to I-saac re-newed
por-tion to stand, the coun-try of Ca-naan, the beau-ti-ful land."
trav-elled a-round; wher-ev-er they wan-dered, no rest could be found.
Me they be-long; re-spect My own pro-phets and do them no wrong

7. The LORD called down famine upon the whole land;
   their food was destroyed at His sovereign command.
   But He sent beforehand, His people to save,
   His chosen one, Joseph, sold off as a slave.

8. His feet within shackles of bronze were confined,
   his neck put in irons; for freedom he pined.
   The word of the LORD was a test to be passed
   till what He foretold was accomplished at last.

9. The king sent an order to let him go free;
   the ruler of nations gave him liberty.
   He put him in charge of his house and his lands;
   his princes and elders obeyed his commands.

10. Then Israel came down into Egypt to stay,
    in Ham's land to sojourn for many a day.
    The LORD caused His people to prosper and grow,
    and so they were seen as a threat to their foe.

11. He turned the Egyptians against Israèl,
    and caused them to plot His own servants to kill.
    Then Moses and Aaron, His chosen, He sent;
    performing His wonders, to Egypt they went.

12. Because the Egyptians despised His command,
    He sent utter darkness to cover the land.
    Their waters and rivers He turned into blood;
    the fish of the Nile were destroyed by the LORD.

13. Their land teemed with frogs, which invaded their rooms;
    at His word swarms of flies and of gnats filled their homes.
    The rain became hail, and the lightning bolts flashed;
    He struck down their vines, and their fig trees were smashed.

14. He spoke, and the locusts and grasshoppers came;
    and every green thing was consumed as by flame.
    And then He took vengeance on all the first-born—
    the firstfruits of manhood of Egypt were gone.

15. He brought Isr'el out, bearing silver and gold;
    their tribes all marched forwards both steadfast and bold.
    Then Egypt was joyful to see them depart,
    For terror of them had laid hold of their heart.

16. He spread out a cloud to protect them from sight,
    and fire to illumine the hours of the night.
    They asked, and with quails were abundantly fed;
    He filled them with manna, the heavenly bread.

17. He opened the rock to give waters to them,
    and there in the desert it flowed like a stream—
    Because He remembered the promise He swore
    to Abr'ham His servant, long ages before.

18. He brought out His chosen ones, shouting with joy;
    He granted to them without toil to enjoy
    the lands of the nations—that they might regard
    His laws and His precepts. All praise to the LORD!

106   O Praise the Lord, for He Is Good

The Psalter, 1912, alt.   OESTREICH   Josh Bauder © 2017
                CMD

1. O praise the LORD, for He is good, give thanks and bless His name; His lov-ing-kind-ness chang-es not, from age to age the same. What tongue can tell His

2. The LORD will bless and pros-per those— yea, blest in-deed are they— whose ways are just, who con-stant-ly His right-eous laws o-bey. O LORD, re-mem-ber

3. Let me be-hold Your peo-ple's good and in their joy re-joice; with Your tri-um-phant her-i-tage let me lift up my voice. In e-vil we have

4. Tho' they re-belled, yet for their help in sav-ing strength He came to make His pow'r al-might-y known and glo-ri-fy His name. He brought them safe-ly

5. For-get-ful soon, they tempt-ed God, nor for His coun-sel cared; He sent them lean-ness in their souls, while they earth's boun-ties shared. Their God and Sav-ior

6. But they de-spised the pleas-ant land, the prom-ised land of God, and tempt-ed Him to make them fall and scat-tered them a-broad. A-gainst His own in-

7. Save us, O LORD, our gra-cious God, from a-lien lands re-claim, that we may tri-umph in Your praise and bless Your ho-ly name. Blest be the Lord, our

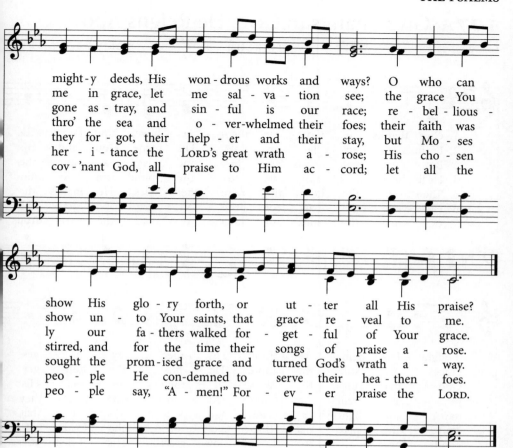

might-y deeds, His won-drous works and ways? O who can
me in grace, let me sal - va - tion see; the grace You
gone as - tray, and sin - ful is our race; re - bel - lious -
thro' the sea and o - ver-whelmed their foes; their faith was
they for - got, their help - er and their stay, but Mo - ses
her - i - tance the LORD's great wrath a - rose; His cho - sen
cov - 'nant God, all praise to Him ac - cord; let all the

show His glo - ry forth, or ut - ter all His praise?
show un - to Your saints, that grace re - veal to me.
ly our fa - thers walked for - get - ful of Your grace.
stirred, and for the time their songs of praise a - rose.
sought the prom - ised grace and turned God's wrath a - way.
peo - ple He con-demned to serve their hea - then foes.
peo - ple say, "A - men!" For - ev - er praise the LORD.

107A Give Thanks to God, He Reigns Above

Isaac Watts, 1719

PUER NOBIS
LM

Trier manuscript, 15th cent
adapt. Michael Praetorius, 160

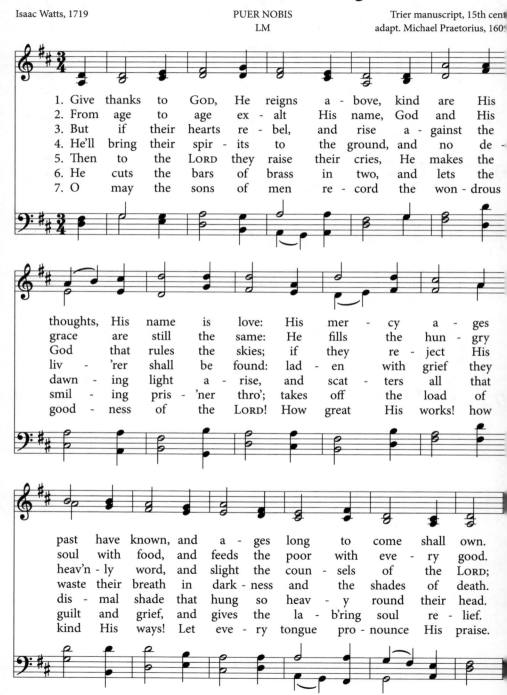

1. Give thanks to God, He reigns above, kind are His
2. From age to age ex-alt His name, God and His
3. But if their hearts re-bel, and rise a-gainst the
4. He'll bring their spir-its to the ground, and no de-
5. Then to the Lord they raise their cries, He makes the
6. He cuts the bars of brass in two, and lets the
7. O may the sons of men re-cord the won-drous

thoughts, His name is love: His mer-cy a-ges
grace are still the same: He fills the hun-gry
God that rules the skies; if they re-ject His
liv-'rer shall be found: lad-en with grief they
dawn-ing light a-rise, and scat-ters all that
smil-ing pris-'ner thro'; takes off the load of
good-ness of the Lord! How great His works! how

past have known, and a-ges long to come shall own.
soul with food, and feeds the poor with eve-ry good.
heav'n-ly word, and slight the coun-sels of the Lord;
waste their breath in dark-ness and the shades of death.
dis-mal shade that hung so heav-y round their head.
guilt and grief, and gives the la-b'ring soul re-lief.
kind His ways! Let eve-ry tongue pro-nounce His praise.

Praise the LORD, for He Is Good   107B

the Psalter, 1912

DIX
77 77 77

Conrad Kocher, 1838
adapt. William Henry Monk, 1861
harm. *The English Hymnal*, 1906

1. Praise the LORD, for He is good, for His mer - cies ev - er sure
2. From cap - ti - vi - ty re - leased, from the south and from the north,
3. Wan - d'ring in the wil - der - ness, far they roamed the des - ert way,
4. To Je - ho - vah then they cried in their trou - ble, and He saved;
5. Sons of men, a - wake to praise God the LORD who reigns a - bove,

from e - ter - ni - ty have stood, to e - ter - ni - ty en - dure;
from the west and from the east, in His love He brought them forth,
found no set - tled dwell - ing - place where in peace se - cure to stay,
He Him - self be - came their guide, led them to the rest they craved
gra - cious in His works and ways, won - drous in re - deem - ing love;

let His ran - somed peo - ple raise songs to their Re - deem - er's praise.
ran - somed out of eve - ry land from the ad - ver - sar - y's hand.
till with thirst and hun - ger pressed cour - age sank with - in their breast.
by a path - way straight and sure, to a cit - y strong, se - cure.
long - ing souls He sat - is - fies, hun - gry hearts with good sup - plies.

108   O Lord God, My Heart Is Steadfast

Sing Psalms © 2003   PLEADING SAVIOR   Leavitt's *The Christian Lyre*, 183
               87 87 D

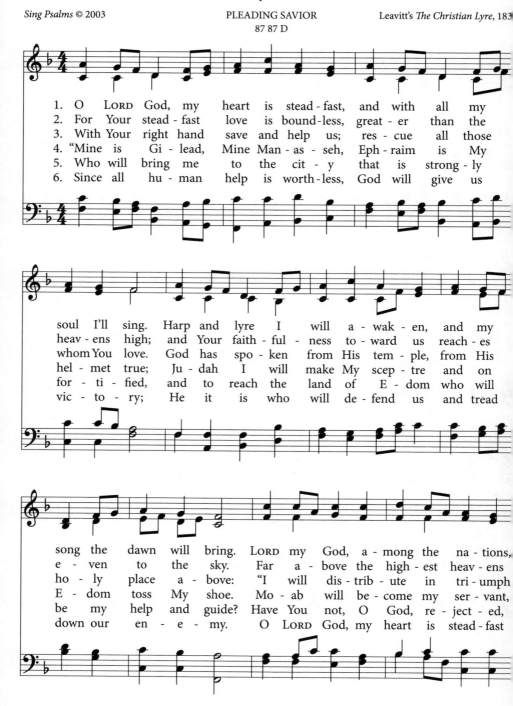

1. O Lord God, my heart is stead-fast, and with all my
2. For Your stead-fast love is bound-less, great-er than the
3. With Your right hand save and help us; res-cue all those
4. "Mine is Gi-lead, Mine Man-as-seh, Eph-raim is My
5. Who will bring me to the cit-y that is strong-ly
6. Since all hu-man help is worth-less, God will give us

soul I'll sing. Harp and lyre I will a-wak-en, and my
heav-ens high; and Your faith-ful-ness to-ward us reach-es
whom You love. God has spo-ken from His tem-ple, from His
hel-met true; Ju-dah I will make My scep-tre and on
for-ti-fied, and to reach the land of E-dom who will
vic-to-ry; He it is who will de-fend us and tread

song the dawn will bring. Lord my God, a-mong the na-tions,
e-ven to the sky. Far a-bove the high-est heav-ens
ho-ly place a-bove: "I will dis-trib-ute in tri-umph
E-dom toss My shoe. Mo-ab will be-come my ser-vant,
be my help and guide? Have You not, O God, re-ject-ed,
down our en-e-my. O Lord God, my heart is stead-fast

I will ev - er give You praise; in the midst of
be ex - alt - ed, O my God; and through all the
eve - ry part of She - chem's land, and the whole of
and up - on Phil - is - tia's shore I will shout a -
turned us o - ver to our foe? When our ar - mies
and with all my soul I'll sing. Harp and lyre I

all the peo - ples I will sing of You al - ways.
earth a - round us let Your glo - ry spread a - broad.
Suc - coth val - ley I will mea - sure with My hand."
loud in tri - umph; I am LORD and Con - quer - or."
go to bat - tle, with them You no long - er go.
will a - wak - en, and my song the dawn shall bring.

109 God of My Mercy and My Praise

st. 1 Isaac Watts, 1719　　　　　　ST. ETHELDREDA　　　　　　Thomas Turton, 18(

st. 2–5 *The Psalter*, 1912　　　　　　CM

1. God of my mer - cy and my praise, Thy glo - ry is my song;
2. O GOD, my Lord, for Thy Name's sake in mer - cy deal with me;
3. O Thou who art my LORD and God, Thy gra - cious help ex - tend,
4. My voice shall great - ly bless the LORD and sing His worth - y praise
5. The LORD be praised, for ev - er near the help - less poor He stands

tho' sin - ners speak a - gainst Thy grace with a blas - phem - ing tongue
be - cause Thy kind - ness is so great, from trou - ble set me free.
and for Thy lov - ing - kind - ness' sake O save me and de - fend.
and I a - mid the mul - ti - tude my thank - ful song will raise.
pro - tect - ing them with won - drous pow'r from their op - pres - sors' hands.

The LORD Declares unto My Lord — 110

avid P. Regier © 2017

ELLACOMBE
CMD

Vollstandige-Sammlung, 1827
adapt. William Henry Monk, 1868

1. The LORD de-clares un-to my Lord, "Be seat-ed by My throne,
2. Thy youth, Thy peo-ple, on that day, shall rise up in Thy pow'r;
3. The Lord is at the LORD's right hand to shat-ter in that day

un-til Thine en-e-mies shall be a foot-stool of Thine own."
in ho-ly splen-dor's fine ar-ray to greet dawn's warm-ing hour.
the kings of earth in His bright wrath, His judg-ment to dis-play.

From Zi-on shall Thy scep-ter be ex-tend-ed forth in strength;
The LORD hath sworn and will not change; e-ter-nal, His de-cree:
He crush-es rul-ers from a-broad, fills na-tions with their dead;

and by Thy God, Thine en-e-my shall bow be-fore Thy name.
as once Mel-chiz-e-dek did reign, Thou Priest and King shall be.
He drinks from streams be-side the road, and there lifts up His head.

111 Praise the LORD with Exaltation

Charles H. Spurgeon, 1866   STUTTGART   Witt's *Psalmodia Sacra*, Gotha, 1715
                                     87 87

1. Praise the LORD with ex - al - ta - tion, my whole
2. All His works are great and glo - rious, saints re -
3. Strength He gives to those who fear Him, of His
4. For His grace stands fast for - ev - er, His de -
5. There - fore be His praise un - ceas - ing, be His

heart my LORD shall praise; with the ran - somed
view them with de - light; His re - demp - tion
cov - 'nant mind - ful still; wise they are who
crees the saints se - cure; from His oath He
name for ev - er blest; and with con - fi -

con - gre - ga - tion wor - thy hal - le - lu - jahs raise.
all vic - to - rious we rem - em - ber day and night.
much re - vere Him, and re - joice to do His will.
turn - eth nev - er, eve - ry prom - ise stand - eth sure.
dence in - creas - ing, let us on His prom - ise rest.

Praise God! Blessed Is the Man

112

ng Psalms © 2003

TOULON
10 10 10 10

Geneva *Psalter*, 1551

1. Praise God! Blessed is the man who fears the LORD and finds de-
2. Rich - es and wealth with - in his house are found; his right-eous-
3. Good is the man who gives and free - ly lends; to his af -
4. Though bad news comes, he will not be a - fraid; his heart is
5. He free - ly shares his rich - es with the poor; his right-eous-
6. The wick - ed, see - ing this, will feel dis - may; he'll gnash his

light in fol - low - ing His word. His chil - dren will be might - y
ness for ev - er will a - bound. The man who stands for mer - cy,
fairs with jus - tice he at - tends. Sure - ly a right - eous man will
firm; he trusts the LORD for aid. He will not be a - larmed, his
ness for ev - er will en - dure. The LORD Him - self ex - alts His
teeth and soon will waste a - way. The wick - ed and their dreams will

in the land; his line will know the bless - ing of God's hand.
truth, and right will find the dark - ness turn to morn - ing light.
stand se - cure; his mem - o - ry for ev - er will en - dure.
heart holds fast; he'll view his foes in tri - umph at the last.
ser - vant's name; He gives him strength and dig - ni - ty and fame.
come to nought; they nev - er will en - joy what they have sought.

113 Hallelujah! Raise, O Raise

Josiah Conder, 1854

MONKLAND   J. Freylinghausen's *Geistreiches Gesangbuch*, 1704
77 77
adapt. John Antes, c. 1800
arr. John Wilkes, 1861

1. Hal - le - lu - jah! raise, O raise to the LORD our song of praise;
2. Bless - ed be for - ev - er - more that great name which we a - dore;
3. O'er all na - tions God a - lone, high - er than the heav'ns His throne
4. From the dust He lifts the poor, from the ash - es those for - lorn;
5. He the bar - ren wo - man takes, and a joy - ful moth - er makes;

praise, O ser - vants of the LORD, praise the name of God our LORD!
dawn to dusk, from east to west let the LORD's great name be blest.
who is like the LORD most high, gaz - ing down on earth and sky?
those He's raised up from the pit with His peo - ple's princ - es sit.
she finds joy in His re - ward. Hal - le - lu - jah! Praise the LORD!

When Israel out of Egypt Went

114

Psalter, 1912   DUKE STREET   John Hatton, 1793
LM

1. When Is - rael out of E - gypt went, from peo - ple
2. The sea be - held and fled a - way, the Jor - dan's
3. What ail - eth thee, O trou - bled sea? Thou Jor - dan,
4. O trem - ble, earth, be - fore the LORD, in pres - ence

of a speech un - known, the LORD a - mong His
wa - ters back - ward turned, the loft - y moun - tains
why thy riv - en tide? Ye moun - tains and ye
of Je - ho - vah fear, be - neath whose touch the

peo - ple dwelt, and there He set His roy - al throne.
and the hills with trem - bling awe our God dis - cerned.
lit - tle hills, why thus dis - mayed on eve - ry side?
flint - y rock be - came a fount of wa - ters clear.

115 Not to Our Names, Thou Only Just

Isaac Watts, 1719

FINLANDIA
10 10 10 10 10 10

Jean Sibelius, 18

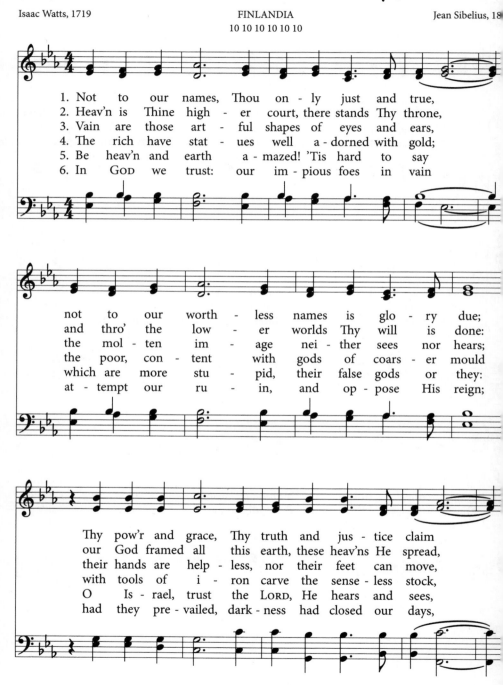

1. Not to our names, Thou on - ly just and true,
2. Heav'n is Thine high - er court, there stands Thy throne,
3. Vain are those art - ful shapes of eyes and ears,
4. The rich have stat - ues well a - dorned with gold;
5. Be heav'n and earth a - mazed! 'Tis hard to say
6. In GOD we trust: our im - pious foes in vain

not to our worth - less names is glo - ry due;
and thro' the low - er worlds Thy will is done;
the mol - ten im - age nei - ther sees nor hears;
the poor, con - tent with gods of coars - er mould
which are more stu - pid, their false gods or they:
at - tempt our ru - in, and op - pose His reign;

Thy pow'r and grace, Thy truth and jus - tice claim
our God framed all this earth, these heav'ns He spread,
their hands are help - less, nor their feet can move,
with tools of i - ron carve the sense - less stock,
O Is - rael, trust the LORD, He hears and sees,
had they pre - vailed, dark - ness had closed our days,

im - mor - tal hon - ors to Thy sov - 'reign name.
but fools a - dore the gods their hands have made;
they have no speech, nor thought, nor pow'r, nor love;
lopped from a tree, or bro - ken from a rock;
He knows thy sor - rows and re - stores thy peace:
and death and si - lence had for - bid His praise;

Shine thro' the earth from heav'n, Thy blest a - bode
the kneel - ing crowd, with looks de - vout, be - hold
yet fool - ish mor - tals make their long com - plaints
peo - ple and priests drive on the sol - emn trade,
His wor - ship does a thou - sand com - forts yield,
but we are saved and live: let songs a - rise,

nor let the heath - ens say, "And where's your God?"
their sil - ver - sav - iors, and their saints of gold.
to their deaf i - dols, and un - mov - ing saints.
and trust the gods that saws and ham - mers made.
He is thy help, and He thy heav'n - ly shield.
and Zi - on bless the GOD that built the skies.

116   I Love the LORD, Who Heard My Cry

The Psalter, 1912

LAND OF REST
CM

Traditional American melody
arr. Annabel M. Buchanan, 1938

1. I love the LORD, who heard my cry and
2. With dead - ly sor - rows com - passed round, my
3. The Lord is just and mer - ci - ful, and
4. Re - turn un - to thy rest, my soul, no
5. Be - fore my Sav - ior I will live, from
6. What shall I ren - der to the Lord, what

grant - ed my re - quest; in Him who hears and
heart was full of grief; then to the LORD I
gra - cious to the meek; He saved me when I
long - er trou - bled be; the Lord sus - tains thee,
death He saved my soul, my eyes from tears, my
shall my of - f'ring be, for all the gra - cious

an - swers pray'r my trust through life shall rest.
made my pray'r that He would send re - lief.
cried to Him, though I was poor and weak.
and has dealt most gra - cious - ly with thee.
feet from falls, and He has made me whole.
ben - e - fits He has be - stowed on me?

7. Salvation's cup my soul will take
while to the Lord I pray,
and with His people I will meet,
my thankful vows to pay.

8. Not lightly does the Lord permit
His chosen saints to die;
from death Thou hast delivered me,
Thy servant, Lord, am I.

9. The sacrifice of praise I bring
while to the Lord I pray,
and with His people I will meet,
my thankful vows to pay.

10. Within His house, the house of prayer,
my soul shall bless the Lord,
and praise to His holy Name
let all His saints accord.

Praise Jehovah, All Ye Nations

117

e Psalter, 1912   AUSTRIAN HYMN   Franz Joseph Haydn, 1797
87 87 D

Praise Je-hov-ah, all ye na-tions, all ye peo-ple, praise pro-claim;

for His grace and lov-ing-kind-ness, O, sing prais-es to His name.

For the great-ness of His mer-cy con-stant praise to Him ac-cord;

ev - er-more His truth en-dur-eth; hal - le - lu - jah, praise the LORD.

118   The Glorious Gates of Righteousness

The Psalter, 1912   CORONATION   Oliver Holden, 17
                                86 86 86

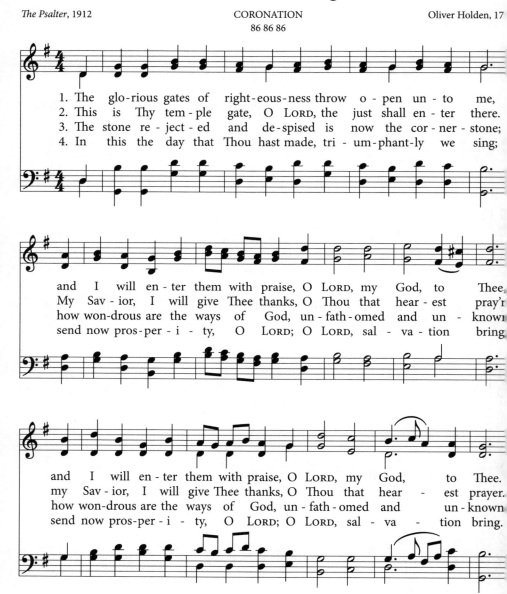

1. The glo-rious gates of right-eous-ness throw o-pen un-to me,
2. This is Thy tem-ple gate, O Lord, the just shall en-ter there.
3. The stone re-ject-ed and de-spised is now the cor-ner-stone;
4. In this the day that Thou hast made, tri-um-phant-ly we sing;

and I will en-ter them with praise, O Lord, my God, to Thee,
My Sav-ior, I will give Thee thanks, O Thou that hear-est pray'r
how won-drous are the ways of God, un-fath-omed and un-known
send now pros-per-i-ty, O Lord; O Lord, sal-va-tion bring

and I will en-ter them with praise, O Lord, my God, to Thee.
my Sav-ior, I will give Thee thanks, O Thou that hear-est prayer.
how won-drous are the ways of God, un-fath-omed and un-known
send now pros-per-i-ty, O Lord; O Lord, sal-va-tion bring.

How Blessed the Perfect in the Way **119A**

e Psalter, 1912
1–8

ROCKINGHAM
LM

A. Williams's *Supplement to Psalmody*, 1780
harm. Edward Miller, 1790

1. How blessed the per - fect in the way who from GOD's
2. Yea, they are kept from paths of sin who walk in
3. My wav - 'ring heart is now re - solved Thy ho - ly
4. Up - on Thy pre - cepts and Thy ways my heart will

law do not de - part, who, hold - ing fast the
God's ap - point - ed way; Thy pre - cepts Thou hast
stat - utes to ful - fill; no more shall I be
med - i - tate with awe; Thy word shall be my

word of truth, seek Him with un - di - vid - ed heart.
giv - en us that we should faith - ful - ly o - bey.
brought to shame when I re - gard Thy ho - ly will.
chief de - light, and I will not for - get Thy law.

119B How Shall the Young Direct Their Way?

The Psalter, 1912
vv 9–16

MARYTON
LM

H. Percy Smith, 1874

1. How shall the young di - rect their way? What light shall
2. Sin - cere - ly I have sought Thee, Lord, O let me
3. O bless - ed LORD, teach me Thy law, Thy right - eous
4. Up - on Thy pre - cepts and Thy ways my heart will

be their per - fect guide? Thy word, O LORD, will
not from Thee de - part; to know Thy will and
judg - ments I de - clare; Thy tes - ti - mo - nies
med - i - tate with awe; Thy word shall be my

safe - ly lead, if in its wis - dom they con - fide.
keep from sin Thy word I cher - ish in my heart.
make me glad, for they are wealth be - yond com - pare.
chief de - light, and I will not for - get Thy law.

Thy Servant, Blessed by Thee, Shall Live 119C

The Psalter, 1912
vv 17–24

ARLINGTON
CM

Thomas Arne, 1762

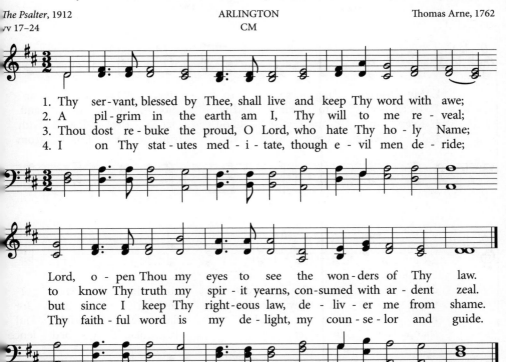

1. Thy ser-vant, blessed by Thee, shall live and keep Thy word with awe;
2. A pil-grim in the earth am I, Thy will to me re-veal;
3. Thou dost re-buke the proud, O Lord, who hate Thy ho-ly Name;
4. I on Thy stat-utes med-i-tate, though e-vil men de-ride;

Lord, o-pen Thou my eyes to see the won-ders of Thy law.
to know Thy truth my spir-it yearns, con-sumed with ar-dent zeal.
but since I keep Thy right-eous law, de-liv-er me from shame.
Thy faith-ful word is my de-light, my coun-se-lor and guide.

Most merciful God, author of all good things, who has given Thy holy commandments unto us whereby we should direct our life; imprint them in our hearts by Thy Holy Spirit; and grant that we may so renounce all our fleshly desires and all the vanities of this world, that our whole pleasure and delight may be in Thy law; that we, being always governed by Thy holy word, may in the end attain to that eternal salvation, which You have promised through Christ Jesus, Thy Son. Amen.

The Scottish Collects, 1595

119D   My Grieving Soul Revive, O Lord

The Psalter, 1912   MARTYRDOM   Hugh Wilson, 1824
vv 25–32   CM

1. My griev - ing soul re - vive, O Lord, ac -
2. Teach me to know Thy ho - ly way and
3. Keep me from false - hood, let Thy law with
4. I cleave un - to Thy truth, O LORD; from

cord - ing to Thy word; to Thee my ways I
think up - on Thy deeds; in grief I ask for
me in grace a - bide; the way of faith - ful -
shame de - liv - er me; in glad o - bed - ience

have de - clared, and Thou my prayer hast heard.
prom - ised grace ac - cord - ing to my needs.
ness I choose, Thy pre - cepts are my guide.
I will live through strength be - stowed by Thee.

Teach Me, O Lord, Thy Way of Truth **119E**

e *Psalter*, 1912
33–40

OLIVE'S BROW
LM

William B. Bradbury, 1853

1. Teach me, O Lord, Thy way of truth, and from it
2. In Thy com-mand-ments make me walk, for in Thy
3. Turn Thou my eyes from van - i - ty, and cause me
4. Turn Thou a - way re - proach and fear; Thy right - eous

I will not de - part; that I may stead - fast -
law my joy shall be; give me a heart that
in Thy ways to tread; O let Thy ser - vant
judg - ments I con - fess; to know Thy pre - cepts

ly o - bey, give me an un - der - stand - ing heart.
loves Thy will, from dis - con - tent and en - vy free.
prove Thy word and thus to god - ly fear be led.
I de - sire, re - vive me in Thy right - eous - ness.

119F Thy Promised Mercies Send to Me

The Psalter, 1912
vv 41–48

ST. AGNES
CM

John B. Dykes, 18

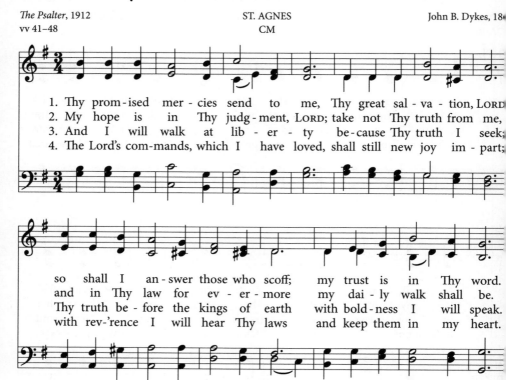

1. Thy prom-ised mer - cies send to me, Thy great sal - va - tion, LORD,
2. My hope is in Thy judg - ment, LORD; take not Thy truth from me,
3. And I will walk at lib - er - ty be-cause Thy truth I seek;
4. The Lord's com-mands, which I have loved, shall still new joy im - part;

so shall I an - swer those who scoff; my trust is in Thy word.
and in Thy law for ev - er - more my dai - ly walk shall be.
Thy truth be - fore the kings of earth with bold-ness I will speak.
with rev-'rence I will hear Thy laws and keep them in my heart.

Lord, Thy Word to Me Remember · 119G

ıe Psalter, 1912   EBENEZER   Thomas J. Williams, 1890
49–56   87 87

1. Lord, Thy word to me re-mem-ber, Thou hast made me hope in Thee;
2. Wick-ed men Thy law for-sak-ing stirred my in-dig-na-tion strong,

this my com-fort in af-flic-tion that Thy word hath quick-ened me.
for in all my pil-grim jour-ney Thy com-mand-ments are my song.

Mocked by those who are un-right-eous, still to Thy com-mands I cleave;
Thou hast been my med-i-ta-tion and Thy law hath been my guide;

think-ing on Thy form-er judg-ments, help and com-fort I re-ceive.
I have kept Thy right-eous pre-cepts, and have found them true and tried.

119H Thou Art My Portion, LORD

The Psalter, 1912
vv 57–64

BOYLSTON
SM

Lowell Mason, 18?

1. Thou art my por - tion, LORD; Thy words I ev - er heed;
2. I thought up - on my ways, Thy tes - ti - mo - nies learned
3. While snares be - set my path, Thy law I keep in view;
4. All those who fear Thy Name shall my com-pan - ions be;

with all my heart Thy grace I seek, Thy prom - is - es I plead.
with ear - nest haste, and wait - ing not, to Thy com-mands I turned.
at mid-night I will give Thee praise for all Thy judg - ments true.
Thy mer - cy fills the earth, O LORD; Thy stat - utes teach Thou me.

According to Your Word, O Lord　1191

Book of Psalms for Worship © 2010
vv 65–72

WINCHESTER OLD
CM

Este's *Psalmes*, 1592

1. Ac - cord - ing　to　Your word, O Lord, You　have Your　ser - vant blessed.
2. I　strayed　be - fore　You hum - bled me; Your　word　I　now　o - bey.
3. The proud have smeared me with their lies; Your　pre - cepts　are　my　choice.
4. Af - flic - tion　has　been　good　for me, Your　laws　I've learned to　hold

Teach me　good judg - ment, knowl - edge give;　on　Your com - mands I　rest.
For　You　are　good; Your　deeds　are　good. Teach me Your　stat - utes'　way.
Their hearts, en - closed　in　fat,　are　dull;　I　in　Your　law re - joice.
as　far　more pre - cious　than great stores of　sil - ver　and　of　gold.

119J Thou, Who Didst Make and Fashion Me

The Psalter, 1912
vv 73–80

BLOCKLEY
LM

Thomas Blockley, 186

1. Thou, who didst make and fash - ion me, O make me wise, Thy law to learn; then they that fear Thee shall be glad when they my hope in God dis - cern.

2. Thou, LORD, art just in all Thy ways, and faith - ful when Thou chast'n - est me; I pray Thee, let Thy prom - ised grace Thy ser - vant's help and com - fort be.

3. Show mer - cy, Lord, that I may live, for in Thy law is all my joy; while those who wrong me are re - buked, Thy pre - cepts shall my thought em - ploy.

4. Let those that fear Thee turn to me, Thy truth to them will I pro - claim; in - struct my heart to keep Thy law, that I may not be put to shame.

My Soul for Thy Salvation Faints   **119K**

The Psalter, 1912   ESSLINGEN   Adam Krieger, 1667
v 81–88   CM

1. My soul for Thy sal - va - tion faints, but still I hope in Thee;
2. Thy stat - utes I do not for - get, though wast-ing grief I know;
3. The proud, dis - dain - ful of Thy law, en - trap me wrong-ful - ly;
4. Al - most con-sumed, yet from Thy law I have not turned a - way;

I long to see Thy prom-ised help, when Thou shalt com-fort me.
Thy ser-vant's days are few, O Lord; when wilt Thou judge my foe?
O Thou, whose law is just and true, help and de - liv - er me.
in lov - ing-kind-ness give me strength, that I may still o - bey.

119L Forever Settled in the Heavens

The Psalter, 1912
vv 89–96

BOURBON
LM

Hesperian Harp, 184
harm. Louise McAllister, 195

1. For - ev - er set - tled in the heav'ns, Thy word, O
2. Thy word and works un - moved re - main, Thy eve - ry
3. I should have per - ished in my woe had not I
4. The wick - ed would de - stroy my soul, but on Thy

LORD, shall firm - ly stand; Thy faith - ful - ness shall
pur - pose to ful - fill; all things are Thine and
loved Thy law di - vine; that law I nev - er
truth I muse with awe; im - per - fect I have

nev - er fail; the earth a - bides at Thy com - mand.
Thee o - bey, and all as ser - vants wait Thy will.
can for - get; O save me, Lord, for I am Thine.
found all else, but bound - less is Thy won - drous law.

How I Love Thy Law, O Lord! 119M

The Psalter, 1912
v 97–104

CANTERBURY
77 77

Orlando Gibbons, 1623

1. How I love Thy law, O Lord! Dai - ly joy its truths af - ford;
2. Thy com-mand-ments in my heart tru - est wis - dom can im - part;
3. While my heart Thy word o - beys, I am kept from e - vil ways;
4. Sweet - er are Thy words to me than all oth - er good can be;

in its con - stant light I go, wise to con - quer eve - ry foe.
to my eyes Thy pre - cepts show wis - dom more than sa - ges know.
from Thy law, with Thee to guide, I have nev - er turned a - side.
safe I walk, Thy truth my light, hat - ing false-hood, lov - ing right.

119N Thy Word Sheds Light upon My Path

The Psalter, 1912
vv 105–112

DISTRESS
LM

William Walker's *Southern Harmony*, 183

1. Thy Word sheds light up - on my path; a shin - ing
2. In my dis - tress I plead with Thee, send help ac -
3. In dan - ger oft and nigh to death, Thy law re -
4. Thy pre - cepts are my her - i - tage, for dai - ly

light, it guides my feet; Thy right - eous judg - ments
cord - ing to Thy Word; ac - cept my sac - ri -
mem - bered is my aid; the wick - ed seek my
they my heart re - joice; to keep Thy stat - utes

to ob - serve my sol - emn vow I now re - peat.
fice of praise and make me know Thy judg - ments, Lord.
o - ver - throw, yet from Thy truth I have not strayed.
faith - ful - ly shall ev - er be my will - ing choice.

Deceit and Falsehood I Abhor   **1190**

The Psalter, 1912
v 113–120

VATER UNSER
88 88 88

attr. Martin Luther,
Valentin Schumann's *Geistliche Lieder*, 1539

1. De - ceit and false - hood I ab - hor, but love Thy
2. Ac - cord - ing to Thy gra - cious word up - hold me,
3. The fro - ward Thou hast set at naught who vain - ly

law, Thy truth re - vealed; my stead - fast hope is in Thy word;
Lord, de - liv - er me; O do not let me be a - shamed
wan - der from the right; the wick - ed Thou dost count as dross;

Thou art my ref - uge and my shield; the paths of
of pa - tient hope and trust in Thee; O hold Thou
Thy just de - crees are my de - light; for fear of

sin I have not trod, but kept the pre - cepts of my God.
me, and I shall stand and ev - er fol - low Thy com - mand.
Thee I stand in awe and rev - 'rence Thy most ho - ly law.

119P   I Have Followed Truth and Justice

The Psalter, 1912   RESTORATION   William Walker's *Southern Harmony,* 183
vv 121–128   87 87

1. I   have fol-lowed truth and jus - tice; leave me not in   deep dis-tress
2. For Thy word and Thy sal - va - tion, Lord, my eyes with long-ing fail;
3. I   am Thine, O   give me   wis - dom, make me know Thy truth, I pray:
4. Lord, I   love Thy good com-mand-ments and es-teem them more than gold

be   my help and my pro - tec - tion, let the proud no   more op-press.
teach Thy stat - utes to Thy ser - vant, let Thy mer - cy   now pre-vail.
sin - ners have de-spised Thy stat - utes; now, O LORD, Thy pow'r dis-play.
all   Thy pre-cepts are most right-eous; hat - ing sin, to   these I hold.

Thy Wondrous Testimonies, Lord   119Q

ie Psalter, 1912   QUEBEC   Henry Baker, 1854
129–136   LM

1. Thy won - drous tes - ti - mo - nies, Lord, my soul will
2. I thirst for Thy com - mand - ments, Lord, and for Thy
3. Di - rect my foot - steps in Thy word, from sin's do -
4. O make Thy face to shine on me, and teach me

keep and great - ly praise; Thy word, by faith - ful
mer - cy press my claim; O look on me, and
min - ion save my soul, from man's op - pres - sion
all Thy laws to keep; be - cause Thy stat - utes

lips pro - claimed, to sim - plest minds the truth con - veys.
show the grace dis - played to all who love Thy name.
set me free, that I may yield to Thy con - trol.
are de - spised, with o - ver - whelm - ing grief I weep.

119R O Lord, Thy Perfect Righteousness

The Psalter, 1912
vv 137–144

BURFORD
CM

A. Williams's *Supplement to Psalmody*, c. 178
harm. Edward Miller, 179

1. O Lord, Thy per - fect right - eous - ness is
2. Be - cause Thy foes for - get Thy law my
3. Though I am hum - ble and de - spised, I
4. De - light a - mid dis - tress and pain do

in Thy judg - ments shown; in Thy un - chang - ing
soul is great - ly stirred; Thy ser - vant loves the
strive Thy will to do; e - ter - nal is Thy
Thy com - mand - ments give; Thy word is right - eous

faith - ful - ness Thy truth Thou hast made known.
pu - ri - ty of Thy most ho - ly word.
right - eous - ness, and all Thy law is true.
ev - er - more, teach me that I may live.

O Lord, My Earnest Cry

119S

The Psalter, 1912
vv 145–152

SOUTHWELL
SM

William Daman
The Psalmes of David, 1579

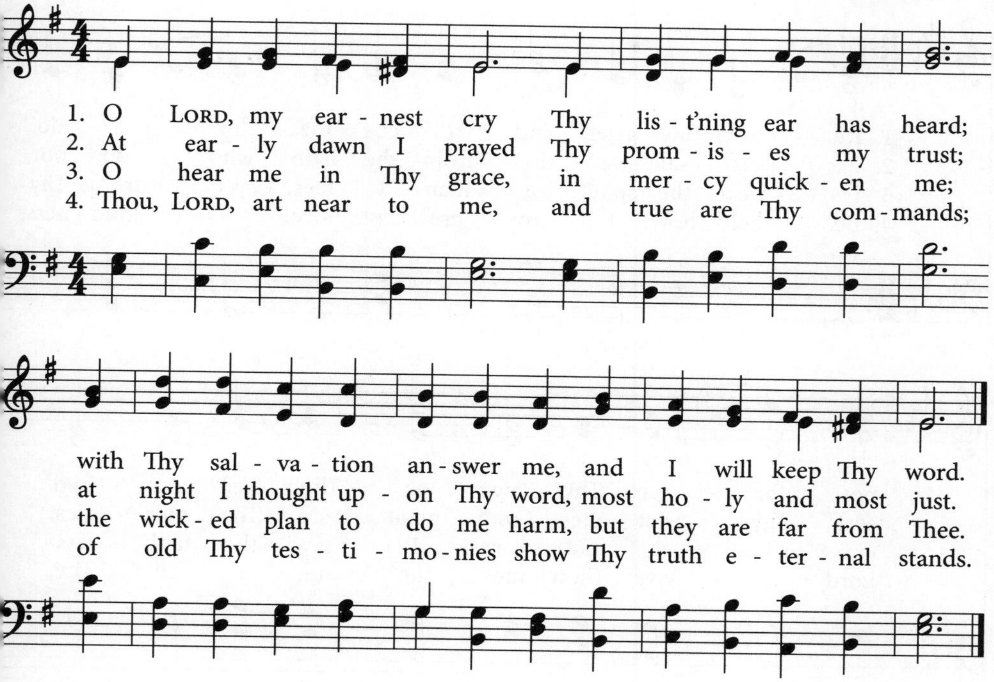

1. O Lord, my ear - nest cry Thy lis - t'ning ear has heard;
2. At ear - ly dawn I prayed Thy prom - is - es my trust;
3. O hear me in Thy grace, in mer - cy quick - en me;
4. Thou, Lord, art near to me, and true are Thy com - mands;

with Thy sal - va - tion an - swer me, and I will keep Thy word.
at night I thought up - on Thy word, most ho - ly and most just.
the wick - ed plan to do me harm, but they are far from Thee.
of old Thy tes - ti - mo - nies show Thy truth e - ter - nal stands.

119T Regard My Grief and Rescue Me

The Psalter, 1912
vv 153–160

KEDRON
LM

attr. Elkanah Kelsay Dare, 179[?]

1. Re - gard my grief and res - cue me, for I do
2. Far is sal - va - tion from the man who do not
3. I bear the spite of man - y foes, yet from Thy
4. Be - hold how I Thy pre - cepts love! In kind - ness,

not for - get Thy laws; as Thou hast prom - ised,
seek Thy stat - utes, LORD; great are Thy mer - cies,
law I do not swerve; I saw the faith - less
Lord, re - vive Thou me; the sum of all Thy

save me, Lord; re - deem my soul, and plead my cause.
quick - en me ac - cord - ing to Thy ho - ly word.
and was grieved, for they Thy word do not ob - serve.
word is truth, Thy word a - bides e - ter - nal - ly.

Though Mighty Foes Assail Me, Lord 119U

Psalter, 1912
161–168

MORNING SONG
CM

Traditional American melody
Kentucky Harmony, 1813

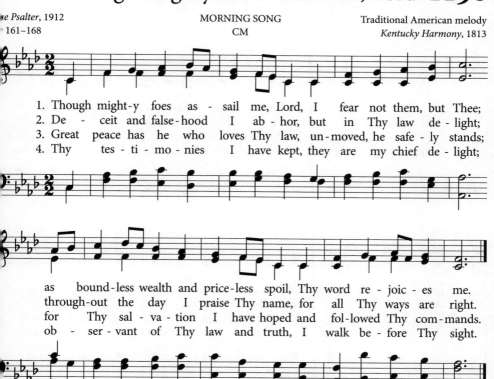

1. Though might-y foes as - sail me, Lord, I fear not them, but Thee;
2. De - ceit and false-hood I ab - hor, but in Thy law de - light;
3. Great peace has he who loves Thy law, un - moved, he safe - ly stands;
4. Thy tes - ti - mo - nies I have kept, they are my chief de - light;

as bound-less wealth and price-less spoil, Thy word re - joic - es me.
through-out the day I praise Thy name, for all Thy ways are right.
for Thy sal - va - tion I have hoped and fol-lowed Thy com-mands.
ob - ser - vant of Thy law and truth, I walk be - fore Thy sight.

119V O Let My Supplicating Cry

The Psalter, 1912
vv 169–176

DISTRESS
LM

William Walker's *Southern Harmony*, 183

1. O let my sup - pli - cat - ing cry by Thee, my
2. In - struct - ed in Thy ho - ly law, to praise Thy
3. For Thy sal - va - tion I have longed, and in Thy
4. Thy ser - vant like a wan - d'ring sheep has lost the

gra - cious LORD, be heard; give wis - dom and de -
word I lift my voice; O Lord, be Thou my
law is my de - light; en - rich my soul with
path and gone a - stray; re - store my soul and

liv - er me ac - cord - ing to Thy faith - ful word.
pres - ent help, for Thy com - mand - ments are my choice.
life di - vine, and help me by Thy judg - ments right.
lead me home, for Thy com - mands I would o - bey.

In My Distress to GOD I Cried

120

ottish Psalter, 1650

KINGSFOLD
CMD

English County Songs, 1893
harm. Ralph Vaughan Williams, 1906

1. In my dis - tress to GOD I cried, and He gave ear to me.
2. Woe's me that I in Mesh - ech am a so - jour - ner so long;

From ly - ing lips, and guile - ful tongue, O LORD, my soul set free.
that I in tab - er - nac - les dwell to Ke - dar that be - long.

What shall be giv'n thee? Or what shall be done to thee, false tongue?
My soul with him that hat - eth peace hath long a dwell - er been.

E'en burn - ing coals of ju - ni - per, sharp ar - rows of the strong.
I am for peace; but when I speak, for bat - tle they are keen.

121   I to the Hills Will Lift Mine Eyes

Scottish Psalter, 1615   DUNDEE   *Scottish Psalter, 16[]*
CM

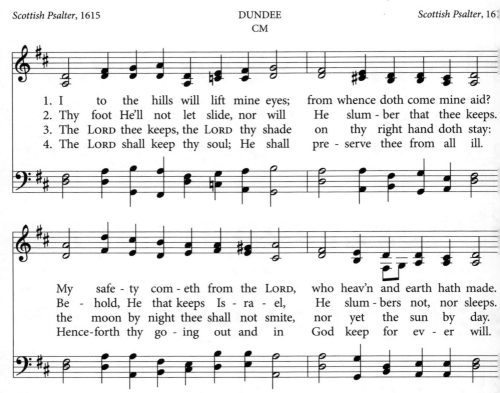

1. I to the hills will lift mine eyes; from whence doth come mine aid?
2. Thy foot He'll not let slide, nor will He slum-ber that thee keeps.
3. The LORD thee keeps, the LORD thy shade on thy right hand doth stay:
4. The LORD shall keep thy soul; He shall pre-serve thee from all ill.

My safe-ty com-eth from the LORD, who heav'n and earth hath made.
Be-hold, He that keeps Is-ra-el, He slum-bers not, nor sleeps.
the moon by night thee shall not smite, nor yet the sun by day.
Hence-forth thy go-ing out and in God keep for ev-er will.

O heavenly Father, creator of heaven and earth, who has received us into Thy protection; suffer not our afflictions so overcome us that we cast off all confidence in Thee, but rather prosper and conduct all our enterprises, and give a happy end and completion to all our businesses that we may continually be more and more assured that we are of the number of them whom You have chosen to salvation, through Jesus Christ, Thy Son. Amen.

The Scottish Collects, 1595

Oh, I Was Glad They Said to Me

Ryan J. Martin © 2023

JERUSALEM
LMD

Hubert Parry, 1916
adapt. Ryan J. Martin © 2016

1. Oh I was glad they said to me, "Come to God's house with us to pray!"
2. We've come to thank Je-ho-vah's name, where jus-tice flows from Da-vid's throne,

In-side your gates, Je-ru-sa-lem, our feet have stood and will for aye!
to sing His grace and spread His fame and make His splen-did glo-ry known!

O cit-y— built and bound in peace, to which tribes go by God's de-cree;
Zi-on we love, and pray for peace! "Her saints, her walls and tow'rs se-cure!

the tribes as-cend Je-ru-sa-lem to wor-ship God in u-ni-ty.
For broth-ers, friends, im-part your peace; here dwells our God, her good make sure!"

123 Lord, unto You I Lift My Eyes

David P. Regier © 2019

O WALY WALY
LM

Folk Songs from Somerset, 1906
arr. Dan Kreider © 2018

1. Lord, un-to You I lift my eyes; You are en-throned in heav'n a-bove. Your ser-vants gaze to You shall rise, seek-ing our Mas-ter's gra-cious love.

2. Lord, how the proud have heaped their scorn; our souls are filled with their great shame. Our gra-cious Lord, our souls a-dorn with Your great mer-cies, by Your name.

If the Lord Had Not Been with Us   **124**

...ie and Timothy Tennent © 2017

BEACH SPRING
87 87 D

Traditional American melody
The Sacred Harp, 1844

1. "If the Lord had not been with us," O let Is - ra - el now say:
2. Bless - ed be the Lord who has not let us be torn from His care.

"If the Lord had not been with us, when we were a - midst the fray;
Like a bird, we have es - caped from out of the cruel fowl - er's snare.

when at - tack - ers in their an - ger would have put us in the grave;
For the snare has now been bro - ken; we've es - caped as in new birth;

tor - rents would have there en - gulfed us, rag - ing floods swept us a - way."
our help's ev - er in the Lord's name, who made heav - en and the earth.

125 All Who, with Heart Confiding

The Psalter, 1912 AURELIA Samuel Sebastian Wesley, 18
76 76 D

1. All who, with heart con - fid - ing, de - pend on GOD a - lone
2. No scep - ter of op - pres - sion shall hold un - bro - ken sway
3. The men who false-hood cher - ish, for - sak - ing truth and right

like Zi - on's mount a - bid - ing, shall ne'er be o - ver-throw
lest un - to base trans - gres - sion the right - eous turn a - way
with wick - ed men shall per - ish, GOD will their sin re - quite

Like Zi - on's cit - y bound - ed by guard - ing moun-tains broa
Thy fa - vor be im - part - ed to god - ly men, O LORI
From sin Thy saints de - fend - ing, their joy, O LORD, in - creas

His peo - ple are sur - round - ed for - ev - er by their GOD
bless all that are pure - heart - ed, the good with good re - ward
with mer - cy nev - er end - ing and ev - er - last - ing peace

When God Revealed His Gracious Name 126

Isaac Watts, 1719   AZMON   Carl G. Gläser, 1828
                                  CM   arr. Lowell Mason, 1839

1. When GOD   re - vealed His   gra - cious name, and   changed my
2. The   world be - held   the   glo - rious change, and   did   Thy
3. "Great is   the work," my   neigh - bors cried, and   owned Thy
4. The   LORD   can clear   the   dark - est   skies, can   give   us
5. Let   those that sow   in   sad - ness   wait   till the   fair
6. Though seed lie bur - ied   long in   dust,   it   shan't de -

mourn - ful   state,   my   rap - ture seemed   a
hand   con - fess;   my   tongue broke out   in
pow'r di - vine;   "Great is   the   work,"   my
day   for   night,   make   drops of   sa - cred
har - vest   come,   they   shall con - fess   their
ceive their   hope;   the   pre - cious grain   can

pleas - ing   dream,   the   grace ap - peared   so   great.
un - known   strains, and   sung   sur - pris - ing   grace.
heart re - plied,   "and   be   the   glo - ry   Thine."
sor - row   rise   to   riv - ers of   de -   light.
sheaves are   great,   and   shout the   bless - ings   home.
ne'er be   lost,   for   grace en - sures the   crop.

127 Unless the Lord the House Shall Build

The Psalter, 1912   HERONGATE   English folk melo
     LM   arr. Ralph Vaughan Williams, 19

1. Un - less the LORD the house shall build, the wea - ry
2. In vain you rise ere morn - ing break, and late your
3. Lo, chil - dren are a great re - ward, a gift from
4. And blest the man whose age is cheered by stal - wart

build - ers toil in vain; un - less the LORD the
night - ly vig - ils keep, and of the bread of
GOD in ver - y truth; with ar - rows in his
sons and daugh - ters fair; no en - e - mies by

cit - y shield, the guards a use - less watch main - tain.
toil par - take; God gives to His be - lov - ed sleep.
quiv - er stored who joys in chil - dren of his youth
him are feared, no lack of love, no want of care.

Blessed the Man That Fears Jehovah **128**

e Psalter, 1912 · RATHBURN · Ithamar Conkey, 1849

87 87

1. Blessed the man that fears Jehovah, walk - ing
2. In thy wife thou shalt have glad - ness, she shall
3. Joy - ful chil - dren, sons and daugh - ters, shall a -
4. Lo, on him that fears Je - ho - vah shall this
5. Thou shalt see God's king - dom pros - per all thy

ev - er in His ways; by thy toil thou shalt be
fill thy home with good, hap - py in her lov - ing
bout thy ta - ble meet, o - live plants, in strength and
bless - ed - ness at - tend, for Je - ho - vah out of
days, till life shall cease, thou shalt see thy chil - dren's

pros - pered and be hap - py all thy days.
ser - vice and the joys of moth - er - hood.
beau - ty, full of hope and prom - ise sweet.
Zi - on shall to thee His bless - ing send.
chil - dren; on thy peo - ple, LORD, be peace.

129 From My Youth up, May Israel Say

Tate and Brady's *New Version*, 1696   MARTYRDOM   Hugh Wilson, 18.
                                                  CM

1. From my youth up, may Is - rael say, they
2. They oft have ploughed my pa - tient back with
3. De - feat, con - fu - sion, shame - ful rout, be
4. Like corn up - on our hous - es' tops, un
5. Which in his arms no reap - er takes, but
6. No trav - el - er that pass - es by, vouch

oft have me as - sailed, re - duced me oft to
fur - rows deep and long; but our just GOD has
still the doom of those, their right - eous doom, who
time - ly let them fade, which too much heat, and
un - re - gard - ed leaves; nor bind - er thinks it
safes a min - ute's stop, to give it one kind

heav - y straits, but nev - er quite pre - vailed.
broke the chains, and res - cued us from wrong.
Zi - on hate, and Zi - on's God op - pose.
want of root, has blast - ed in the blade,
worth his pains to fold it in - to sheaves.
look, or crave heav'n's bless - ing on the crop.

Out of the Depths I Cry to Thee

130

Martin Luther, 1524;
trans. Catherine Winkworth, 1863, alt.

AUS TIEFER NOT
87 87 88 7

Martin Luther, 1524

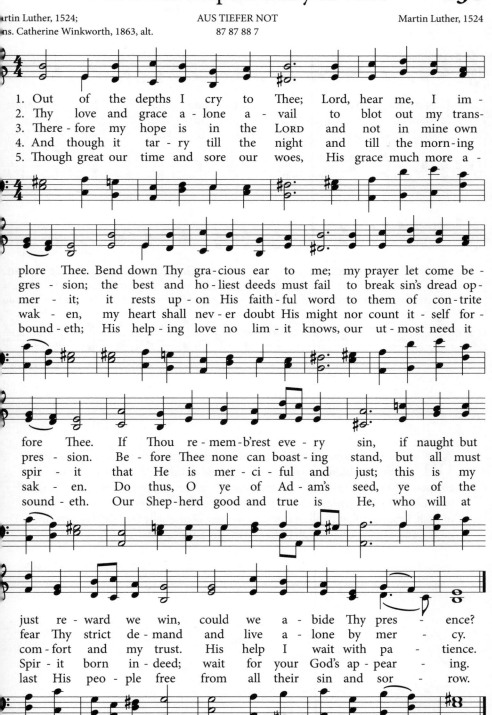

1. Out of the depths I cry to Thee; Lord, hear me, I im-plore Thee. Bend down Thy gra-cious ear to me; my prayer let come be-fore Thee. If Thou re-mem-b'rest eve-ry sin, if naught but just re-ward we win, could we a-bide Thy pres-ence?

2. Thy love and grace a-lone a-vail to blot out my trans-gres-sion; the best and ho-liest deeds must fail to break sin's dread op-pres-sion. Be-fore Thee none can boast-ing stand, but all must fear Thy strict de-mand and live a-lone by mer-cy.

3. There-fore my hope is in the LORD and not in mine own mer-it; it rests up-on His faith-ful word to them of con-trite spir-it that He is mer-ci-ful and just; this is my com-fort and my trust. His help I wait with pa-tience.

4. And though it tar-ry till the night and till the morn-ing wak-en, my heart shall nev-er doubt His might nor count it-self for-sak-en. Do thus, O ye of Ad-am's seed, ye of the Spir-it born in-deed; wait for your God's ap-pear-ing.

5. Though great our time and sore our woes, His grace much more a-bound-eth; His help-ing love no lim-it knows, our ut-most need it sound-eth. Our Shep-herd good and true is He, who will at last His peo-ple free from all their sin and sor-row.

131 Not Haughty Is My Heart

The Psalter, 1912

SOUTHWELL
SM

William Dam[...]
The Psalmes of David, 15[...]

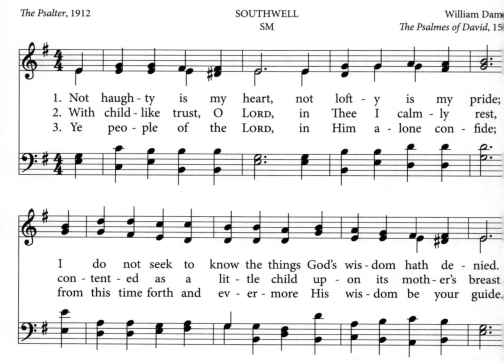

1. Not haugh-ty is my heart, not loft-y is my pride;
I do not seek to know the things God's wis-dom hath de - nied.

2. With child-like trust, O LORD, in Thee I calm-ly rest,
con - tent - ed as a lit - tle child up - on its moth-er's breast

3. Ye peo - ple of the LORD, in Him a - lone con - fide;
from this time forth and ev - er - more His wis-dom be your guide.

Mighty Lord, who resists the proud and gives strength to the humble; suffer not that we lift up ourselves in any proud opinion or conceit of ourselves in any good thing, but grant that we may humbly perceive ourselves without charade before Thy divine majesty; and that we may mortify ourselves daily more and more in such a manner that in all our doings we may continually feel Thy fatherly favor, mercy, and assistance, through Jesus Christ Thy Son. Amen.

The Scottish Collects, 1595

Arise, O Lord, Our God, Arise

e Psalter, 1912   HERR JESU CHRIST   *Pensum Sacrum*, 1648
     LM   arr. Johann Sebastian Bach, 1750

1. A - rise, O Lord, our God, a - rise, and en - ter
2. Thy gra - cious cov - 'nant, Lord, ful - fill, turn not a -
3. Thy Zi - on Thou hast cho - sen, Lord, and Thou hast

now in - to Thy rest: O let this house be
way from us Thy face; es - tab - lish Thou Mes -
said, "I love her well, this is My con - stant

Thine a - bode, for - ev - er with Thy pres - ence blest.
si - ah's throne and let Him reign with - in this place.
rest - ing place, and here will I de - light to dwell."

133 How Beautiful the Sight

James Montgomery, 1854

MILLENNIUM
66 66 88

English melody
Plymouth Collection of Hymns and Tunes, 1855

1. How beau-ti-ful the sight of breth-ren who a-gree
2. 'Tis like the dews that fill the cups of Her-mon's flow'rs;
3. For there the LORD com-mands bless-ings, a bound-less store,

in friend-ship to u-nite, and bonds of char-i-ty!
or Zi-on's fruit-ful hill, bright with the drops of show'rs,
from His un-spar-ing hands— yea, life for ev-er-more;

'Tis like the pre-cious oint-ment, shed
when min-gling o-dors breathe a-round,
thrice hap-py those who meet a-bove

o'er all his robes, from Aa-ron's head.
and glo-ry rests on all the ground.
to spend e-ter-ni-ty in love.

You Faithful Servants of the Lord **134**

vid T. Koyzis © 2021

OLD HUNDREDTH
LM

Louis Bourgeois
Genevan Psalter, 1551

1. You faith - ful ser - vants of the LORD, sing
2. Un - to His house lift up your hand and

out His praise with one ac - cord, while serv - ing Him with
to the LORD your prais - es send. May the LORD who made

all your might and keep - ing vig - il through the night.
earth and sky be - stow His bless - ings from on high.

135 Praise the LORD! O Praise the LORD's Name

Julie and Timothy Tennent © 2017   ODE TO JOY   Ludwig van Beethoven, 18
                87 87 D   adapt. Edward Hodges, 18

1. Praise the LORD! O praise the LORD's name; praise Him, ser - vant
2. I know that the LORD is great— that He is great - er
3. He struck down all E - gypt's first - born, of both an - i
4. He gave all their land to Is - rael, an in - her - i
5. They have mouths, but can - not speak; and they have eyes, but
6. Praise the LORD, O house of Le - vi— praise the LORD, and

of the LORD— You who serve with - in the LORD's house
than all gods; and the LORD does what He pleas - es,
mals and men. He sent signs in your midst, E - gypt,
tance for them. Your name, LORD, en - dures for - ev - er;
can - not see; they have ears, but can - not hear; though
Him re - vere. Praise the LORD, all you who fear Him;

in the courts of God the LORD. Praise the LORD, for that is
in the heav'ns, on earth a - broad. He works in the depths of
a - gainst Phar - aoh and his men. He struck down the man - y
Your fame's told each age a - gain. God will vin - di - cate His
they have mouths, they can - not breathe. Those who make them will be
bless the LORD who brings you near. Praise be to the LORD from

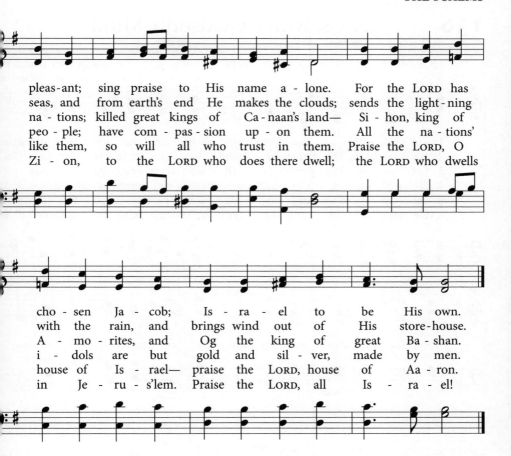

pleas-ant;   sing   praise   to   His   name   a - lone.   For   the   LORD   has
seas, and   from earth's   end   He   makes the clouds;   sends   the   light - ning
na - tions;   killed   great   kings   of   Ca - naan's land—   Si - hon,   king   of
peo - ple;   have   com - pas - sion   up - on   them.   All   the   na - tions'
like them,   so   will   all   who   trust   in   them.   Praise   the   LORD,   O
Zi - on,   to   the   LORD who   does there dwell;   the   LORD who   dwells

cho - sen   Ja - cob;   Is - ra - el   to   be   His   own.
with   the   rain,   and   brings wind   out   of   His   store - house.
A - mo - rites,   and   Og   the   king   of   great   Ba - shan.
i - dols   are   but   gold   and   sil - ver,   made   by   men.
house of   Is - rael—   praise   the   LORD, house   of   Aa - ron.
in   Je - ru - s'lem.   Praise   the   LORD,   all   Is - ra - el!

136   Let Us, with a Gladsome Mind

John Milton, 1624, alt.

MONKLAND   J. Freylinghausen's *Geistreiches Gesangbuch*, 17
77 77
adapt. John Antes, c. 18
arr. John Wilkes, 18

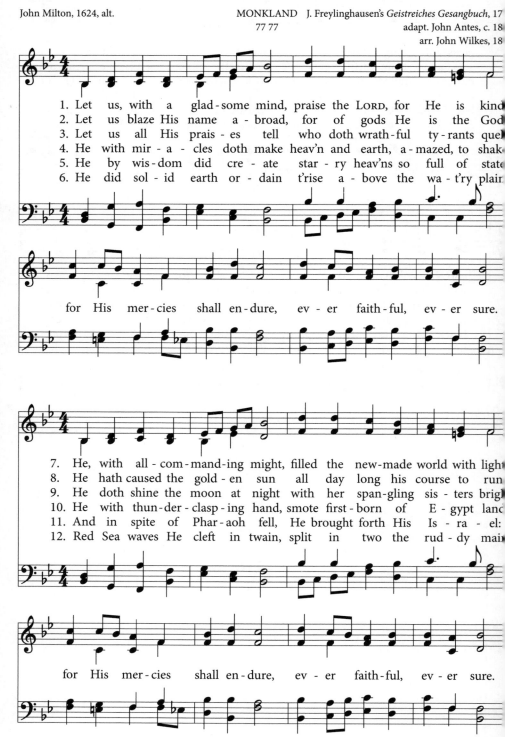

1. Let us, with a glad-some mind, praise the LORD, for He is kind
2. Let us blaze His name a-broad, for of gods He is the God
3. Let us all His prais-es tell who doth wrath-ful ty-rants quel
4. He with mir-a-cles doth make heav'n and earth, a-mazed, to shak
5. He by wis-dom did cre-ate star-ry heav'ns so full of state
6. He did sol-id earth or-dain t'rise a-bove the wa-t'ry plain

for His mer-cies shall en-dure, ev-er faith-ful, ev-er sure.

7. He, with all-com-mand-ing might, filled the new-made world with light
8. He hath caused the gold-en sun all day long his course to run
9. He doth shine the moon at night with her span-gling sis-ters brigh
10. He with thun-der-clasp-ing hand, smote first-born of E-gypt land
11. And in spite of Phar-aoh fell, He brought forth His Is-ra-el:
12. Red Sea waves He cleft in twain, split in two the rud-dy main

for His mer-cies shall en-dure, ev-er faith-ful, ev-er sure.

13. Floods stood still like walls of glass, while the He-brew bands did pass:
14. But full soon did they de-vour E-gypt's king with all his pow'r:
15. He His cho-sen race did bless in the waste-ful wil-der-ness:
16. He in bat-tle has brought down kings of prow-ess and re-nown:
17. Con-quered Si-hon and his host of the A-mor-re-an coast:
18. Large-limbed Og He did sub-due, with his o-ver-har-dy crew.

for His mer-cies shall en-dure, ev-er faith-ful, ev-er sure.

19. To His ser-vant Is-ra-el, gave their land there-in to dwell:
20. He hath with a pit-eous eye looked up-on our mis-er-y:
21. Freed us from the slav-er-y of th'in-vad-ing en-e-my:
22. All things liv-ing He doth feed; His full hand sup-plies their need:
23. Let us there-fore war-ble forth His high maj-es-ty and worth:
24. He His man-sion hath on high out of reach of mor-tal eye:

for His mer-cies shall en-dure, ev-er faith-ful, ev-er sure.

137   By Rivers of Cruel Babylon

Julie and Timothy Tennent © 2017   MORNING SONG   Traditional American melod
                            CM   *Kentucky Harmony, 181.*

1. By riv - ers of cruel Bab - y - lon, there we sat down and wept
2. Up - on the trees we hung our harps, for they de - mand - ed song;
3. How can we sing songs of the LORD while in a for - eign land?
4. May my tongue cleave to my mouth's roof if I do not re - call;
5. Re - mem - ber, LORD, all E - dom's sons who razed Je - ru - sa - lem;
6. O daught - er of doomed Ba - by - lon, your end will sure - ly come
7. How blessed will be the one who thus does end your cru - el - ty:

when we re - mem - bered Zi - on's land—our home we'll not for - get.
our cap - tors, with tri - umph - ant scorn, said, "Sing songs of Zi - on."
If I for - get Je - ru - sa - lem, let skill leave my right hand.
if I don't praise Je - ru - sa - lem, my chief joy a - bove all.
who said, "Tear down, tear down its walls un - to its foun - da - tion."
how blessed will be the one who pays to you as you have done.
who takes your in - fants, dash - ing them up - on the rocks just - ly.

With All My Heart My Thanks I'll Bring 138

Book of Psalms for Worship © 2010   WESLEY   Isaac B. Woodbury, 1819–1858
                                                LM

1. With all my heart my thanks I'll bring, be - fore the gods
2. For You have mag - ni - fied Your word, so far a - bove
3. All kings of earth will thank You, LORD; they'll sing when they
4. The LORD, al - though ex - alt - ed high, on low - ly ones
5. Through trou - ble though my path - way be, my life You will
6. Your right hand, LORD, will set me free and work out what

Your praise I'll sing. I'll bow down toward Your ho - ly
Your name a - dored. You an - swered me the day I
have heard Your word. The LORD's ways they will cel - e -
will keep His eye; but those who proud and haugh - ty
pre - serve for me; with out - stretched hand You will op -
per - tains to me. Your love, O LORD, for - ev - er

place, and praise Your name for truth and grace;
called, You strength - ened me and made me bold.
brate; the glo - ry of the LORD is great.
are, He knows them on - ly from a - far.
pose the wrath and an - ger of my foes.
stands; leave not the works done by Your hands.

139 LORD, Thou Hast Searched Me

The Psalter, 1912   FEDERAL STREET   Henry K. Oliver, 1832
                                   LM

1. LORD, Thou hast searched me, and dost know where-e'er I rest, where-e'er I go; Thou know-est all that I have planned, and all my ways are in Thy hand.

2. My words from Thee I can-not hide, I feel Thy pow'r on eve-ry side; O won-drous knowl-edge, aw-ful might, un-fath-omed depth, un-meas-ured height!

3. Where can I go a-part from Thee, or whith-er from Thy pres-ence flee? In heav'n? it is Thy dwell-ing fair; in death's a-bode? lo, Thou art there.

4. If I the wings of morn-ing take, and far a-way my dwell-ing make, the hand that lead-eth me is Thine, and my sup-port Thy pow'r di-vine.

5. If deep-est dark-ness cov-er me, the dark-ness hid-eth not from Thee; to Thee both night and day are bright, the dark-ness shin-eth as the light.

Deliver Me from Evil

...e Psalter, 1912

PASSION CHORALE
76 76 D

Hans Leo Hassler, 1601
adapt. Johann Sebastian Bach, 1729

1. De - liv - er me from e - vil, pre - serve me, LORD, from wrong;
2. O LORD, I have con - fessed Thee to be my God a - lone;
3. Let e - vil smite the e - vil and cause their o - ver - throw;

a - gainst the foes that gath - er be Thou my Help - er strong.
O hear my sup - pli - ca - tion and be Thy mer - cy shown;
the need - y and af - flict - ed the LORD will help, I know;

From those who plot to hurt me and spread their treach - 'rous snare
O God the LORD, my Sav - ior, my Shield a - mid the strife,
Thy saints, re - deemed from e - vil, their thanks to Thee shall give;

pre - serve me, LORD, and keep me safe - guard - ed in Thy care.
let not the wick - ed tri - umph who plot a - gainst my life.
the right - eous and the up - right shall in Thy pres - ence live.

141

O Lord, I Call upon You

Julie and Timothy Tennent © 2017   LLANGLOFFAN   Welsh hymn melody
                                                          CMD

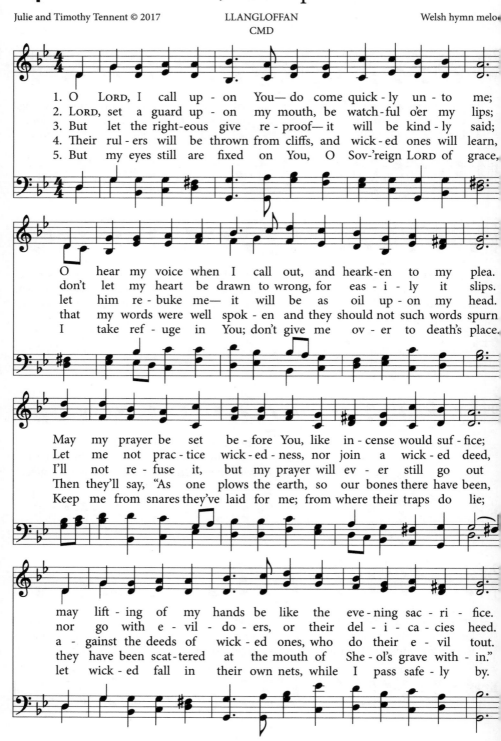

1. O Lord, I call up-on You— do come quick-ly un-to me;
2. Lord, set a guard up-on my mouth, be watch-ful o'er my lips;
3. But let the right-eous give re-proof— it will be kind-ly said,
4. Their rul-ers will be thrown from cliffs, and wick-ed ones will learn,
5. But my eyes still are fixed on You, O Sov-'reign Lord of grace,

O hear my voice when I call out, and heark-en to my plea.
don't let my heart be drawn to wrong, for eas-i-ly it slips.
let him re-buke me— it will be as oil up-on my head.
that my words were well spok-en and they should not such words spurn
I take ref-uge in You; don't give me ov-er to death's place.

May my prayer be set be-fore You, like in-cense would suf-fice;
Let me not prac-tice wick-ed-ness, nor join a wick-ed deed,
I'll not re-fuse it, but my prayer will ev-er still go out
Then they'll say, "As one plows the earth, so our bones there have been,
Keep me from snares they've laid for me; from where their traps do lie;

may lift-ing of my hands be like the eve-ning sac-ri-fice.
nor go with e-vil-do-ers, or their del-i-ca-cies heed.
a-gainst the deeds of wick-ed ones, who do their e-vil tout.
they have been scat-tered at the mouth of She-ol's grave with-in."
let wick-ed fall in their own nets, while I pass safe-ly by.

To God I Made My Sorrows Known   **142**

Isaac Watts, 1719   SASHA   Joan J. Pinkston © 2017
CMD

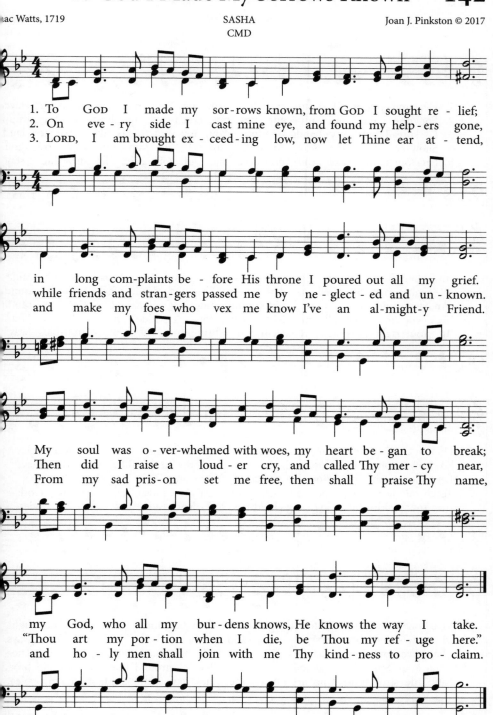

1. To GOD I made my sor-rows known, from GOD I sought re - lief;
2. On eve - ry side I cast mine eye, and found my help - ers gone,
3. LORD, I am brought ex - ceed-ing low, now let Thine ear at - tend,

in long com-plaints be - fore His throne I poured out all my grief.
while friends and stran-gers passed me by ne - glect - ed and un - known.
and make my foes who vex me know I've an al-might-y Friend.

My soul was o - ver-whelmed with woes, my heart be - gan to break;
Then did I raise a loud - er cry, and called Thy mer - cy near,
From my sad pris-on set me free, then shall I praise Thy name,

my God, who all my bur - dens knows, He knows the way I take.
"Thou art my por - tion when I die, be Thou my ref - uge here."
and ho - ly men shall join with me Thy kind-ness to pro - claim.

143 Hear My Prayer, O Lord, and Listen

Julie and Timothy Tennent © 2017
BEACH SPRING
87 87 D

Traditional American melo
The Sacred Harp, 18

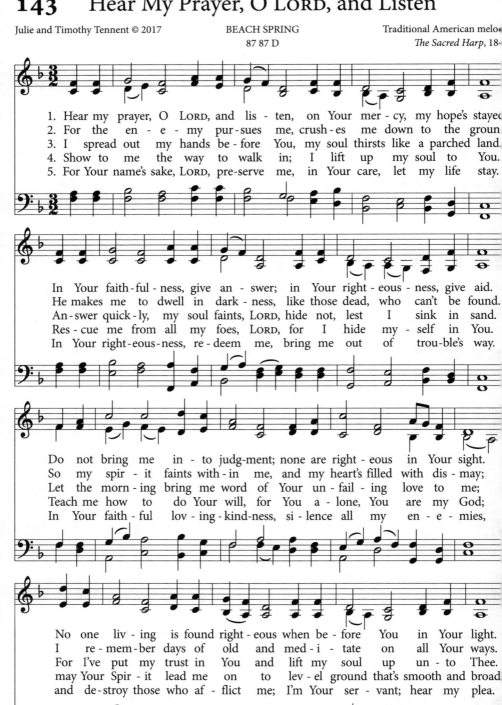

1. Hear my prayer, O Lord, and lis - ten, on Your mer - cy, my hope's stayed
2. For the en - e - my pur - sues me, crush - es me down to the groun
3. I spread out my hands be - fore You, my soul thirsts like a parched land.
4. Show to me the way to walk in; I lift up my soul to You.
5. For Your name's sake, Lord, pre-serve me, in Your care, let my life stay.

In Your faith - ful - ness, give an - swer; in Your right - eous - ness, give aid.
He makes me to dwell in dark - ness, like those dead, who can't be found.
An - swer quick - ly, my soul faints, Lord, hide not, lest I sink in sand.
Res - cue me from all my foes, Lord, for I hide my - self in You.
In Your right - eous - ness, re - deem me, bring me out of trou - ble's way.

Do not bring me in - to judg-ment; none are right - eous in Your sight.
So my spir - it faints with - in me, and my heart's filled with dis - may;
Let the morn - ing bring me word of Your un - fail - ing love to me;
Teach me how to do Your will, for You a - lone, You are my God;
In Your faith - ful lov - ing - kind-ness, si - lence all my en - e - mies,

No one liv - ing is found right - eous when be - fore You in Your light.
I re - mem - ber days of old and med - i - tate on all Your ways.
For I've put my trust in You and lift my soul up un - to Thee.
may Your Spir - it lead me on to lev - el ground that's smooth and broad
and de-stroy those who af - flict me; I'm Your ser - vant; hear my plea.

Blessed Be the Lord, My Rock

ook of Psalms for Worship © 2010

LENOX
66 66 888

Lewis Edson, 1782

1. Blessed be the Lord, my Rock, who trains my hands for war,
2. O Lord, what then is man that You take note of him?
3. O bow Your heav - ens, Lord, may You Your - self come down!
4. From heav - en stretch Your hand; reach down to res - cue me,

my fin - gers for the fight. My Stead - fast Love, my Fort,
What is the son of man that You con - sid - er him?
Yes, touch the moun - tain - tops that they may burn with smoke.
and save me from the floods, the grip of for - eign pow'rs,

my Strong - hold, my De - liv - er - er, my Shield in
The life of man is like a breath; the to - tal
Make light - ning flash and scat - ter them. O may Your
the ones whose mouth speaks what is false, the ones whose

whom I ref - uge take, He brings my peo - ple un - der me.
num - ber of his days is like a shad - ow pass - ing by.
ar - rows be sent forth to trou - ble and dis - qui - et them!
right hand is the same, a right hand of de - ceit - ful - ness.

145   I Will Extol You, God My King

The Psalter, 1912   JERUSALEM   Hubert Parry, 191•
                          LMD   adapt. Ryan J. Martin © 201•

1. I will ex - tol You, God my King; and I will ev - er praise Your name. I will ex - alt you eve - ry day and ev - er - more Your praise pro - claim.

2. On Your most glo - rious maj - es - ty and on Your deeds my mind will dwell. Your deeds will fill the world with awe, and all Your great - ness I will tell.

3. The LORD our God is rich in grace, ten - der to us, com - pas - sion - ate. His an - ger is most slow to rise, His love and kind - ness are most great.

4. All You have made will praise You, LORD; Your might - y acts Your saints will show, till all the peo - ples on the earth the splen - dor of Your king - dom know.

5. The LORD is faith - ful to His word; He will ex tend His gra - cious hand. The LORD up - holds the fal - t'ring feet and makes the weak se - cure - ly stand.

6. The LORD is just in all His ways; in all His works He is most kind, and all who call on Him in truth in Him a pres - ent help - er find.

7. The LORD in grace pre - serves His saints, re - deem - ing those who love His name. The wick - ed He will o - ver - throw and put His en - e - mies to shame.

You, LORD, are great - ly to be praised; Your great - ness
Your match - less good - ness and Your grace Your peo - ple
The LORD is good in all His ways. His crea - tures
E - ter - nal is Your king - dom, LORD, for - ev - er
The eyes of all look up to You for food and
He will ful - fill the heart's de - sire of those who
My mouth will sing the glo - rious praise of God, whom

is be - yond all thought. From age to age Your peo - ple
will com - mem - o - rate; and all Your truth and right - eous-
know His con - stant care. To all His works His love ex -
strong, for - ev - er sure. While gen - er - a - tions rise and
drink, which You sup - ply; Your o - pen hand is boun - ti -
fear Him and o - bey. The LORD will sure - ly hear their
earth and heav'n a - dore. Let eve - ry crea - ture praise His

tell the might - y won - ders You have wrought.
ness our joy - ful song will cel - e - brate.
tends; all crea - tures in His mer - cies share.
die, Your glo - rious reign will still en - dure.
ful, and eve - ry need You sat - is - fy.
cry, will save them when to Him they pray.
name for - ev - er and for - ev - er - more!

146 I'll Praise My Maker with My Breath

Isaac Watts, 1719   OLD 113TH   Matthäus Greiter

88 88 88   *Strassburger Kirchenamt, 152*

1. I'll praise my Mak - er with my breath, and when my
2. Why should I make a man my trust? Prin - ces must
3. Hap - py the man whose hopes re - ly on Is - rael's
4. The LORD hath eyes to give the blind; the LORD sup -
5. He loves His saints, He knows them well, but turns the
6. I'll praise Him while He lends me breath; and when my

voice is lost in death, praise shall em - ploy my nob - ler pow'rs;
die and turn to dust; vain is the help of flesh and blood:
God; He made the sky and earth and seas, with all their train;
ports the sink - ing mind; He sends the la - b'ring con - science peace,
wick - ed down to hell; thy God, O Zi - on, ev - er reigns;
voice is lost in death, praise shall em - ploy my nob - ler pow'rs;

my days of praise shall ne'er be past, while life, and
their breath de - parts, their pomp and pow'r, and thoughts all
His truth for ev - er stands se - cure; He saves th'op -
He helps the stran - ger in dis - tress, the wid - ow
let eve - ry tongue, let eve - ry age, in this ex -
my days of praise shall ne'er be past, while life, and

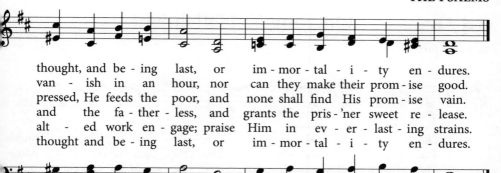

thought, and be - ing	last,	or	im - mor - tal - i - ty	en - dures.
van - ish in an	hour,	nor	can they make their prom - ise	good.
pressed, He feeds the	poor,	and	none shall find His prom - ise	vain.
and the fa - ther - less,	and	grants the pris - 'ner sweet re - lease.
alt - ed work en - gage;	praise	Him in ev - er - last - ing strains.
thought and be - ing	last,	or	im - mor - tal - i - ty	en - dures.

With Songs and Honors Sounding Loud 147A

aac Watts, 1719, alt.   ST. MAGNUS (295)
                                          CM

1. With songs and honors sounding loud,
   O praise the LORD on high;
   over the heav'ns He spreads His cloud,
   and waters veil the sky.

2. He sends His show'rs of blessing down
   to cheer the plains below;
   He makes the grass the mountains crown,
   and corn in valleys grow.

3. His steady counsels change the face
   of the declining year;
   He bids the sun cut short his race,
   and wintry days appear.

4. His icy frost, His fleecy snow,
   descend and clothe the ground;
   the liquid streams forbear to flow,
   in icy fetters bound.

5. He sends His Word, and melts the snow,
   the fields no longer mourn;
   He calls the warmer gales to blow,
   and bids the spring return.

6. The changing wind, the flying cloud,
   obey His mighty Word:
   with songs and honors sounding loud,
   praise ye the sovereign LORD.

147B Oh, Sing Ye Hallelujah!

The Psalter, 1912   PSALM 147   Gregory D. Wilbur © 200[

76 76 D

1. Oh, sing ye hal - le - lu - jah! 'Tis good our God to praise;
2. The star - ry host He num - bers, He calls them all by name;
3. The heav'ns with clouds He cov - ers, He sends the cheer-ing rain;
4. No hu - man pow'r de - lights Him, no earth - ly pomp or pride;
5. He sends His swift com - mand - ment, and snow and ice en - fold
6. His stat - utes and His judg - ments He makes His peo - ple know;

'tis pleas - ant and be - com - ing to Him our songs to raise;
His great - ness and His wis - dom His won-drous works pro - claim;
the slopes of all the moun-tains He fills with grass and grain;
He loves the meek who fear Him and in His love con - fide;
the world, and none are a - ble to stand be - fore His cold.
to them as to no oth - ers His grace He loves to show;

He builds the walls of Zi - on, He seeks her wan - d'ring sons,
the meek He lifts to hon - or, He hum - bles sin - ful pride;
to beast and bird His good - ness their dai - ly food sup - plies;
then praise thy God, O Zi - on, His gra - cious aid con - fess;
A - gain He gives com - mand-ment; the winds of sum - mer blow;
for match - less grace and mer - cy Your grate - ful prais - es bring;

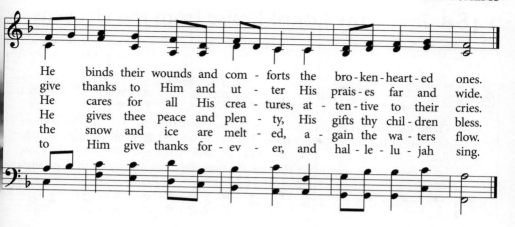

He   binds their wounds and com - forts the   bro - ken - heart - ed   ones.
give   thanks to   Him and ut - ter His   prais - es   far and   wide.
He   cares for   all His crea - tures, at - ten - tive to   their cries.
He   gives thee peace and plen - ty, His   gifts thy chil - dren bless.
the   snow and   ice are melt - ed, a - gain the wa - ters flow.
to   Him   give thanks for - ev - er, and hal - le - lu - jah sing.

From Heav'n O Praise the Lord!   148A

The Book of Psalms for Worship © 2010   DARWALL (291)
66 66 88

1. From heav'n O praise the Lord!
   On high the Lord O praise!
   All angels, praise accord;
   let all His host give praise.
   Praise Him on high, sun, moon, and star,
   you heav'ns afar,
   and cloudy sky.

2. O let them glorify
   the Lord's majestic name;
   when He spoke from on high,
   they into being came.
   And He arranged where they should stand
   by His command
   cannot be changed.

3. From earth O praise the Lord,
   you deeps and all below,
   wild winds that do His word,
   you clouds, fire, hail, and snow,
   hills low and high, and cedars tall,
   beasts great and small,
   and birds that fly.

4. Let all the peoples praise,
   and kings of every land;
   let all their voices raise
   who judge and give command.
   By young and old, by girl and boy,
   His name with joy
   should be extolled.

5. The Lord alone be praised
   above the earth and sky!
   He for his saints has raised
   a king to rule on high;
   so praise accord, O Israel;
   who near Him dwell,
   O praise the Lord!

148B Praise the LORD! Praise from the Heavens

Julie and Timothy Tennent © 2017

ODE TO JOY
87 87 D

Ludwig van Beethoven, 182
adapt. Edward Hodges, 186

1. Praise the LORD! Praise from the heav-ens; praise Him in the heights a-bove!
2. Let them praise the LORD's name, for He spoke and they all came to be;
3. Praise Him, moun-tains and all hills, all fruit trees and all ce-dars too;
4. Let them ev-er praise the LORD's name; His name is ex-alt-ed high;

Praise Him, all His an-gels; praise Him, all His hosts who know His love.
He set them in place for-ev-er— ev-er-last-ing His de-cree.
creep-ing things and fly-ing birds, all cat-tle and wild crea-tures too.
for His splen-dor and His glo-ry are a-bove the earth and sky.

Praise Him, sun and moon, and praise Him all you shin-ing stars of light.
Praise the LORD from all the earth, all o-cean depths and crea-tures there;
Kings of earth and all you na-tions, princ-es, rul-ers eve-ry-where;
He has lift-ed up a horn for His own peo-ple all their days;

Praise Him, all you high-est heav-ens, and you wa-ters in the height.
light-ning, hail, snow, clouds, and winds that do His bid-ding eve-ry-where.
young men, maid-ens, old men, chil-dren— let all earth His praise de-clare.
Is-ra-el, the peo-ple near Him— give the LORD whole-heart-ed praise.

O Praise Ye the LORD

e Psalter, 1912

LYONS
10 10 11 11

attr. J. Michael Haydn, 18th cent.
arr. Joseph Martin Kraus, 1784

1. O praise ye the LORD and sing a new song,
2. With tim - brel and harp and joy - ful ac - claim,
3. In glo - ry ex - ult, ye saints of the LORD;
4. For this is His word: His saints shall not fail,

a - mid all His saints His prais - es pro - long;
with glad - ness and mirth, sing praise to His name;
with songs in the night high prais - es ac - cord;
but o - ver the earth their pow'r shall pre - vail;

the praise of their Mak - er His peo - ple shall sing,
for God in His peo - ple His pleas - ure doth seek,
go forth in His ser - vice, be strong in His might
all king - doms and na - tions shall yield to their sway.

and chil - dren of Zi - on re - joice in their King.
with robes of sal - va - tion He cloth - eth the meek.
to con - quer all e - vil and stand for the right.
To God give the glo - ry and praise Him for aye.

150 Praise the LORD Who Reigns Above

Charles Wesley, 1743, alt.

AMSTERDAM
76 76 77 76

Foundery Collection, 17

1. Praise the LORD who reigns a - bove and keeps His courts be - low;
2. Cel - e - brate th'e - ter - nal God with harp and psal - ter - y;
3. Him, in whom they move and live, let eve - ry crea - ture sing,

praise the ho - ly God of love, and all His great - ness show.
tim - brels soft and cym - bals loud in His high praise a - gree.
glo - ry to their Mak - er give, and hom - age to their King.

Praise Him for His no - ble deeds, praise Him for His match - less pow'r;
Praise Him, eve - ry tune - ful string, all the reach of heav'n - ly art;
Hal - lowed be His name be - neath, as in heav'n, on earth a - dored;

Him from whom all good pro - ceeds let earth and heav'n a - dore.
all the pow'rs of mu - sic bring, the mu - sic of the heart.
praise the LORD in eve - ry breath, let all things praise the LORD!

Morning Prayer 151

mas Ken, 1674, alt.   TALLIS CANON   Thomas Tallis, 1567
                              LM

1. A - wake, my soul, and with the sun thy dai - ly stage of du - ty run;
2. Lord, I my vows to Thee re - new. Dis - perse my sins as morn-ing dew;
3. Di - rect, con - trol, sug - gest, this day, all I de - sign or do or say,
4. Praise God, from whom all bless-ings flow; praise Him all crea-tures here be - low;

shake off dull sloth, and ear - ly rise to pay thy morn-ing sac - ri - fice.
guard my first springs of thought and will; and with Thy - self my spir - it fill.
that all my pow'rs, with all their might, in Thy sole glo - ry may u - nite.
praise Him a - bove, ye heav'n - ly host; praise Fa - ther, Son, and Ho - ly Ghost.

Evening Prayer 152

mas Ken, 1674, alt.   TALLIS CANON (151)
                              LM

1. All praise to Thee, my God, this night,
   for all the blessings of the light.
   Keep me, O keep me, King of kings,
   beneath Thine own almighty wings.

2. Forgive me, Lord, for Thy dear Son,
   the ill that I this day have done;
   that with the world, myself, and Thee,
   I, ere I sleep, at peace may be.

3. O may my soul on Thee repose,
   and may sweet sleep mine eyelids close;
   sleep, that may me more vig'rous make,
   to serve my God, when I awake.

4. Praise God, from whom all blessings flow;
   praise Him all creatures here below;
   praise Him above, ye heav'nly host;
   praise Father, Son, and Holy Ghost.

153 Holy, Holy, Holy!

Reginald Heber, 1826   NICAEA   John B. Dykes, 18
11 12 12 10

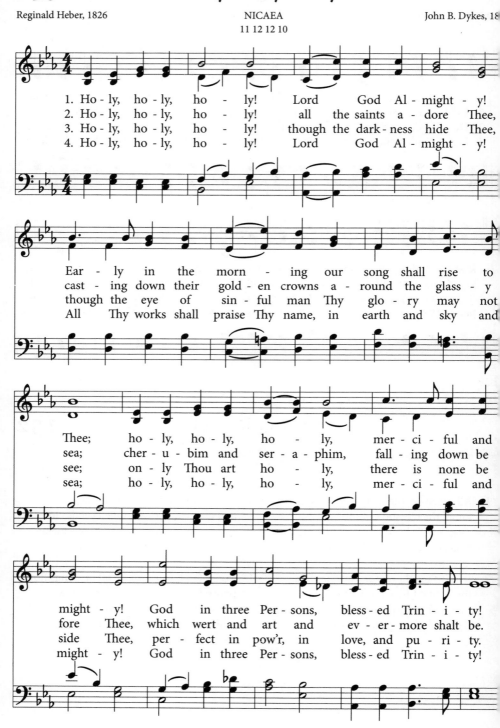

1. Ho - ly, ho - ly, ho - ly! Lord God Al - might - y!
2. Ho - ly, ho - ly, ho - ly! all the saints a - dore Thee,
3. Ho - ly, ho - ly, ho - ly! though the dark - ness hide Thee,
4. Ho - ly, ho - ly, ho - ly! Lord God Al - might - y!

Ear - ly in the morn - ing our song shall rise to
cast - ing down their gold - en crowns a - round the glass - y
though the eye of sin - ful man Thy glo - ry may not
All Thy works shall praise Thy name, in earth and sky and

Thee; ho - ly, ho - ly, ho - ly, mer - ci - ful and
sea; cher - u - bim and ser - a - phim, fall - ing down be
see; on - ly Thou art ho - ly, there is none be
sea; ho - ly, ho - ly, ho - ly, mer - ci - ful and

might - y! God in three Per - sons, bless - ed Trin - i - ty!
fore Thee, which wert and art and ev - er - more shalt be.
side Thee, per - fect in pow'r, in love, and pu - ri - ty.
might - y! God in three Per - sons, bless - ed Trin - i - ty!

Round the Lord in Glory Seated   154

Deum, c. 4th cent.
‑hard Mant, 1837

EBENEZER
87 87 D

Thomas J. Williams, 1897

1. Round the Lord in glo - ry seat - ed, cher - u - bim and ser - a - phim
2. Heav'n is still with glo - ry ring - ing; earth takes up the an - gels' cry,
3. With His ser - aph train be - fore Him, with His ho - ly church be - low,
4. This Thy glo - rious name con - fess - ing, with Thine an - gel hosts we cry,

filled His tem - ple, and re - peat - ed each to each the_al - ter - nate hymn:
"Ho - ly, ho - ly, ho - ly," sing - ing, "Lord of Hosts, the Lord Most High!"
thus con - spire we to a - dore Him, bid we thus our an - them flow:
"Ho - ly, ho - ly, ho - ly," bless - ing Thee, the Lord of Hosts Most High.

"Lord, Thy glo - ry fills the heav - en, earth is with its full - ness stored;

un - to Thee be glo - ry giv - en, ho - ly, ho - ly, ho - ly Lord."

155 The God of Abraham Praise

Moses Maimonides, 12th cent.
vers. Daniel ben Judah, 1404
para. Thomas Olivers, c. 1770, alt.

LEONI
66 84 D

Hebrew melody, 17th ce
adapt. Meyer Lyon, c. 17

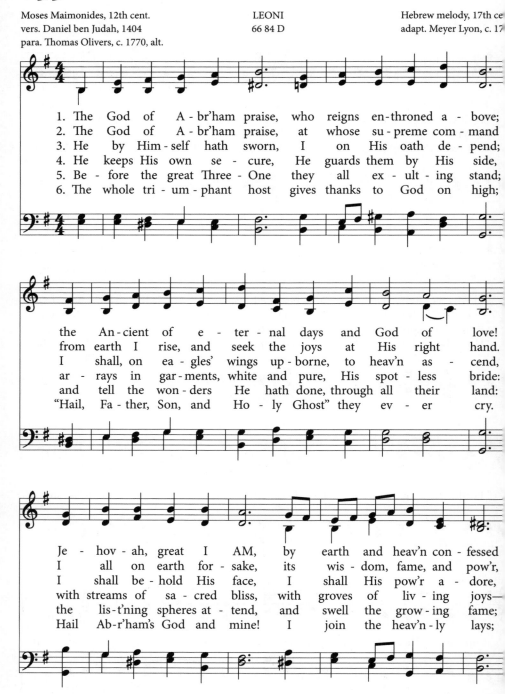

1. The God of A-br'ham praise, who reigns en-throned a-bove;
2. The God of A-br'ham praise, at whose su-preme com-mand;
3. He by Him-self hath sworn, I on His oath de-pend;
4. He keeps His own se-cure, He guards them by His side,
5. Be-fore the great Three-One they all ex-ult-ing stand;
6. The whole tri-um-phant host gives thanks to God on high;

the An-cient of e-ter-nal days and God of love!
from earth I rise, and seek the joys at His right hand.
I shall, on ea-gles' wings up-borne, to heav'n as-cend;
ar-rays in gar-ments, white and pure, His spot-less bride.
and tell the won-ders He hath done, through all their land.
"Hail, Fa-ther, Son, and Ho-ly Ghost" they ev-er cry.

Je-hov-ah, great I AM, by earth and heav'n con-fessed;
I all on earth for-sake, its wis-dom, fame, and pow'r,
I shall be-hold His face, I shall His pow'r a-dore,
with streams of sa-cred bliss, with groves of liv-ing joys—
the lis-t'ning spheres at-tend, and swell the grow-ing fame;
Hail Ab-r'ham's God and mine! I join the heav'n-ly lays;

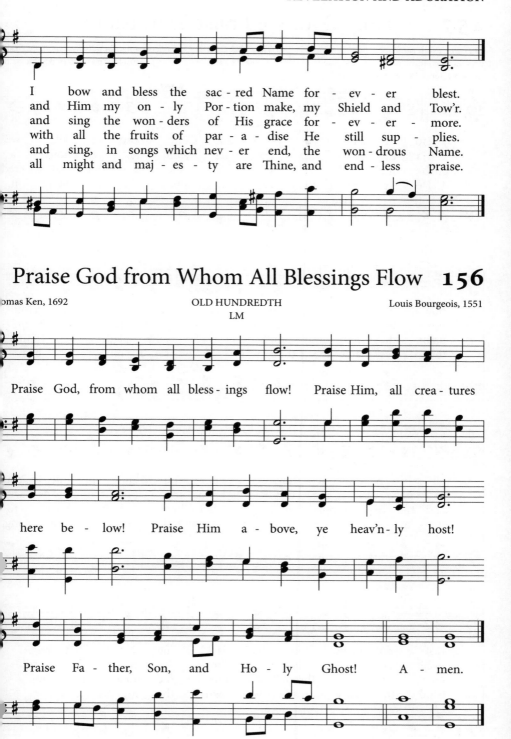

I bow and bless the sac - red Name for - ev - er blest.
and Him my on - ly Por - tion make, my Shield and Tow'r.
and sing the won - ders of His grace for - ev - er - more.
with all the fruits of par - a - dise He still sup - plies.
and sing, in songs which nev - er end, the won - drous Name.
all might and maj - es - ty are Thine, and end - less praise.

Praise God from Whom All Blessings Flow 156

omas Ken, 1692   OLD HUNDREDTH   Louis Bourgeois, 1551
LM

Praise God, from whom all bless - ings flow! Praise Him, all crea - tures

here be - low! Praise Him a - bove, ye heav'n - ly host!

Praise Fa - ther, Son, and Ho - ly Ghost! A - men.

157 Holy God, We Praise Your Name

Te Deum, c. 4th cent.,
vers. Ignace Franz, 1768
trans. Clarence Walworth, 1853, alt.

GROSSER GOTT
78 78 77

Allgemeines Katholisches Gesangbuch, 17
harm. Johann Gottfried Schicht, 18

1. Ho - ly God, we praise Your name; Lord of all, we
2. Hark, the glad ce - les - tial hymn an - gel choirs a
3. Lo, the ap - os - tol - ic train joins Your sa - cred
4. Ho - ly Fa - ther, Ho - ly Son, Ho - ly Spir - it,

bow be - fore You. Saints on earth Your scep - ter claim;
bove are rais - ing; cher - u - bim and ser - a - phim,
name to hal - low; proph - ets swell the glad re - frain,
three we name You, though in es - sence on - ly one;

all in heav'n a - bove a - dore You. In - fi - nite, Your
in un - ceas - ing cho - rus prais - ing, fill the heav'ns with
and the white - robed mar - tyrs fol - low; and from morn to
un - di - vid - ed God, we claim You, and, a - dor - ing,

vast do - main; ev - er - last - ing is Your reign.
sweet ac - cord: "Ho - ly, ho - ly, ho - ly Lord!"
set of sun, through the church the song goes on.
bend the knee while we own the mys - ter - y.

Come, Thou Almighty King 158

Anonymous, 1757

ITALIAN HYMN
66 4 66 64

Felice de Giardini, ca. 1762

1. Come, Thou Al - might - y King, help us Thy name to sing;
2. Come, Thou In - car - nate Word, gird on Thy might - y sword,
3. Come, Ho - ly Com - fort - er, Thy sa - cred wit - ness bear
4. To Thee, great One in Three, e - ter - nal prais - es be

help us to praise: Fa - ther, all glo - ri - ous, o'er all vic -
our prayer at - tend: come, and Thy peo - ple bless, and give Thy
in this glad hour: Thou who al - might - y art, now rule in
hence, ev - er - more. His sov - 'reign maj - es - ty may we in

to - ri - ous, come, and reign o - ver us, An - cient of Days.
word suc - cess: Spir - it of ho - li - ness, on us de - scend.
eve - ry heart, and ne'er from us de - part, Spir - it of pow'r.
glo - ry see, and to e - ter - ni - ty love and a - dore!

159 All Creatures of Our God and King

Francis of Assisi, 1225
trans. William H. Draper, 1919

LASST UNS ERFREUEN
LM with alleluias

Geistliche Kirchengesäng, 16
harm. Ralph Vaughan Williams, 19

1. All   crea-tures of our God and King,   lift   up your voice and
2. Thou rush-ing wind that art so strong,   ye   clouds that sail in
3. And all ye men of ten-der heart,   for - giv-ing oth-ers,
4. Let   all things their Cre-a-tor bless,   and   wor-ship Him in

with us sing,   "Al - le - lu - ia! Al - le - lu - ia!"
heav'n a - long,   O   praise Him! Al - le - lu - ia!
take your part;   O   sing ye! Al - le - lu - ia!
hum - ble - ness;   O   praise Him! Al - le - lu - ia!

Thou   burn-ing sun with gold-en beam,   thou   sil - ver moon with
Thou   ris - ing morn, in praise re - joice,   ye   lights of eve - ning
Ye   who long pain and sor - row bear,   praise   God and on Him
Praise, praise the Fa-ther, praise the Son,   and   praise the Spir - it,

soft - er gleam,
find a voice,   O praise Him, O praise Him, al - le
cast your care;
Three in One;

lu - ia, al - le - lu - ia, al - le - lu - - - ia!

Holy Trinity, Thanks and Praise to Thee 160

renz T. Nyberg, 1754 SEELENBRÄUTIGAM Adam Drese, 1665
55 88 55

1. Ho - ly Trin - i - ty, thanks and praise to Thee, that our life
2. Had we an - gels' tongues, with ser - aph - ic songs, bow - ing hearts

and whole sal - va - tion flow from Christ's blest in - car - na - tion
and knees be - fore Thee, Tri - une God, we would a - dore Thee

and His death for us on the shame - ful cross.
in the high - est strain for the Lamb once slain.

161 Glory Be to the Father

Gloria Patri, 2nd cent.   GREATOREX   Henry W. Greatorex, 18

Glory be to the Father, and to the Son, and to the

Holy Ghost; as it was in the beginning, is now, and ever

shall be, world without end. A - men, a - men.

162 Come, We That Love the Lord

Isaac Watts, 1707   ST. THOMAS   Aaron Williams, 17(
                                          SM

1. Come, we that love the Lord, and let our joys be known;
2. Let those re-fuse to sing who nev - er knew our God;
3. The hill of Zi - on yields a thou-sand sa - cred sweets
4. Then let our songs a - bound, and eve - ry tear be dry;

join   in   a   song with sweet ac - cord, and   thus   sur-round the throne.
but   chil - dren of   the heav'n - ly King may speak their joys   a - broad.
be - fore   we   reach the heav'n - ly fields, or   walk the gold - en   streets.
we're march-ing through Em - man - uel's ground to   fair - er worlds on   high.

My God, How Wonderful Thou Art   **163**

alm 113; Frederich W. Faber, 1848   ST. ETHELDREDA   Thomas Turton, 1860
CM

1. My   God, how won - der - ful Thou art, Thy   maj - es - ty   how bright,
2. How dread are Thine   e - ter - nal years, O   ev - er - last - ing LORD;
3. How won - der - ful, how beau - ti - ful, the   sight of Thee must   be,
4. O   how   I   fear Thee, Liv - ing God, with   deep - est, ten - d'rest fears,
5. Yet   I   may love Thee too, O LORD, Al - might - y   as   Thou   art;
6. No   earth - ly   fa - ther loves like Thee, no moth - er e'er   so   mild,
7. Fa - ther   of   Je - sus, love's re - ward, what rap - ture will   it   be,

How beau - ti - ful Thy   mer - cy   seat, in depths of burn-ing   light!
by   pros-trate spir - its,   day and night, in - ces-sant-ly   a - dored.
Thine end - less   wis - dom, bound-less pow'r, and   aw - ful pu - ri - ty.
and   wor - ship Thee with   trem-bling hope, and   pen - i - ten - tial   tears.
for   Thou hast stooped to   ask   of   me   the   love of my poor   heart.
bears and for - bears, as   Thou hast done with   me, Thy sin - ful   child.
pros - trate be - fore Thy   throne to   lie, and   ev - er gaze on   Thee!

164   Lo! God Is Here, Let Us Adore

Gerhard Tersteegen, 1729   VATER UNSER   attr. Martin Luth
trans. John Wesley, 1739   88 88 88   Valentin Schumann's *Geistliche Lieder*, 15

1. Lo! God is here; let us a - dore, and own how dread - ful
2. Lo! God is here, whom day and night u - nit - ed choirs of
3. Al - might - y Fa - ther, may our praise Thy courts with grate - ful

is this place; let all with - in us feel His pow'r,
an - gels praise; to Him, en - throned a - bove all height,
fra - grance fill; still may we stand be - fore Thy face,

and hum - bly bow be - fore His face. Who knows His
the host of heav'n their an - thems raise. Dis - dain not,
still hear and do Thy sov - 'reign will. To God whom

pow'r, His grace who proves, serve Him with awe, with rev - 'rence love.
Lord, our mean - er song, who praise Thee with a stam-m'ring tongue.
earth and heav'n a - dore, be praise and glo - ry ev - er - more.

Angel Voices, Ever Singing

165

ancis Pott, 1861

ANGEL VOICES
85 85 87

Edwin George Monk, 1861

1. An - gel voic - es ev - er sing - ing round Thy throne of light,
2. Thou who art be - yond the far - thest mor - tal eye can scan,
3. Yea, we know Thy love re - joic - es o'er each work of Thine;
4. Here, great God, to - day we of - fer of Thine own to Thee;
5. Hon - or, glo - ry, might, and mer - it Thine shall ev - er be,

an - gel harps, for - ev - er ring - ing, rest not day nor night;
can it be that Thou re - gard - est songs of sin - ful man?
Thou didst ears and hands and voic - es for Thy praise com - bine;
and for Thine ac - cept - ance prof - fer, all un - worth - i - ly,
Fa - ther, Son, and Ho - ly Spir - it, bless - ed Trin - i - ty:

thou - sands on - ly live to bless Thee and con - fess Thee Lord of might.
Can we feel that Thou art near us and wilt hear us? Yea, we can.
crafts - man's art and mu - sic's meas - ure for Thy plea - sure didst de - sign.
hearts and minds and hands and voic - es in our choic - est mel - o - dy.
of the best that Thou hast giv - en earth and heav - en ren - der Thee.

166 Sing Praise to God Who Reigns Above

Johann Jakob Schütz, 1675
trans. Frances E. Cox, 1864, alt.

MIT FREUDEN ZART
87 87 88 7

Bohemian Brethren's *Kirchengesänge*, 15[...]

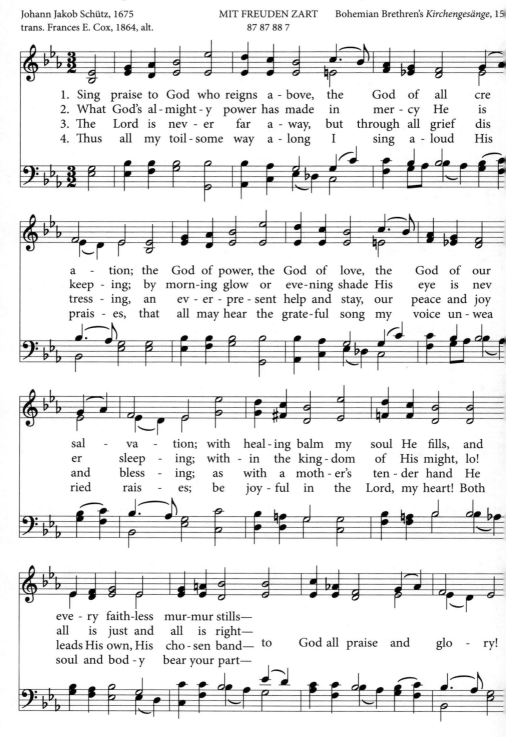

1. Sing praise to God who reigns a-bove, the God of all cre-
2. What God's al-might-y power has made in mer-cy He is
3. The Lord is nev-er far a-way, but through all grief dis-
4. Thus all my toil-some way a-long I sing a-loud His

a - tion; the God of power, the God of love, the God of our
keep - ing; by morn-ing glow or eve-ning shade His eye is nev-
tress - ing, an ev-er-pre-sent help and stay, our peace and joy
prais - es, that all may hear the grate-ful song my voice un-wea-

sal - va - tion; with heal-ing balm my soul He fills, and
er sleep - ing; with-in the king-dom of His might, lo!
and bless - ing; as with a moth-er's ten-der hand He
ried rais - es; be joy-ful in the Lord, my heart! Both

eve - ry faith-less mur-mur stills—
all is just and all is right—
leads His own, His cho-sen band— to God all praise and glo - ry!
soul and bod-y bear your part—

God Himself Is with Us

167

rhard Tersteegen, 1729; trans. composite   ARNSBERG   Joachim Neander, 1680
6 68 6 68 6 66

1. God Him-self is with us; let us now a - dore Him and with awe ap -
2. God Him-self is with us; hear the harps re - sound-ing; see the hosts the
3. Light of light e - ter - nal, all things pen - e - trat - ing, for Your rays our
4. Come, ce - les - tial Be - ing, make our hearts Your dwell-ing, eve - ry car - nal

pear be - fore Him! God is in His tem - ple; all with-in keep
throne sur-round - ing! "Ho - ly, ho - ly, ho - ly!" Hear the hymn as -
soul is wait - ing. As the ten-der flow - ers, will-ing-ly un -
thought dis - pel - ling. By Your Ho - ly Spir - it sanc - ti - fy us

si - lence, pros-trate lie with deep-est rev - 'rence. Him a - lone God we own,
cend-ing, songs of saints and an-gels blend - ing. Bow Your ear to us here:
fold - ing, to the sun their fac - es hold - ing: e - ven so would we do,
tru - ly, teach-ing us to love You on - ly. Where we go here be-low,

Him, our God and Sav - ior; praise His name for - ev - er!
hear, O Christ, the prais - es that Your church now rais - es.
light from You ob - tain - ing, strength to serve You gain - ing.
let us bow be - fore You and in truth a - dore You.

168 Sing Hallelujah, Praise the Lord!

John Swertner, 1789

BECHLER
86 86 88 86

John Christian Bechler, 19th cen

1. Sing hal - le - lu - jah, praise the Lord! Sing with a cheer - ful voice;
2. There we to all e - ter - ni - ty shall join th' an - gel - ic lays

ex - alt our God with one ac - cord, and in His Name re - joice.
and sing in per - fect har - mo - ny to God our Sav - ior's praise;

Ne'er cease to sing, O ran - somed host, praise Fa - ther, Son, and Ho - ly Ghost
He has re - deemed us by His blood, and made us kings and priests to God

un - til in realms of end - less light your prais - es shall u - nite.
for us, for us, the Lamb was slain! Praise ye the Lord! A - men.

Thee We Adore, Eternal Lord! 169

atin, 4th or 5th cent.
ans. Thomas Cotterill, 1815

MENDON
LM

Traditional German melody
arr. Samuel Dyer, 1828

1. Thee we a - dore, e - ter - nal Lord! We praise Thy
2. To Thee a - loud all an - gels cry, the heav'ns and
3. Th'a - pos - tles join the glo - rious throng; the proph - ets
4. From day to day, O Lord, do we high - ly ex -
5. Vouch-safe, O Lord, we hum - bly pray, to keep us

Name with one ac - cord, Thy saints, who here Thy
all the pow'rs on high: Thee, ho - ly, ho - ly,
swell th'im - mor - tal song; the mar - tyrs' no - ble
alt and hon - or Thee! Thy Name we wor - ship
safe from sin this day; have mer - cy, Lord, we

good - ness see, through all the world do wor - ship Thee.
ho - ly King, Lord God of hosts, they ev - er sing.
ar - my raise e - ter - nal an - thems to Thy praise.
and a - dore, world with - out end, for ev - er - more!
trust in Thee; O let us ne'er con - found - ed be!

170 Father, Most Holy

Latin, *O Pater Sancte*, c. 900
trans. Percy Dearmer, 1906

CHRISTE SANCTORUM
11 11 11 5

Paris Antiphoner, 16

1. Fa - ther, most ho - ly, mer - ci - ful, and ten - der; Je - sus our
2. Trin - i - ty bless - ed, U - ni - ty un - shak - en; De - i - ty
3. Mak - er of all things, all Thy crea-tures praise Thee; lo, all thing
4. To the al - might - y tri - une God be glo - ry: high - est and

Sav - ior, with the Fa - ther reign - ing; Spir - it of mer - cy,
per - fect, giv - ing and for - giv - ing, Light of the an - gels,
serve Thee through Thy whole cre - a - tion: hear us, Al - might - y,
great - est, help Thou our en - deav - or; we, too, would praise Thee,

Ad - vo - cate, De - fend - er, Light nev - er wan - ing;
Life of the for - sak - en, Hope of all liv - ing;
hear us as we raise Thee, heart's ad - o - ra - tion.
giv - ing hon - or wor - thy, now and for - ev - er.

O Worship the King

Robert Grant, 1833

LYONS
10 10 11 11

attr. J. Michael Haydn, 18th cent.
arr. Joseph Martin Kraus, 1784

1. O wor-ship the King, all glo-rious a-bove, and grate-ful-ly sing
2. O tell of His might, O sing of His grace, whose robe is the light,
3. The earth with its store of won-ders un-told, Al-might-y, Thy pow'r
4. Thy boun-ti-ful care, what tongue can re-cite? It breathes in the air,
5. Frail chil-dren of dust, and fee-ble as frail, in Thee do we trust,

His pow'r and His love; our Shield and De-fend-er, the An-cient of
whose can-o-py space. His char-iots of wrath the deep thun-der-clouds
hath found-ed of old; hath stab-lished it fast by a change-less de-
it shines in the light. It streams from the hills, it de-scends to the
nor find Thee to fail; Thy mer-cies, how ten-der, how firm to the

Days, pa-vil-ioned in splen-dor, and gird-ed with praise.
form, and dark is His path on the wings of the storm.
cree, and round it hath cast, like a man-tle, the sea.
plain, and sweet-ly dis-tills in the dew and the rain.
end, our Mak-er, De-fend-er, Re-deem-er, and Friend.

172 Praise, My Soul, the King of Heaven

Henry F. Lyte, 1834, alt.

ANDREWS
87 87 87

Mark Andrews, 193

1. Praise, my soul, the King of heav - en; to His feet thy
2. Praise Him for His grace and fa - vor to our fa - ther
3. Fa - ther - like He tends and spares us; well our fee - ble
4. Frail as sum - mer's flow'r we flour - ish— blows the wind and
5. An - gels, help us to a - dore Him— ye be - hold Him

trib - ute bring. Ran - somed, healed, re - stored, for - giv - en,
in dis - tress. Praise Him, still the same for - ev - er,
frame He knows. In His hands He gent - ly bears us,
it is gone. But, while mor - tals rise and per - ish,
face to face. Sun and moon, bow down be - fore Him,

ev - er - more His prais - es sing. Al - le - lu - ia!
slow to chide, and swift to bless. Al - le - lu - ia!
res - cues us from all our foes. Al - le - lu - ia!
God en - dures un - chang-ing on! Al - le - lu - ia!
gath - ered in from eve - ry race. Al - le - lu - ia!

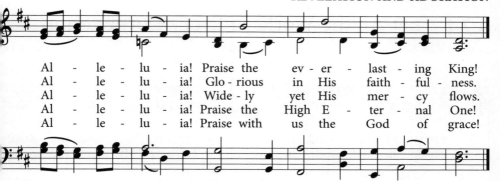

Al - le - lu - ia! Praise the ev - er - last - ing King!
Al - le - lu - ia! Glo - rious in His faith - ful - ness.
Al - le - lu - ia! Wide - ly yet His mer - cy flows.
Al - le - lu - ia! Praise the High E - ter - nal One!
Al - le - lu - ia! Praise with us the God of grace!

Immortal, Invisible, God Only Wise 173

Walter C. Smith, 1867   ST. DENIO   Welsh melody,
11 11 11 11   from John Roberts's *Caniadau y Cyssegr*, 1839

1. Im - mor - tal, in - vis - i - ble, God on - ly wise, in light in - ac-
2. Un - rest - ing, un - hast - ing, and si - lent as light, nor want - ing, nor
3. To all, life Thou giv - est, to both great and small; in all life Thou
4. Great Fa - ther of glo - ry, pure Fa - ther of light, Thine an - gels a -

ces - si - ble hid from our eyes; most bless - ed, most glo - rious, the
wast - ing Thou rul - est in might; Thy jus - tice, like moun - tains, high
liv - est, the true life of all; we blos - som and flour - ish as
dore Thee, all veil - ing their sight. All praise we would ren - der; O

An - cient of Days, Al - might - y, vic - to - rious, Thy great name we praise.
soar - ing a - bove Thy clouds, which are foun - tains of good - ness and love.
leaves on the tree, and with - er and per - ish— but naught chang - eth Thee.
help us to see 'tis on - ly the splen - dor of light hid - eth Thee!

174 Let All the World in Every Corner Sing

George Herbert, 1633   LUCKINGTON   Basil Harwood, 190|

10 4 66 66 10 4

1. Let all the world in eve-ry cor-ner sing, "My God and King!"
2. Let all the world in eve-ry cor-ner sing, "My God and King!"

The heav'ns are not too high, God's praise may thith - er fly;
The church with psalms must shout: no door can keep them out.

the earth is not too low, God's prais - es there may grow.
But, more than all, the heart must bear the long - est part.

Let all the world in eve-ry cor-ner sing, "My God and King!"
Let all the world in eve-ry cor-ner sing, "My God and King!"

How Marvelous God's Greatness! 175

Valdimar Briem, 1886
trans. Charles Venn Pilcher, 1958

BLOMSTERTID
76 76 D

Swedish *Koralbok*, 1697

1. How mar - vel - ous God's great - ness! How glo - ri - ous His might!
2. Each ti - ny flow - 'ret whis - pers the great Life - giv - er's Name;
3. The o - cean's vast a - byss - es in one grand psalm re - cord
4. The star - ry hosts are sing - ing thro' all the light-strewn sky

To this the world bears wit - ness in won - ders day and night—
the might - y moun - tain mass - es His maj - es - ty pro - claim;
the deep mys - te - rious coun - sels and mer - cies of the Lord;
of God's maj - es - tic tem - ple and pal - ace courts on high;

in form of flow'r and snow - flake, in morn's re - splen - dent birth,
in hol - low vales are hymn - ing God's shel - ter for His own;
the ic - y waves of win - ter are thun - d'ring on the strand;
when in these out - er cham - bers such glo - ry gilds the night,

in af - ter - glow at ev - en, in sky and sea and earth.
the snow-capped peaks are point - ing to God's al - might - y throne.
and grief's chill stream is guid - ed by God's all - gra - cious hand.
O, what tran - scen - dent bright - ness is God's e - ter - nal light!

176 Stand Up and Bless the Lord

James Montgomery, 1824

ST. MICHAEL
SM

Genevan Psalter, 1551
adapt. William Crotch, 1836

1. Stand up and bless the Lord, ye peo - ple of His choice;
2. Though high a - bove all praise, a - bove all bless - ing high,
3. O for the liv - ing flame from His own al - tar brought,
4. There, with be - nign re - gard, our hymns He deigns to hear;
5. God is our strength and song, and His sal - va - tion ours;
6. Stand up and bless the Lord; the Lord your God a - dore;

stand up and bless the Lord your God with heart and soul and voice.
who would not fear His ho - ly name and laud and mag - ni - fy?
to touch our lips, our minds in - spire, and wing to heav'n our thought!
tho' un - re - vealed to mor - tal sense, the spir - it feels Him near.
then be His love in Christ pro-claimed with all our ran-somed pow'rs.
stand up and bless His glo - rious name hence-forth and ev - er - more.

177 O Lord of Heaven and Earth and Sea

Christopher Wordsworth, 1863

ES IST KEIN TAG
888 4

Geistliche Seelen-Freud, 1692

1. O Lord of heav'n and earth and sea, to Thee all praise and
2. The gold - en sun - shine, ver - nal air, sweet flow'rs and fruits Thy
3. For peace-ful homes and health-ful days, for all the bless - ings
4. Thou didst not spare Thine on - ly Son, but gav'st Him for a
5. Thou giv'st the Spir - it's bless - ed dow'r, Spir - it of life and
6. For souls re - deemed, for sins for - giv'n, for means of grace and

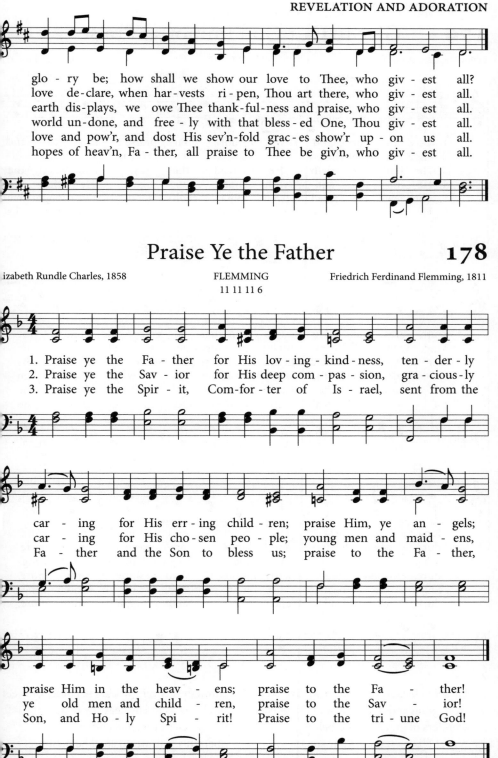

glo - ry be; how shall we show our love to Thee, who giv - est all?
love de - clare, when har - vests ri - pen, Thou art there, who giv - est all.
earth dis - plays, we owe Thee thank - ful - ness and praise, who giv - est all.
world un - done, and free - ly with that bless - ed One, Thou giv - est all.
love and pow'r, and dost His sev'n - fold grac - es show'r up - on us all.
hopes of heav'n, Fa - ther, all praise to Thee be giv'n, who giv - est all.

Praise Ye the Father

178

izabeth Rundle Charles, 1858   FLEMMING   Friedrich Ferdinand Flemming, 1811
11 11 11 6

1. Praise ye the Fa - ther for His lov - ing - kind - ness, ten - der - ly
2. Praise ye the Sav - ior for His deep com - pas - sion, gra - cious - ly
3. Praise ye the Spir - it, Com - for - ter of Is - rael, sent from the

car - ing for His err - ing child - ren; praise Him, ye an - gels;
car - ing for His cho - sen peo - ple; young men and maid - ens,
Fa - ther and the Son to bless us; praise to the Fa - ther,

praise Him in the heav - ens; praise to the Fa - ther!
ye old men and child - ren, praise to the Sav - ior!
Son, and Ho - ly Spi - rit! Praise to the tri - une God!

179   Give to Our God Immortal Praise

Psalm 136; Isaac Watts, 1719   WARRINGTON   Ralph Harrison, 178
                                          LM

1. Give to our God im - mor - tal praise; mer - cy and
2. Give to the LORD of lords re - known, the King of
3. He built the earth, He spread the sky, and fixed the
4. He fills the sun with morn - ing light, He bids the
5. The Jews He freed from Pha - raoh's hand and brought them
6. He saw the Gen - tiles dead in sin and felt His

truth are all His ways; won-ders of grace to God be -
kings with glo - ry crown; His mer-cies ev - er shall en -
star - ry lights on high; won-ders of grace to God be -
moon di - rect the night; His mer-cies ev - er shall en -
to the prom - ised land; won-ders of grace to God be -
pit - y move with - in; His mer-cies ev - er shall en -

long, re - peat His mer - cies in your song.
dure, when lords and kings are known no more.
long, re - peat His mer - cies in your song.
dure, when suns and moons shall shine no more.
long, re - peat His mer - cies in your song.
dure, when death and sin shall reign no more.

7. He sent His Son with pow'r to save
   from guilt, and darkness, and the grave;
   wonders of grace to God belong,
   repeat His mercies in your song.

8. Through this vain world He guides our feet
   and leads us to His heav'nly seat;
   His mercies ever shall endure,
   when this vain world shall be no more.

Safely Through Another Week

180

...hn Newton, 1774

DIX
77 77 77

Conrad Kocher, 1838
adapt. William Henry Monk, 1861
harm. *The English Hymnal*, 1906

1. Safe - ly through an - oth - er week God has brought us on our way;
2. While we pray for par-d'ning grace, through the dear Re - deem-er's name,
3. Here we come Thy name to praise, let us feel Thy pres-ence near;
4. May Thy gos - pel's joy - ful sound con - quer sin - ners, com - fort saints;

let us now a bless - ing seek, wait - ing in His courts to - day;
show Thy rec - on - cil - ing face; take a - way our sin and shame;
may Thy glo - ry meet our eyes, while we in Thy house ap - pear:
may the fruits of grace a - bound, bring re - lief for all com-plaints:

day of all the week the best, em - blem of e - ter - nal rest.
from our world - ly cares set free, may we rest this day in Thee.
here af - ford us, Lord, a taste of our ev - er - last - ing feast.
thus may all our Sab - baths prove, till we join the church a - bove.

181   This Is My Father's World

Maltbie D. Babcock, 1901   TERRA BEATA   English folk melod
                    SMD   adapt. Franklin L. Sheppard, 191

1. This is my Fa-ther's world, and to my lis-t'ning ears
2. This is my Fa-ther's world; the birds their car-ols raise;
3. This is my Fa-ther's world; O let me ne'er for-get

all na-ture sings, and 'round me rings the mu-sic of the spheres
the morn-ing light, the lil-y white de-clare their Mak-er's praise
that though the wrong seems oft so strong, God is the Rul-er yet.

This is my Fa-ther's world; I rest me in the thought of
This is my Fa-ther's world; He shines in all that's fair; in the
This is my Fa-ther's world; the bat-tle is not done; Je -

rocks and trees, of skies and seas; His hand the won-ders wrought
rus-tling grass I hear Him pass, He speaks to me eve-ry-where.
sus who died shall be sat-is-fied, and earth and heav-en be one.

O Father, Thou Whose Love Profound **182**

Edward Cooper, 1805 ROCKINGHAM A. Williams's *Supplement to Psalmody*, 1780
LM harm. Edward Miller, 1790

1. O Father, Thou whose love pro - found a ran - som
2. Al - might - y Son, In - car - nate Word, our Proph - et,
3. E - ter - nal Spir - it, by whose breath the soul is
4. Je - ho - vah! Fa - ther, Spir - it, Son, mys - ter - ious

for our souls hath found, be - fore Thy throne we
Priest, Re - deem - er, Lord, be - fore Thy throne we
raised from sin and death, be - fore Thy throne we
God - head, Three in One, be - fore Thy throne we

sin - ners bend; to us Thy par - d'ning love ex - tend.
sin - ners bend; to us Thy sav - ing grace ex - tend.
sin - ners bend; to us Thy quick - 'ning pow'r ex - tend.
sin - ners bend; grace, par - don, life, to us ex - tend.

183   O Splendor of God's Glory Bright

Ambrose of Milan, 4th cent.   PUER NOBIS   Trier manuscript, 15th cen
trans. composite   LM   adapt. Michael Praetorius, 16(

1. O Splen - dor of God's glo - ry bright, from Light e
2. Come, ver - y Sun of heav - en's love, in last - ing
3. And now to Thee our pray'rs as - cend, O Fa - ther,
4. Con - firm our will to do the right, and keep our
5. O joy - ful be the pass - ing day with thoughts as
6. Dawn's glo - ry gilds the earth and skies, let Him, our

ter - nal bring - ing light, O Light of light, light's
ra - diance from a - bove, and pour the Ho - ly
glo - rious with - out end; we plead with sov - 'reign
hearts from en - vy's blight; let faith her ea - ger
pure as morn - ing's ray, with faith like noon - tide
per - fect Morn, a - rise, the Word in God the

liv - ing Spring, true Day, all days il - lu - min - ing.
Spir - it's ray on all we think or do to - day.
grace for pow'r to con - quer in temp - ta - tion's hour.
fires re - new, and hate the false, and love the true.
shin - ing bright, our souls un - shad - owed by the night.
Fath - er one, the Fath - er im - aged in the Son.

All Things Bright and Beautiful   **184**

cil F. Alexander, 1848   ALL THINGS BRIGHT   William Henry Monk, 1887
76 76 with refrain

Refrain

All things bright and beau - ti - ful, all crea - tures great and small,

all things wise and won - der - ful, the Lord God made them all.

1. Each lit - tle flow'r that o - pens, each lit - tle bird that sings,
2. The pur - ple - head - ed moun - tain, the riv - er run - ning by,
3. The cold wind in the win - ter, the pleas - ant sum - mer sun,
4. He gave us eyes to see them, and lips that we might tell

to Refrain

He made their glow-ing col - ors, He made their ti - ny wings.
the sun - set and the morn - ing that bright - ens up the sky.
the ripe fruits in the gar - den: He made them eve - ry one.
how great is God Al - might - y, who has made all things well.

185 Great Is Thy Faithfulness

Thomas O. Chisholm, 1923

FAITHFULNESS
11 10 11 10 with refrain

William M. Runyan, 19.

1. Great is Thy faith-ful-ness, O God my Fath-er; there is no
shad-ow of turn-ing with Thee; Thou chang-est not, Thy com
pas-sions, they fail not; as Thou hast been, Thou for-ev-er wilt be.

2. Sum-mer and win-ter, and spring-time and har-vest, sun, moon, and
stars in their cours-es a-bove join with all na-ture in
man-i-fold wit-ness to Thy great faith-ful-ness, mer-cy, and love.

3. Par-don for sin and a peace that en-dur-eth, Thine own dea
pres-ence to cheer and to guide; strength for to-day and brigh
hope for to-mor-row: bless-ings all mine, with ten thou-sand be-side!

Great is Thy faith-ful-ness! Great is Thy faith-ful-ness! Morn-ing by
morn-ing new mer-cies I see; all I have need-ed Thy

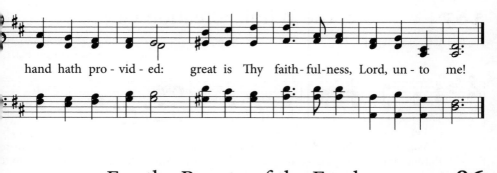

hand hath pro - vid - ed: great is Thy faith-ful-ness, Lord, un - to me!

For the Beauty of the Earth 186

liott Sandford Pierpoint, 1864, alt. DIX Conrad Kocher, 1838
77 77 77 adapt. William Henry Monk, 1861
harm. *The English Hymnal*, 1906

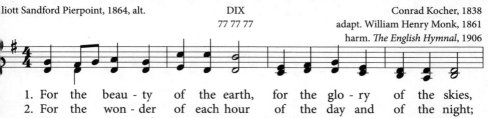

1. For the beau - ty of the earth, for the glo - ry of the skies,
2. For the won - der of each hour of the day and of the night;
3. For the joy of hu - man love, broth - er, sis - ter, par - ent, child;
4. For Thy church that ev - er - more lifts her ho - ly hands a - bove,
5. For the joy of ear and eye, for the heart and mind's de - light,
6. For Thy - self, best gift di - vine, to our world so free - ly giv'n;

for the love which from our birth o - ver and a - round us lies:
hill and vale, and tree and flow'r, sun and moon, and stars of light:
friends on earth, and friends a - bove, pleas-ures pure and un - de - filed:
of - f'ring up on eve - ry shore her pure sac - ri - fice of love:
for the mys - tic har - mon - y link - ing sense and sound and sight:
for that great, great love of Thine, peace on earth and joy in heav'n:

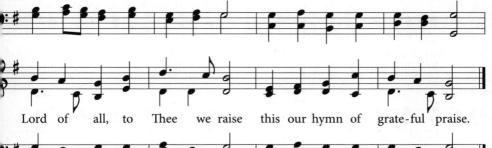

Lord of all, to Thee we raise this our hymn of grate-ful praise.

187 Let the Whole Creation Cry

Stopford A. Brooke, 1881, alt.   SALZBURG   Jakob Hintze, 16
77 77 D   harm. Johann Sebastian Bach, 18th ce

1. Let the whole cre - a - tion cry, "Glo - ry to the Lord on high
2. War - riors fight - ing for the Lord, proph - ets burn - ing with His word
3. Men and wom - en, young and old, raise the an - them man - i - fold

Heav'n and earth, a - wake and sing, "God is good, and God is King!
those to whom the arts be - long, add their voic - es to the song,
and let chil - dren's hap - py hearts in this wor - ship bear their parts

Praise Him, an - gel hosts a - bove, ev - er bright and fair in love;
Kings of knowl - edge and of law, to the glo - rious cir - cle draw
from the north to south - ern pole let the might - y cho - rus roll:

sun and moon, lift up your voice, night and stars, in God re - joice!
all who work and all who wait, sing, "The Lord is good and great!
"Ho - ly, ho - ly, ho - ly One! Glo - ry be to God a - lone!"

I Sing the Mighty Power of God 188

Isaac Watts, 1715 ELLACOMBE *Vollstandige-Sammlung*, 1827
CMD adapt. William Henry Monk, 1868

1. I sing the might-y pow'r of God that made the moun-tains rise,
2. I sing the good-ness of the Lord that filled the earth with food.
3. There's not a plant or flower be-low but makes Thy glo-ries known.

that spread the flow-ing seas a-broad and built the loft-y skies.
He formed the crea-tures with His word, and then pro-nounced them good.
And clouds a-rise, and tem-pests blow, by or-der from Thy throne.

I sing the wis-dom that or-dained the sun to rule the day.
Lord, how Thy won-ders are dis-played, wher-e'er I turn my eye,
While all that bor-rows life from Thee is ev-er in Thy care,

The moon shines full at His com-mand, and all the stars o-bey.
if I sur-vey the ground I tread, or gaze up-on the sky.
and eve-ry-where that man can be, Thou, God, art pres-ent there.

189   Give Praise to God

James Montgomery Boice © 1999   SOLI DEO   Paul S. Jones © 19

LM with refrain

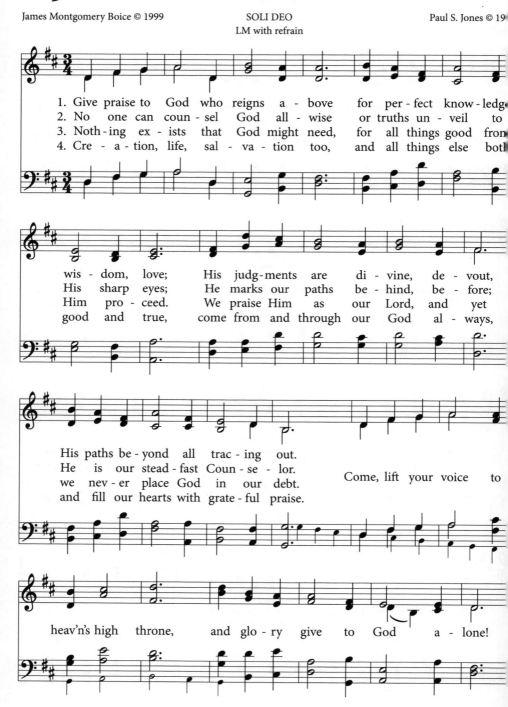

1. Give praise to God who reigns a - bove for per - fect know - ledg
2. No one can coun - sel God all - wise or truths un - veil to
3. Noth - ing ex - ists that God might need, for all things good from
4. Cre - a - tion, life, sal - va - tion too, and all things else both

wis - dom, love; His judg - ments are di - vine, de - vout,
His sharp eyes; He marks our paths be - hind, be - fore,
Him pro - ceed. We praise Him as our Lord, and yet
good and true, come from and through our God al - ways,

His paths be - yond all trac - ing out.
He is our stead - fast Coun - se - lor.
we nev - er place God in our debt.
and fill our hearts with grate - ful praise.

Come, lift your voice to

heav'n's high throne, and glo - ry give to God a - lone!

Now Thank We All Our God   190

Martin Rinkart, 1636   NUN DANKET   Johann Crüger, 1647
trans. Catherine Winkworth, 1858   67 67 66 66   harm. Felix Mendelssohn, 1840

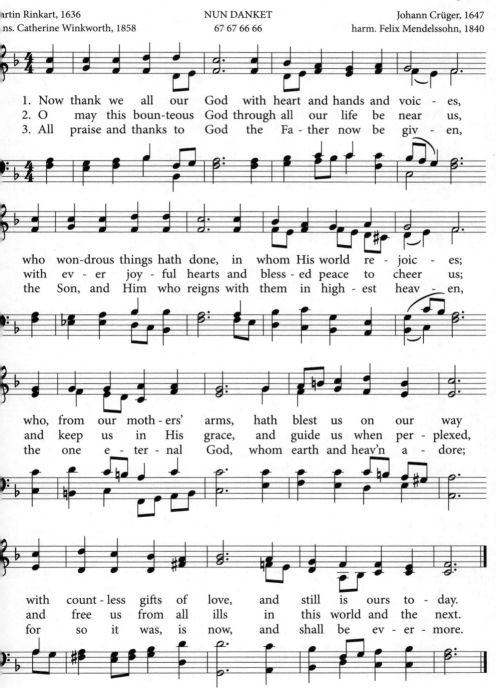

1. Now thank we all our God with heart and hands and voic - es,
2. O may this boun-teous God through all our life be near us,
3. All praise and thanks to God the Fa - ther now be giv - en,

who won-drous things hath done, in whom His world re - joic - es;
with ev - er joy - ful hearts and bless - ed peace to cheer us;
the Son, and Him who reigns with them in high - est heav - en,

who, from our moth - ers' arms, hath blest us on our way
and keep us in His grace, and guide us when per - plexed,
the one e - ter - nal God, whom earth and heav'n a - dore;

with count - less gifts of love, and still is ours to - day.
and free us from all ills in this world and the next.
for so it was, is now, and shall be ev - er - more.

191 Praise to the Lord, the Almighty

Joachim Neander, 1680
trans. Catherine Winkworth, 1863, alt.

LOBE DEN HERREN
14 14 4 7 8

Siraslund Gesangbuch, 1665

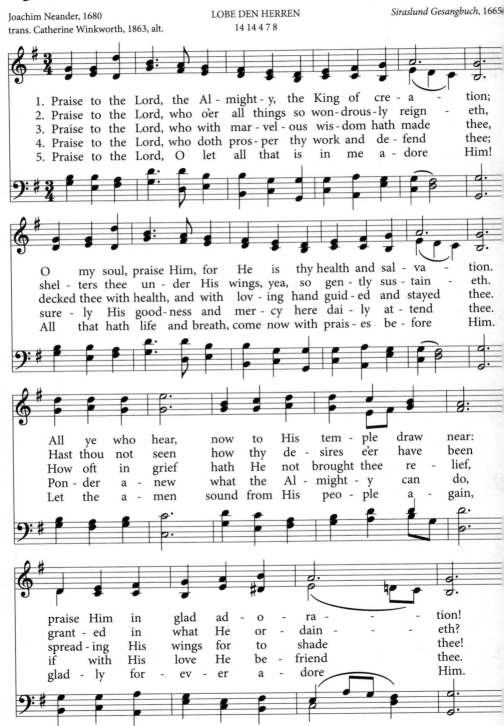

1. Praise to the Lord, the Al - might - y, the King of cre - a - tion;
   O my soul, praise Him, for He is thy health and sal - va - tion.
   All ye who hear, now to His tem - ple draw near:
   praise Him in glad ad - o - ra - tion!

2. Praise to the Lord, who o'er all things so won - drous - ly reign - eth,
   shel - ters thee un - der His wings, yea, so gen - tly sus - tain - eth.
   Hast thou not seen how thy de - sires e'er have been
   grant - ed in what He or - dain - eth?

3. Praise to the Lord, who with mar - vel - ous wis - dom hath made thee,
   decked thee with health, and with lov - ing hand guid - ed and stayed thee.
   How oft in grief hath He not brought thee re - lief,
   spread - ing His wings for to shade thee!

4. Praise to the Lord, who doth pros - per thy work and de - fend thee;
   sure - ly His good - ness and mer - cy here dai - ly at - tend thee.
   Pon - der a - new what the Al - might - y can do,
   if with His love He be - friend thee.

5. Praise to the Lord, O let all that is in me a - dore Him!
   All that hath life and breath, come now with prais - es be - fore Him.
   Let the a - men sound from His peo - ple a - gain,
   glad - ly for - ev - er a - dore Him.

Rejoice, Ye Pure in Heart

192

ward H. Plumptre, 1865   MARION   Arthur H. Messiter, 1883

SM with refrain

1. Re - joice, ye pure in heart, re - joice, give thanks and sing:
2. With all the an - gel choirs, with all the saints of earth,
3. Yes, on through life's long path, still chant - ing as ye go;
4. Still lift your stand- ard high, still march in firm ar - ray;

your fes - tal ban - ner wave on high, the cross of Christ your King.
pour out the strains of joy and bliss, true rap - ture, no - blest mirth!
from youth to age, by night and day, in glad- ness and in woe.
as war - riors thro' the dark - ness toil till dawns the gold - en day.

Re - joice, re - joice, re - joice, give thanks, and sing!
Re - joice, re - joice,

193   We Gather Together

Adrianus Valerius, 1626   KREMSER   *Neder-landtsch Gedenck-Clank,* 16
trans. Theodore Baker, 1894   12 11 12 11   harm. Eduard Kremser, 18

1. We gath - er to - geth - er to ask the Lord's bless - ing;
2. Be - side us to guide us, our God with us join - ing,
3. We all do ex - tol Thee, Thou lead - er tri - um - phant,

He chas - tens and has - tens His will to make known;
or - dain - ing, main - tain - ing His king - dom di - vine;
and pray that Thou still our de - fend - er wilt be.

the wick - ed op - press - ing now cease from dis - tress - ing.
so from the be - gin - ning the fight we were win - ning;
Let Thy con - gre - ga - tion es - cape trib - u - la - tion;

Sing prais - es to His name; He for - gets not His own.
the Lord was at our side— the glo - ry be Thine!
Thy name be ev - er praised! O Lord, make us free!

We Praise Thee, O God, Our Redeemer 194

Julia C. Cory, 1902

KREMSER
12 11 12 11

Neder-landtsch Gedenck-Clank, 1626
harm. Eduard Kremser, 1877

1. We praise Thee, O God, our Re - deem - er, Cre - a - tor,
2. We wor - ship Thee, God of our fa - thers, we bless Thee;
3. With voic - es u - nit - ed our prais - es we of - fer,

in grate - ful de - vo - tion our trib - ute we bring;
through life's storm and tem - pest, our Guide hast Thou been;
to Thee, great Je - ho - vah, glad an - thems we raise;

we lay it be - fore Thee, we kneel and a - dore Thee,
when per - ils o'er - take us, es - cape Thou wilt make us,
Thy strong arm will guide us, our God is be - side us,

we bless Thy ho - ly name, glad prais - es we sing.
and with Thy help, O Lord, our bat - tles we win.
to Thee, our great Re - deem - er, for - ev - er be praise.

195 King of Glory, King of Peace

George Herbert, 1633   GWALCHMAI   Joseph David Jones, 18
74 74 D

1. King of glo - ry, King of peace, I will love Thee;
2. Where-fore with my ut - most art I will sing Thee,
3. Sev'n whole days, not one in sev'n, I will praise Thee;

and that love may nev - er cease, I will move Thee.
and the cream of all my heart I will bring Thee.
in my heart, though not in heav'n, I can raise Thee.

Thou hast grant - ed my re - quest, Thou hast heard me;
Though my sins a - gainst me cried, Thou didst clear me;
Small it is, in this poor sort to en - roll Thee:

Thou didst note my work - ing breast, Thou hast spared me.
and a - lone, when they re - plied, Thou didst hear me.
e'en e - ter - ni - ty's too short to ex - tol Thee.

Lord, We Bow Before Your Glory   **196**

ic J. Alexander © 2001

KIMARSONEVY
87 87 D

Paul S. Jones © 2001

1. Lord, we bow be - fore Your glo - ry man - i - fest - ed in Your Son.
2. Such a Sav - ior, now ex - alt - ed, well de - serves our heart - felt praise.
3. O that we might know You bet - ter, Je - sus Christ, our liv - ing Lord.

Ra - diant with Your per - fect beau - ty, He is heav'n's Be - lov - ed One.
Dy - ing He has death de - feat - ed; ris'n He reigns for end - less days.
Let our love grow dai - ly great - er as we hear Your ho - ly word.

Sav - ing grace has giv'n us vi - sion, o - pened eyes that once were blind.
Now in heav - en in - ter - ced - ing, Je - sus, Friend of sin - ners, prays
There You have re - vealed Your glo - ry, there we mar - vel at Your grace.

He on whom we brought de - ri - sion now de - lights our heart and mind.
for the weak - est, dai - ly plead - ing; all suf - fi - cient is His grace.
Feed our souls and make us like You till we see You face to face.

197 When Morning Gilds the Skies

Sebastian Portner's
Katholisches Gesangbuch, 1828
trans. Edward Caswall, 1858

LAUDES DOMINI
66 6 66 6

Joseph Barnby, 18

1. When morn-ing gilds the skies, my heart a-wak-ing cries,
2. Does sad-ness fill my mind? A sol-ace here I find,
3. The night be-comes as day when from the heart we say,
4. Let earth's wide cir-cle round in joy-ful notes re-sound,
5. Be this, while life is mine, my can-ti-cle di-vine,

may Je-sus Christ be praised! A-like at work and prayer
may Je-sus Christ be praised! Or fades my earth-ly bliss?
may Je-sus Christ be praised! The pow'rs of dark-ness fear
may Je-sus Christ be praised! Let air and sea and sky
may Je-sus Christ be praised! Be this th'e-ter-nal song

to Je-sus I re-pair, may Je-sus Christ be praised!
My com-fort still is this, may Je-sus Christ be praised!
when this sweet song they hear, may Je-sus Christ be praised!
from depth to height re-ply, may Je-sus Christ be praised!
through all the a-ges long, may Je-sus Christ be praised!

Fairest Lord Jesus

198

ünsterisch Gesangbuch, 1677
ns. Evangelical Christendom (st. 1–3), 1850
d J.A. Seiss (st. 4), 1873

CRUSADER'S HYMN
56 85 58

Silesian folk melody
Schlesische Volkslieder, 1842

1. Fair - est Lord Je - sus, Ru - ler of all na - ture,
2. Fair are the mead - ows, fair - er still the wood - lands,
3. Fair is the sun - shine, fair - er still the moon - light,
4. Beau - ti - ful Sav - ior! Lord of the na - tions!

O Thou of God and man the Son, Thee will I cher - ish,
robed in the bloom - ing garb of spring: Je - sus is fair - er,
and all the twink - ling star - ry host: Je - sus shines bright - er,
Son of God and Son of Man! Glo - ry and hon - or,

Thee will I hon - or, Thou, my soul's glo - ry, joy, and crown!
Je - sus is pur - er, who makes the woe - ful heart to sing.
Je - sus shines pur - er, than all the an - gels heav'n can boast.
praise, ad - o - ra - tion, now and for - ev - er - more be Thine!

199   Jesus, Thy Boundless Love to Me

Paul Gerhardt, 1653   RYBURN   Norman Cocke
trans. John Wesley, 1739, alt.   88 88 88   © 1953 Oxford University Pre

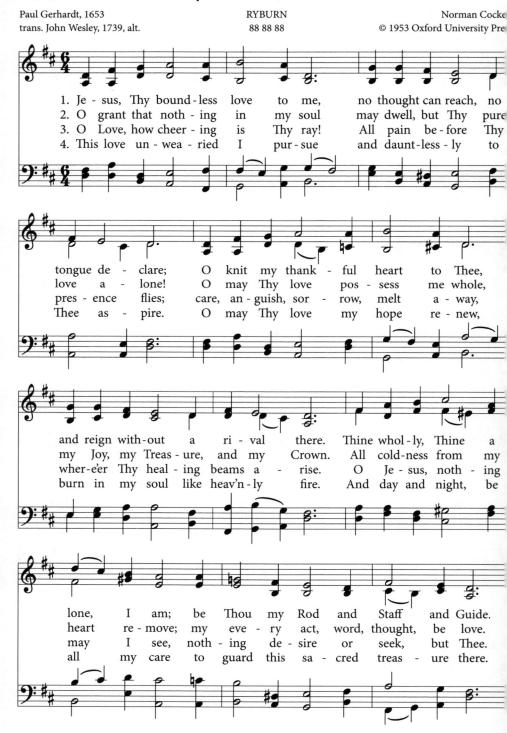

1. Je - sus, Thy bound-less love to me,   no thought can reach, no
2. O grant that noth-ing in my soul   may dwell, but Thy pure
3. O Love, how cheer-ing is Thy ray!   All pain be-fore Thy
4. This love un-wea-ried I pur-sue   and daunt-less-ly to

tongue de - clare;   O knit my thank - ful heart to Thee,
love a - lone!   O may Thy love pos - sess me whole,
pres - ence flies;   care, an-guish, sor - row, melt a - way,
Thee as - pire.   O may Thy love my hope re - new,

and reign with-out a ri - val there. Thine whol-ly, Thine a
my Joy, my Treas - ure, and my Crown. All cold-ness from my
wher-e'er Thy heal - ing beams a - rise. O Je - sus, noth - ing
burn in my soul like heav'n-ly fire. And day and night, be

lone, I am; be Thou my Rod and Staff and Guide.
heart re - move; my eve - ry act, word, thought, be love.
may I see, noth - ing de - sire or seek, but Thee.
all my care to guard this sa - cred treas - ure there.

How Sad Our State

ac Watts, 1707 · SASHA · Joan J. Pinkston © 1998
CMD

1. How sad our state by na - ture is, our sin how deep it stains;
2. My soul o - beys th'_al - might - y call and runs to this re - lief;
3. Stretch out Thine arm, vic - tor - ious King, my reign - ing sins sub - due;

and Sa - tan binds our cap - tive minds fast in his slav - ish chains.
I would be - lieve Thy prom - ise, Lord; O help my un - be - lief.
and drive the drag - on from his seat, with all his hell - ish crew.

But there's a voice of sov - 'reign grace sounds from the sa - cred word,
Un - to the foun - tain of Thy blood, In - car - nate God, I fly;
A guilt - y, weak, and help - less worm, on Thy kind arms I fall;

"Ho! ye de - spair - ing sin - ners, come, and trust up - on the Lord."
here let me wash my spot - ted soul from crimes of deep - est dye.
be Thou my strength and right - eous - ness, my Je - sus, and my all.

201   A Debtor to Mercy Alone

Augustus M. Toplady, 1771, alt.   TREWEN   David Emlyn Evans, 18
                                     LMD

1. A debt-or to mer-cy a-lone, of cov-e-nant mer-cy I sing; nor fear, with Your right-eous-ness on, my per-son and of-f'ring to bring. The ter-rors of law and of God with me can have noth-ing to do; my Sav-ior's o

2. The work which His good-ness be-gan, the arm of His strength will com-plete; His prom-ise is yea and a-men, and nev-er was for-feit-ed yet. Things fu-ture, nor things that are now, nor all things be-low or a-bove, can make Him His

3. My name from the palms of His hands e-ter-ni-ty will not e-rase; im-pressed on His heart it re-mains, in marks of in-del-i-ble grace. Yes, I to the end shall en-dure, as sure as the ear-nest is giv'n; more hap-py, but

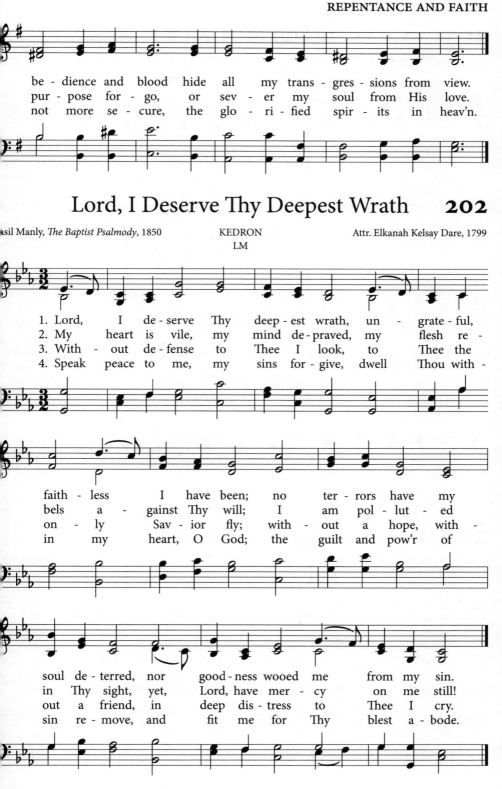

be - dience and blood hide all my trans - gres - sions from view.
pur - pose for - go, or sev - er my soul from His love.
not more se - cure, the glo - ri - fied spir - its in heav'n.

Lord, I Deserve Thy Deepest Wrath 202

Basil Manly, *The Baptist Psalmody*, 1850   KEDRON   Attr. Elkanah Kelsay Dare, 1799
LM

1. Lord, I de - serve Thy deep - est wrath, un - grate - ful,
2. My heart is vile, my mind de - praved, my flesh re -
3. With - out de - fense to Thee I look, to Thee the
4. Speak peace to me, my sins for - give, dwell Thou with -

faith - less I have been; no ter - rors have my
bels a - gainst Thy will; I am pol - lut - ed
on - ly Sav - ior fly; with - out a hope, with -
in my heart, O God; the guilt and pow'r of

soul de - terred, nor good - ness wooed me from my sin.
in Thy sight, yet, Lord, have mer - cy on me still!
out a friend, in deep dis - tress to Thee I cry.
sin re - move, and fit me for Thy blest a - bode.

203   Come, Ye Sinners, Poor and Needy

Joseph Hart, 1759   RESTORATION   William Walker's *Southern Harmony*, 183(

                                   87 87

1. Come, ye sin-ners, poor and need-y, weak and wound-ed, sick and sore;
2. Come, ye thirst-y, come, and wel-come, God's free boun-ty glo-ri-fy;
3. Let not con-science make you lin-ger, nor of fit-ness fond-ly drean
4. Come, ye wea-ry, heav-y la-den, lost and ru-ined by the fall;
5. Lo! th' in-car-nate God, as-cend-ed, pleads the mer-it of His bloo

Je-sus read-y stands to save you, full of pit-y, love, and pow'r.
true be-lief and true re-pen-tance, eve-ry grace that brings you nigh.
all the fit-ness He re-quir-eth is to feel your need of Him.
if you tar-ry till you're bet-ter, you will nev-er come at all.
ven-ture on Him, ven-ture whol-ly; let no oth-er trust in-trude.

204   Lord Jesus, Think on Me

Synesius of Cyrene, c. 410   SOUTHWELL   William Dama
trans. Allen W. Chatfield, 1876   SM   *The Psalmes of David*, 157

1. Lord Je-sus, think on me, and purge a-way my sin;
2. Lord Je-sus, think on me, with care and woe op-pressed,
3. Lord Je-sus, think on me, nor let me go a-stray;
4. Lord Je-sus, think on me, that, when the flood is past,

from   earth-born pas - sions   set   me   free, and   make me pure with - in.
let   me   Thy lov - ing   ser - vant be,   and   taste Thy prom- ised rest.
through dark-ness and per - plex - i - ty point Thou the heav'n- ly   way.
I   may   e - ter - nal bright-ness see, and   share Thy joy   at   last.

Depth of Mercy! Can There Be   205

harles Wesley, 1740   CANTERBURY   adapt. from Orlando Gibbons, 1623
                                    77 77

1. Depth of mer - cy!   Can there be   mer - cy   still   re - served for me?
2. I   have long with-stood His grace, long pro-voked Him to   His face,
3. I   my Mas - ter have de - nied; I   a - fresh have cru - ci - fied,
4. There for me the   Sav- ior stands, shows His wounds and spreads His hands.
5. Now in - cline me   to re - pent, let   me   now   my   fall   la - ment;

Can   my God His wrath for - bear; me, the chief of   sin - ners, spare?
would not hark - en   to   His calls, grieved Him by   a   thou-sand falls.
oft   pro-faned His hal-lowed name, put Him to   an   o - pen shame.
God   is love! I   know, I   feel; Je - sus weeps, but loves me still!
now   my foul re - volt de - plore; weep, be- lieve, and sin   no more.

206   Come to the Waters

Revelation 22   WATER OF LIFE   Paul S. Jones © 200
James Montgomery Boice © 2000   11 10 11 10

1. Come to the wa - ters, who - ev - er is thirst - y; drink from the
2. Come to the Riv - er that flows thro' the ci - ty, forth from the
3. Come to the Foun - tain with - out an - y mon - ey; buy what is
4. Come to the Well of un - mer - it - ed fa - vor; stretch out your
5. Come to the Sav - ior, the God of sal - va - tion. God has pro

Foun - tain that nev - er runs dry. Je - sus, the Liv - ing One, of - fers you
throne of the Fa - ther and Son. Je - sus the Sav - ior says, "Come and drin
giv - en with - out an - y cost. Je - sus, the gra - cious One, wel - comes the
hand; fill your cup to the brim. Je - sus is such a com - pas - sion - ate
vid - ed an end to sin's strife. Why will you suf - fer the Law's con - dem

mer - cy, life more a - bun - dant in bound - less sup - ply.
deep - ly." Drink from the pure, in - ex - haust - i - ble One.
wea - ry; Je - sus, the self - less One, died for the lost.
Sav - ior. Draw from the grace that flows free - ly from Him.
na - tion? Take the free gift of the wa - ter of life.

Ho! Ye That Thirst

207

aiah 55; *Scottish Psalter,* 1880 · FOREST GREEN · English folk tune
CMD · harm. Ralph Vaughan Williams, 1906

1. Ho! Ye that thirst, ap-proach the spring where liv-ing wa-ters flow;
2. My stores af-ford those rich sup-plies that health and pleas-ure give;
3. Be-hold He comes! your Lead-er comes, with might and hon-or crowned;
4. Seek ye the LORD while yet His ear is o-pen to your call;
5. With joy and peace shall then be led the glad con-vert-ed lands;

free to that sa-cred foun-tain all with-out a price may go.
in-cline your ear, and come to Me; the soul that hears shall live.
a Wit-ness who shall spread My Name to earth's re-mot-est bound.
while of-fered mer-cy still is near, be-fore His foot-stool fall.
the loft-y moun-tains then shall sing, the for-ests clap their hands.

How long to streams of false de-light will ye in crowds re-pair?
With you a cov-'nant I will make that ev-er shall en-dure;
See! na-tions has-ten to His call from eve-ry dis-tant shore;
Let sin-ners quit their e-vil ways, their e-vil thoughts fore-go,
Where bri-ars grew 'midst bar-ren wilds, shall firs and myr-tles spring;

How long your strength and sub-stance waste on tri-fles light as air?
the hope which glad-dened Da-vid's heart My mer-cy hath made sure.
isles, yet un-known, shall bow to Him, and Is-rael's God a-dore.
and God, when they to Him re-turn, re-turn-ing grace will show.
and na-ture, thro' its ut-most bounds, e-ter-nal prais-es sing.

208 No, Not Despairingly

Horatius Bonar, 1866 · NENTHORN · Thomas Legerwood Hately, 19th cent
64 64 66 4

1. No, not des - pair - ing - ly come I to Thee; no, not dis -
2. Ah! Mine in - i - qui - ty crim - son has been, in - fi - nite,
3. Lord, I con - fess to Thee sad - ly my sin; all I am,
4. Faith - ful and just art Thou, for - giv - ing all; lov - ing and
5. Then all is peace and light this soul with - in; thus shall I

trust - ing - ly bend I the knee; sin hath gone o - ver me,
in - fi - nite, sin up - on sin; sin of not lov - ing Thee,
tell to Thee, all I have been; purge Thou my sin a - way,
kind art Thou when poor ones call; Lord, let the cleans - ing blood
walk with Thee, the loved Un - seen; lean - ing on Thee, my God,

yet is this still my plea, Je - sus hath died.
sin of not trust - ing Thee, in - fi - nite sin.
wash Thou my soul this day; Lord, make me clean.
blood of the Lamb of God, pass o'er my soul.
guid - ed a - long the road, noth - ing be - tween.

I Lay My Sins on Jesus

209

oratius Bonar, 1848

AURELIA
76 76 D

Samuel Sebastian Wesley, 1864

1. I lay my sins on Je - sus, the spot - less Lamb of God;
2. I lay my wants on Je - sus; all full - ness dwells in Him;
3. I rest my soul on Je - sus, this wear - y soul of mine;
4. I long to be like Je - sus, meek, lov - ing, low - ly, mild;

He bears them all, and frees us from the ac - curs - ed load;
He heals all my dis - eas - es, He doth my soul re - deem;
His right hand me em - brac - es, I on His breast re - cline.
I long to be like Je - sus, the Fa - ther's ho - ly Child;

I bring my guilt to Je - sus, to wash my crim - son stains
I lay my griefs on Je - sus, my bur - dens and my cares;
I love the Name of Je - sus, Im - man - uel, Christ, the Lord;
I long to be with Je - sus a - mid the heav'n - ly throng,

white in His blood most pre - cious, till not a spot re - mains.
He from them all re - leas - es, He all my sor - row shares.
like frag - rance on the breez - es His Name a - broad is poured.
to sing with saints His prais - es, to learn the an - gels' song.

210 Rock of Ages

Augustus M. Toplady, 1776   REDHEAD   Richard Redhead, 185[?]

77 77 77

1. Rock of Ag - es, cleft for me, let me hide my - self in Thee;
2. Not the la - bors of my hands can ful - fil Thy Law's de - mands;
3. Noth-ing in my hand I bring, sim - ply to Thy cross I cling.
4. While I draw this fleet - ing breath, when mine eye - lids close in death,

let the wa - ter and the blood from Thy wound-ed side which flowed,
could my zeal no res - pite know, could my tears for - ev - er flow,
Na - ked, come to Thee for dress; help - less, look to Thee for grace;
when I soar to worlds un-known, see Thee on Thy judg-ment throne,

be of sin the dou - ble cure; cleanse me from its guilt and pow'r.
all for sin could not a - tone; Thou must save, and Thou a - lone.
foul, I to the foun - tain fly; wash me, Sav - ior, or I die!
Rock of Ag - es, cleft for me, let me hide my - self in Thee.

O Come, O Come, Emmanuel 211

tin hymn, 12th cent.
ans. J.M. Neale, 1851

VENI EMMANUEL
88 88 88

Latin hymn, 13th cent.
adapt. Thomas Helmore, 1854

1. O come, O come, Em - man - u - el, and ran - som cap - tive
2. O come, Thou Rod of Jes - se, free Thine own from Sa - tan's
3. O come, Thou Day-spring, come and cheer our spir - its by Thine
4. O come, Thou Key of Da - vid, come, and o - pen wide our

Is - - ra - el, that mourns in low - ly ex - ile here,
tyr - - an - ny; from depths of hell Thy peo - ple save,
ad - - vent here; dis - perse the gloom - y clouds of night,
heav'n - ly home; make safe the way that leads on high,

un - til the Son of God ap - pear.
and give them vic - t'ry o'er the grave.
and death's dark shad-ows put to flight.
and close the path to mis - - er - y.

Re - joice! Re - joice!

Em - man - u - el shall come to thee, O Is - - ra - el.

212 Comfort, Comfort Ye My People

Isaiah 40:1–5; Johann Olearius, 1671
trans. Catherine Winkworth, 1863

GENEVAN 42
87 87 77 88

Genevan Psalter, 155

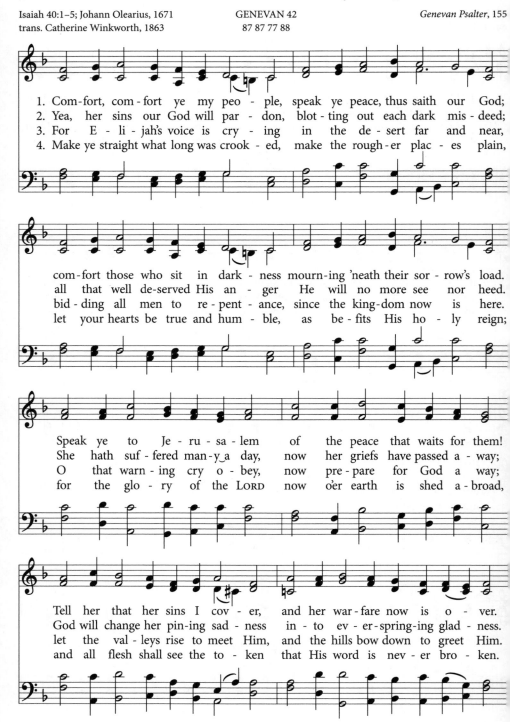

1. Com-fort, com-fort ye my peo - ple, speak ye peace, thus saith our God;
2. Yea, her sins our God will par - don, blot-ting out each dark mis - deed;
3. For E - li - jah's voice is cry - ing in the de - sert far and near,
4. Make ye straight what long was crook - ed, make the rough-er plac - es plain,

com-fort those who sit in dark - ness mourn-ing 'neath their sor - row's load.
all that well de-served His an - ger He will no more see nor heed.
bid-ding all men to re - pent - ance, since the king-dom now is here.
let your hearts be true and hum - ble, as be-fits His ho - ly reign;

Speak ye to Je - ru - sa - lem of the peace that waits for them!
She hath suf - fered man-y a day, now her griefs have passed a - way;
O that warn - ing cry o - bey, now pre - pare for God a way;
for the glo - ry of the LORD now o'er earth is shed a - broad,

Tell her that her sins I cov - er, and her war-fare now is o - ver.
God will change her pin-ing sad - ness in - to ev - er-spring-ing glad - ness.
let the val - leys rise to meet Him, and the hills bow down to greet Him.
and all flesh shall see the to - ken that His word is nev - er bro - ken.

On Jordan's Banks the Baptist's Cry **213**

Charles Coffin, 1736
trans. John Chandler, 1837

PUER NOBIS
LM

Trier manuscript, 15th cent.
adapt. Michael Praetorius, 1609

1. On Jor - dan's banks the Bap - tist's cry an - nounc - es
2. Then cleansed be eve - ry breast from sin; make straight the
3. For Thou art our Sal - va - tion, Lord, our Ref - uge
4. To heal the sick stretch out Thine hand, and bid the
5. All praise, E - ter - nal Son, to Thee, whose Ad - vent

that the Lord is nigh; a - wake, and heark - en,
way for God with - in; pre - pare we in our
and our great Re - ward; with - out Thy grace we
fal - len sin - ner stand; shine forth, and let Thy
doth Thy peo - ple free; whom with the Fa - ther

for he brings glad ti - dings of the King of kings.
hearts a home, where such a might - y Guest may come.
waste a - way, like flow'rs that with - er and de - cay.
light re - store earth's own true love - li - ness once more.
we a - dore, and Ho - ly Ghost for - ev - er - more.

214 Lo! He Comes, with Clouds Descending

Charles Wesley, 1758, alt.

HELMSLEY
87 87 12 7

Select Hymns with Tunes Annext, 176

1. Lo! He comes, with clouds de-scend-ing, once for
2. Eve-ry eye shall now be-hold Him, robed in
3. Eve-ry is - land, sea, and moun-tain, heav'n and
4. Now re - demp - tion, long ex-pect-ed, see in
5. Yea, a - men! Let all a - dore Thee, high on

fa - vored sin - ners slain; thou - sand thou - sand
dread - ful ma - jes - ty; those who set at
earth, shall flee a - way; all who hate Him
sol - emn pomp ap - pear! And His saints, by
Thine e - ter - nal throne; Sav - ior, take the

saints at - tend - ing swell the tri - umph of His train:
naught and sold Him, pierced, and nailed Him to the tree,
must, con - found - ed, hear the trump pro - claim the day:
men re - ject - ed, com - ing with Him in the air.
pow'r and glo - ry, claim the king - dom for Thine own;

al - le - lu - ia, al - le - lu - ia, al - le
deep - ly wail - ing, deep - ly wail - ing, deep - ly
Come to judg - ment! Come to judg - ment! Come to
Al - le - lu - ia! Al - le - lu - ia! Al - le
O come quick - ly, O come quick - ly, O com

lu - ia!	God ap - pears	on earth	to reign.
wail - ing,	shall the	true Mes - si -	ah see.
judg - ment!	Come to	judg - ment, come	a - way!
lu - ia!	See the	day of	God ap - pear!
quick - ly!	Al - le -	lu - ia! Come,	Lord, come!

Hark, the Glad Sound! The Savior Comes   **215**

ilip Doddridge, 1735   GRÄFENBERG   Johann Crüger, c. 1647
                                    CM

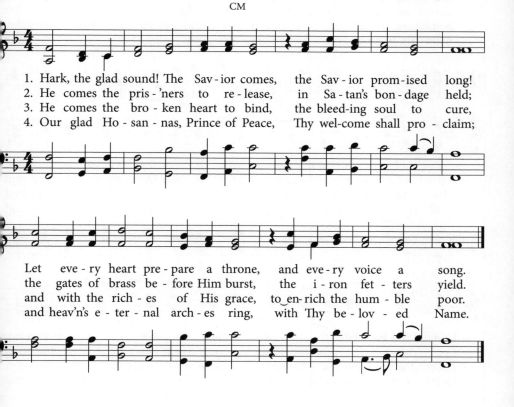

1. Hark, the glad sound! The Sav-ior comes, the Sav-ior prom-ised long!
2. He comes the pris-'ners to re-lease, in Sa-tan's bon-dage held;
3. He comes the bro-ken heart to bind, the bleed-ing soul to cure,
4. Our glad Ho-san-nas, Prince of Peace, Thy wel-come shall pro-claim;

Let eve-ry heart pre-pare a throne, and eve-ry voice a song.
the gates of brass be-fore Him burst, the i-ron fet-ters yield.
and with the rich-es of His grace, to en-rich the hum-ble poor.
and heav'n's e-ter-nal arch-es ring, with Thy be-lov-ed Name.

216   Christ Is Coming! Let Creation

John R. MacDuff, 1853   CWM RHONDDA   John Hughes, 19(

87 87 87 with repeat

1. Christ is com - ing! Let cre - a - tion from her groans and
2. Earth can now but tell the sto - ry of Thy bit - ter
3. Long Thine ex - iles have been pin - ing, far from rest, and
4. With that bless - ed hope be - fore us, let no harp re

tra - vail cease; let the glo - rious proc - la - ma - tion hope re
cross and pain; she shall yet be - hold Thy glo - ry, when Thou
home, and Thee; but, in heav'n - ly ves - tures shin - ing, they their
main un - strung; let the might - y ad - vent chor - us on - ward

store and faith in - crease: Christ is com-ing! Christ is com-ing!
com - est back to reign: Christ is com-ing! Christ is com-ing!
lov - ing Lord shall see: Christ is com-ing! Christ is com-ing!
roll from tongue to tongue: "Christ is com-ing! Christ is com-ing!

Come, Thou bless-ed Prince of Peace, come, Thou bless - ed Prince of Peace.
Let each heart re-peat the strain, let each heart re - peat the strain
Haste the joy-ous ju - bi - lee, haste the joy - ous ju - bi - lee.
Come, Lord Je - sus, quick-ly come, come, Lord Je - sus, quick - ly come!

O Lord, How Shall I Meet You

217

Paul Gerhardt, 1653
Trans. Catherine Winkworth, 1863, alt.

WIE SOLL ICH DICH EMPFANGEN
76 76 D

Johann Crüger, 1653

1. O Lord, how shall I meet You, how wel-come You a - right?
2. Love caused Your in - car - na - tion; love brought You down to me.
3. Re - joice, then, you sad - heart - ed, who sit in deep - est gloom,
4. Sin's debt, that fear - ful bur - den, let not your soul dis - tress;
5. He comes to judge the na - tions, a ter - ror to His foes,

Your peo - ple long to greet You, my Hope, my heart's De - light!
Your thirst for my sal - va - tion pro - cured my lib - er - ty.
who mourn your joys de - part - ed and trem - ble at your doom.
your guilt the Lord will par - don and cov - er by His grace.
a light of con - so - la - tions and bless - ed hope to those

O, kin - dle, Lord most ho - ly, Your lamp with - in my breast
O, love be - yond all tell - ing, that led You to em - brace
De - spair not; He is near you, there, stand-ing at the door,
He comes, for men pro - cur - ing the peace of sin for - giv'n,
who love the Lord's ap - pear - ing. O glo - rious Sun, now come,

to do in spir - it low - ly all that may please You best.
in love, all love ex - cel - ling, our lost and fall - en race.
who best can help and cheer you and bids you weep no more.
for all God's sons se - cur - ing their her - it - age in heav'n.
send forth Your beams so cheer - ing and guide us safe - ly home.

218 Wake, Awake, for Night is Flying

Philipp Nicolai, 1599
trans. Catherine Winkworth, 1858, alt.

WACHET AUF
89 8 89 8 66 488

Hans Sachs, c. 1513
adapt. Philipp Nicolai, 1599
harm. Johann Sebastian Bach, 1731

1. Wake, a-wake, for night is fly-ing, the watch-men on the heights are cry-ing; a-wake, Je-ru-sa-lem, at last. Mid-night hears the wel-come voic-es, and at the thrill-ing cry re-joic-es: "Come forth, you maid-ens! Night is past.

2. Zi-on hears the watch-men sing-ing, and in her heart new joy is spring-ing. She wakes, she ris-es from her gloom, for her Lord comes down all-glo-rious, and strong in grace, in truth vic-to-rious. Her star is ris'n; her light is come.

3. Now let all the heav'ns a-dore You, and saints and an-gels sing be-fore You. The harps and cym-bals all u-nite. Of one pearl each shin-ing por-tal, where, dwel-ling with the choir im-mor-tal, we gath-er 'round Your daz-zling light.

The Bride-groom comes! A - wake; your lamps with glad - ness take!"
O, come, you Bles - sed One, Lord Je - sus, God's own Son.
No eye has seen, no ear has yet been trained to hear

Al - le - lu - ia! Pre - pare your - selves to meet the Lord,
Sing ho - san - na! We go un - til the halls we view
what joy is ours! Cres - cen - dos rise; Your halls re - sound;

whose light has stirred the wait - ing guard.
where You have bid us dine with You.
ho - san - nas blend in cos - mic sound.

219 Joy to the World

Isaac Watts, 1719

ANTIOCH
CM with repeats

George Frederic Handel, 17
alt. Lowell Mason, 18

1. Joy to the world, the Lord is come! Let earth re-ceive her
2. Joy to the earth, the Sav-ior reigns! Let men their songs em
3. No more let sins and sor-rows grow, nor thorns in-fest the
4. He rules the world with truth and grace, and makes the na-tion

King! Let eve-ry heart pre-pare Him room,
ploy, while fields and floods, rocks, hills, and plains
ground; He comes to make His bless-ings flow
prove the glo-ries of His right-eous-ness

and heav'n and na-ture sing, and heav'n and na-ture
re-peat the sound-ing joy, re-peat the sound-ing
far as the curse is found, far as the curse is
and won-ders of His love, and won-ders of His

1. and heav'n and na-ture sing, and

sing, and heav'n, and heav'n and na-ture sing.
joy, re-peat, re-peat the sound-ing joy.
found, far as, far as the curse is found.
love, and won-ders, won-ders of His love.

heav'n and na-ture sing,

Jesus Shall Reign

Isaac Watts, 1719

DUKE STREET
LM

John Hatton, 1793

1. Je - sus shall reign wher - e'er the sun does its suc -
2. To Him shall end - less prayer be made, and end - less
3. Peo - ple and realms of eve - ry tongue dwell on His
4. Bless - ings a - bound wher - e'er He reigns; the pris - 'ners
5. Let eve - ry crea - ture rise and bring their grate - ful

ces - sive jour - neys run; His king - dom spread from
prais - es crown His head; His name like sweet per -
love with sweet - est song, and in - fant voic - es
leap to lose their chains, the wea - ry find e -
hon - ors to our King. An - gels de - scend with

shore to shore, till moons shall wax and wane no more.
fume shall rise with eve - ry morn - ing sac - ri - fice.
shall pro - claim their ear - ly bless - ings on His name.
ter - nal rest, and all who suf - fer want are blest.
songs a - gain, and earth re - peat the loud "A - men!"

221 The King Shall Come

Greek hymn
trans. John Brownlie, 1907

MORNING SONG
CM

Traditional American melody
Kentucky Harmony, 1813

1. The King shall come when morn-ing dawns and light tri - um-phant breaks,
2. Not as of old a lit - tle child, to bear, and fight, and die,
3. O bright - er than the ris - ing morn when He, vic - to - rious, rose
4. O bright - er than that glo-rious morn shall this fair morn - ing be,
5. The King shall come when morn-ing dawns and earth's dark night is past;
6. And let the end - less bliss be - gin, by wea - ry saints fore - told,
7. The King shall come when morn-ing dawns, and light and beau - ty brings;

when beau - ty gilds the east-ern hills and life to joy a - wakes.
but crowned with glo - ry like the sun that lights the morn-ing sky.
and left the lone-some place of death, de - spite the rage of foes.
when Christ, our King, in beau-ty comes, and we His face shall see.
O haste the ris - ing of that morn, the day that aye shall last.
when right shall tri - umph o - ver wrong, and truth shall be ex - tolled.
"Hail, Christ the Lord!" Thy peo-ple pray, come quick - ly, King of kings!

My Soul Now Magnifies the Lord [Magnificat] 222

ke 1:46–55; Hermann Bonnus, 1548   DEO GRACIAS   English melody; harm. from
ns. John T. Mueller, 1967   LM   *Hymns Ancient and Modern*, revised, 1950

1. My soul now mag - ni - fies the Lord; my spir - it
2. Hence-forth shall peo - ple call me blest, for great things
3. His mer - cy is on all who fear, who trust in
4. He brings down ru - lers from their seat and rais - es
5. He helped His ser - vant Is - ra - el, re - mem - b'ring
6. So praise with me the Ho - ly One, who comes in

shall in God re - joice. My hum - ble state He
He has done for me. The might - y God is
Him from age to age. His arm of strength to
those of low de - gree. He fills the hun - gry
His e - ter - nal grace, as from of old He
all hu - mil - i - ty. To our Re - deem - er,

did re - gard, ex - alt - ing me by gra - cious choice.
now my guest; the Ho - ly One has set me free.
all is near; the proud He scat - ters, tho' they rage.
souls with meat; the rich de - part in pov - er - ty.
did fore - tell to Ab - ra - ham and all His race.
God's own Son, be glo - ry in e - ter - ni - ty!

223 Blessed Be God [Benedictus]

Luke 1:68–79

Trinity Psalter Hymnal © 2018

BEACH SPRING
87 87 D

Traditional American melody
The Sacred Harp, 1844

1. Blessed be God, the Lord of Is - rael, He has come to set us free!
2. God has come in might to save us from the ha - tred of our foes.
3. God has sworn to grant de - liv - 'rance and re - store us to our place:
4. Bring the know - ledge of sal - va - tion to God's peo - ple in their sin.

And a horn of full sal - va - tion He has raised from Da - vid's seed.
From their cru - el hand He frees us, and His ten - der mer - cy shows;
serv - ing bold - ly in His pres - ence, just and ho - ly all our days.
Preach that God is ten - der - heart - ed, and by Him are sins for - giv'n.

God has vis - i - ted His peo - ple to re - deem them as fore - told
mer - cy prom - ised in His cov - 'nant to our fa - thers whom He chose.
You, my child, will be His pro - phet, called and sent by God Most High.
His great mer - cy, like the sun - rise, bright - ly shines in deep - est night,

in the prom - ise He had spo - ken thro' His pro - phets from of old.
He will keep His oath to Ab - r'am to re - lease us from our woes.
You must go be - fore the Lord now to pre - pare His ways a - right.
guid - ing those who sit in dark - ness to the way of peace and light.

Angels We Have Heard on High [Gloria] 224

e 2:14; French carol
s. James Chadwick, 1860, alt.

GLORIA
77 77 with refrain

French carol
arr. Edward Shippen Barnes, 1937

1. An - gels we have heard on high, sweet - ly sing - ing o'er the plains,
2. Shep - herds, why this ju - bi - lee? Why your joy - ous strains pro - long?
3. Come to Beth - le - hem and see Him whose birth the an - gels sing;
4. See Him in a man - ger laid, Je - sus, Lord of heav'n and earth!

and the moun - tains in re - ply ech - o - ing their joy - ous strains:
What the glad - some ti - dings be which in - spire your heav'n - ly song?
come, a - dore on bend - ed knee Christ the Lord, the new - born King.
Ma - ry, Jo - seph, lend your aid, sing with us our Sav - ior's birth.

Glo - - - - - - - - - - ri - a,

in ex - cel - sis De - o! Glo - - - - - -

- - - - - ri - a, in ex - cel - sis De - - o!

225 Now Let Your Servant, Lord [Nunc Dimittis]

Luke 2:29–32　　　　　　　　　　NUNC DIMITTIS　　　　　　　　Louis Bourgeois, 15
William Helder © 2009　　　　　　　　67 76 67　　　　　　　　arr. Claude Goudimel, 15

1. Now let Your ser - vant, Lord, ac - cord - ing to Your word,
2. Lord, You have gra - cious - ly pre - pared for all to see

de - part in ex - ult - a - tion; now I in peace may rest:
a light for rev - e - la - tion to peo - ples far and near,

my eyes have seen at last Your won - der - ful sal - va - tion.
and glo - ry bright and clear to Is - ra - el, Your na - tion.

Come, Thou Long-Expected Jesus · **226**

Charles Wesley, 1744   HYFRYDOL   Rowland H. Prichard, 1830
87 87 D   arr. Ralph Vaughan Williams, 1906, alt.

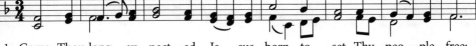

1. Come, Thou long - ex - pect - ed Je - sus, born to set Thy peo - ple free;
2. Joy to those who long to see Thee, Day-spring from on high, ap - pear;
3. Come to earth to taste our sad - ness, He whose glo - ries knew no end;
4. Born Thy peo - ple to de - liv - er, born a child and yet a King,

from our fears and sins re - lease us; let us find our rest in Thee.
come, Thou prom - ised Rod of Jes - se, of Thy birth we long to hear!
by His life He brings us glad - ness, our Re - deem - er, Shep - herd, Friend.
born to reign in us for - ev - er, now Thy gra - cious king - dom bring.

Is - rael's strength and con - so - la - tion, hope of all the earth Thou art,
O'er the hills the an - gels sing - ing news, glad tid - ings of a birth:
Leav - ing rich - es with - out num - ber, born with - in a cat - tle stall;
By Thine own e - ter - nal Spir - it rule in all our hearts a - lone;

dear De - sire of eve - ry na - tion, joy of eve - ry long-ing heart.
"Go to Him, your prais - es bring - ing; Christ the Lord has come to earth."
this the ev - er - last - ing won - der, Christ was born the Lord of all.
by Thine own e - ter - nal mer - it, raise us to Thy glo - rious throne.

227 Hark! the Herald Angels Sing

Charles Wesley, 1739, alt.
MENDELSSOHN
77 77 D with refrain
Felix Mendelssohn, 1840

1. Hark! the her - ald an - gels sing, "Glo - ry to the new-born King.
2. Christ by high - est heav'n a - dored, Christ, the ev - er - last - ing Lord,
3. Hail the heav'n-born Prince of Peace! Hail the Sun of Right-eous-ness!
4. Come, De - sire of na - tions, come, fix in us Thy hum - ble home;

Peace on earth and mer - cy mild, God and sin - ners rec - on - ciled!"
late in time be - hold Him come, off - spring of the vir - gin's womb.
Light and life to all He brings, ris'n with heal - ing in His wings.
rise, the wo - man's con-qu'ring Seed, bruise in us the ser - pent's head.

Joy - ful, all ye na - tions, rise; join the tri - umph of the skies;
Veiled in flesh the God-head see; hail the in-car - nate De - i - ty,
Mild He lays His glo - ry by, born that man no more may die,
A - dam's like - ness now ef - face, stamp Thine im - age in its place;

with the an - gel - ic host pro - claim, "Christ is born in Beth - le - hem!"
pleased as man with men to dwell, Je - sus our Em - man - u - el.
born to raise the sons of earth, born to give them sec - ond birth.
Sec - ond A - dam from a - bove, re - in - state us in Thy love.

Hark! the her-ald an-gels sing, "Glo-ry to the new-born King!"

Savior of the Nations, Come 228

Ambrose of Milan, 4th cent. NUN KOMM, DER HEIDEN HEILAND attr. Martin Luther, 1524
German version, Martin Luther, 1523 77 77 harm. Seth Calvisius, 1594
Trans. William M. Reynolds, 1880, alt.

1. Sav - ior of the na - tions, come; vir - gin's Son, make here Thy home!
2. Not by hu - man flesh and blood, but the Spir - it of our God,
3. Won-drous birth! O won-drous Child of the vir - gin un - de - filed!
4. From the Fa - ther forth He came and re - turn - eth to the same,
5. Thou, the Fa - ther's on - ly Son, hast o'er sin the vic - t'ry won.
6. Bright-ly doth Thy man - ger shine, glo - rious in its light di - vine.
7. Praise to God the Fa - ther, sing, praise to God, the Son, our King.

Mar - vel now, O heav'n and earth, that the Lord chose such a birth.
was the Word of God made flesh— wo - man's off - spring, pure and fresh.
Tho' by all the world dis - owned, still to be in heav'n en - throned.
cap - tive lead - ing death and hell— high the song of tri - umph swell!
Bound-less shall Thy king - dom be; when shall we its glo - ries see?
Let not sin o'er - cloud this light ev - er be our faith thus bright.
Praise to God the Spir - it be ev - er and e - ter - nal - ly.

229   Let All Mortal Flesh Keep Silence

Liturgy of St. James, 4th cent.   PICARDY   French melody, 17th ce
trans. Gerard Moultrie, 1864   87 87 87   arr. Ralph Vaughan Williams, 19

1. Let all mor-tal flesh keep si-lence, and with fear and
2. King of kings, yet born of Mar-y, as of old on
3. Rank on rank the host of heav-en spreads its van-guard
4. At His feet the six-winged ser-aph, cher-u-bim with

trem-bling stand; pon-der noth-ing earth-ly mind-ed,
earth He stood, Lord of lords, in hu-man ves-ture,
on the way, as the Light of light de-scend-eth
sleep-less eye, veil their fac-es to the Pres-ence,

for, with bless-ing in His hand, Christ our God to
in the bod-y and the blood. He will give to
from the realms of end-less day, that the pow'rs of
as with cease-less voice they cry, "Al-le-lu-ia,

earth de-scend-eth, our full hom-age to de-mand.
all the faith-ful His own self for heav'n-ly food.
hell may van-ish as the dark-ness clears a-way.
al-le-lu-ia, al-le-lu-ia, Lord Most High!"

Away in a Manger

1–2, Anonymous, 1885
3, John T. McFarland, 1892

CRADLE SONG
11 11 11 11

William J. Kirkpatrick, 1895

1. A - way in a man - ger, no crib for a bed,
2. The cat - tle are low - ing, the Ba - by a - wakes,
3. Be near me, Lord Je - sus; I ask Thee to stay

the lit - tle Lord Je - sus laid down His sweet head;
but lit - tle Lord Je - sus, no cry - ing He makes.
close by me for - ev - er and love me, I pray.

the stars in the heav - ens looked down where He lay,
I love Thee, Lord Je - sus, look down from the sky
Bless all the dear chil - dren in Thy ten - der care,

the lit - tle Lord Je - sus a - sleep on the hay.
and stay by my side un - til morn - ing is nigh.
and fit us for heav - en, to live with Thee there.

231   What Child Is This?

William Dix, 1868

GREENSLEEVES
87 87 68 67

English folk melod[y]
arr. John Stainer, 18[ ]

1. What Child is this who, laid to rest, on Mar - y's lap is sleep - ing
2. Why lies He in such low es - tate where ox and lamb are feed - ing
3. So bring Him in - cense, gold and myrrh, come peas - ant, king, to own Hir[m]

Whom an - gels greet with an - thems sweet while shep-herds watch are keep - ing
Good Chris - tian, fear: for sin - ners here the si - lent Word is plead - ing
The King of kings sal - va - tion brings; let lov - ing hearts en - throne Hir[m]

This, this is Christ the King, whom shep-herds guard and an - gels sing;
Nails, spear shall pierce Him through; the cross be borne for me, for you.
Raise, raise the song on high. The vir - gin sings her lul - la - by.

haste, haste to bring Him laud, the Babe, the son of Mar - y.
Hail, hail the Word made flesh, the Babe, the son of Mar - y.
Joy, joy for Christ is born, the Babe, the son of Mar - y!

O Little Town of Bethlehem

232

Phillips Brooks, 1868

FOREST GREEN
CMD

English folk tune
harm. Ralph Vaughan Williams, 1906

1. O   lit - tle town of   Beth - le - hem, how   still   we   see   thee   lie!
2. For Christ is born of   Mar   -   y; and, gath - ered   all   a - bove,
3. How   si - lent - ly, how   si - lent - ly,   the   won - drous gift   is   giv'n!
4. O   ho - ly Child of   Beth - le - hem, de - scend   to   us,   we   pray;

A - bove thy deep and   dream - less sleep the   si - lent stars   go   by.
while mor - tals sleep, the   an - gels keep their watch of   won - d'ring love.
So   God im - parts to   hu - man hearts the   bless - ings of   His heav'n.
cast   out   our sin and   en - ter   in;   be   born   in   us   to - day.

Yet   in   thy dark streets shin   -   eth   the   ev - er - last - ing   light;
O   morn - ing stars,   to - geth   -   er   pro - claim   the   ho - ly   birth,
No   ear   may hear   His   com   -   ing, but   in   this world of   sin,
We   hear   the Christ - mas   an   -   gels, the   great glad ti - dings   tell;

the   hopes and fears of   all   the years are   met   in   thee to - night.
and   prais - es   sing to   God   the King, and peace   to   men on   earth.
where   meek souls will   re - ceive Him still,   the dear Christ en - ters   in.
O   come   to   us,   a - bide with us,   our Lord Em - man - u - el!

233 How Bright Appears the Morning Star

Philip Nicolai, 1597
adapt. William Mercer, 1859

WIE SCHÖN LEUCHTET
88 78 87 48 48

Philip Nicolai; 159
arr. Johann Sebastian Bach, 173

1. How bright ap-pears the Morn-ing Star, with mer-cy beam-ing
2. Though cir-cled by the hosts on high, He deigned to cast a
3. Re-joice, O heav'ns, and earth, re-ply; with praise, O sin-ners,

from a-far; the host of heav'n re-joic-es; O Right-eous
pit-ying eye up-on His help-less crea-ture; the whole cre-
fill the sky for this, His in-car-na-tion. In-car-nate

Branch, O Jes-se's Rod! Thou Son of Man and Son of God!
a-tion's Head and Lord, by high-est ser-a-phim a-dored
God, put forth Your pow'r; ride on, ride on, great Con-quer-or,

We, too, will lift our voic-es: Je-sus, Je-sus!
as-sumed our ver-y na-ture; Je-sus, grant us,
till all know Your sal-va-tion. A-men, a-men!

Ho - ly, ho - ly, yet most low - ly, draw Thou near us;
thro' Your mer - it, to in - her - it Your sal - va - tion;
Al - le - lu - ia! Al - le - lu - ia! Praise be giv - en

great Em - man - uel, come and hear us.
hear, O hear our sup - pli - ca - tion.
ev - er - more by earth and heav - en.

Love Came Down at Christmas 234

Christina Rossetti, 1855   CULBACH   Scheffler's *Heilige Seelenlust*, 1657
67 67

1. Love came down at Christ - mas, Love all love - ly, Love di - vine;
2. Wor - ship we the God - head, Love in - car - nate, Love di - vine;
3. Love shall be our to - ken; love be yours and love be mine;

Love was born at Christ - mas; star and an - gels gave the sign.
wor - ship we our Je - sus, but where-with for sa - cred sign?
love to God and oth - ers, love for plea and gift and sign.

235 Gentle Mary Laid Her Child

Joseph Simpson Cook, 1919   TEMPUS ADEST FLORIDUM   *Piae Cantiones*, 158
         76 76 D   arr. Ernest MacMillan, 193

1. Gen-tle Mar-y laid her Child low-ly in a man-ger;
2. An-gels sang a-bout His birth; wise men sought and found Him;
3. Gen-tle Mar-y laid her Child low-ly in a man-ger;

there He lay, the un-de-filed, to the world a stran-ger:
heav-en's star shone bright-ly forth, glo-ry all a-round Him:
He is still the un-de-filed, but no more a stran-ger:

such a Babe in such a place, can He be the Sav-ior?
shep-herds saw the won-drous sight, heard the an-gels sing-ing;
Son of God, of hum-ble birth, beau-ti-ful the sto-ry;

Ask the saved of all the race who have found His fa-vor?
all the plains were lit that night, all the hills were ring-ing.
praise His name in all the earth, hail the King of glo-ry!

Once in Royal David's City

236

Cecil F. Alexander, 1848

IRBY
87 87 77

Henry Gauntlett, 1849

1. Once in roy - al Da - vid's cit - y stood a low - ly cat - tle shed, where a moth - er laid her ba - by in a man - ger for His bed: Mar - y was that moth - er mild, Je - sus Christ her lit - tle Child.

2. He came down to earth from heav - en who is God and Lord of all, and His shel - ter was a sta - ble, and His cra - dle was a stall: with the poor, and meek, and low - ly, lived on earth our Sav - ior ho - ly.

3. And our eyes at last shall see Him, through His own re - deem - ing love; for that Child so dear and gen - tle is our Lord in heav'n a - bove, and He leads His chil - dren on to the place where He is gone.

4. Not in that poor low - ly sta - ble, with the ox - en stand - ing by, we shall see Him, but in heav - en, set at God's right hand on high; when like stars His chil - dren crowned all in white shall wait a - round.

237 Christians, Awake!

John Byrom, 1749   YORKSHIRE   John Wainwright, 175◆
10 10 10 10 10 10

1. Chris-tians, a - wake, sa - lute the hap - py morn, where - on the
2. Then to the watch - ful shep-herds it was told, who heard th'an-
3. He spake, and straight-way the ce - les - tial choir in hymns of
4. To Beth-l'hem straight the hap - py shep-herds ran, to see the
5. Oh, may we keep and pon - der in our mind God's won-drous
6. Then may we hope, th'an - gel - ic throngs a - mong, to sing, re -

Sav - ior of the world was born; rise to a - dore the
gel - ic her - ald's voice: "Be - hold, I bring good tid - ings
joy, un-known be - fore, con - spire; the prais - es of re -
won - der God had wrought for man; and found, with Jo - seph
love in sav - ing lost man - kind! Trace we the Babe, who
deemed, a glad tri - umph - al song; He that was born up -

mys - ter - y of love, which hosts of an - gels chant - ed
of a Sav - ior's birth to you and all the na - tions
deem-ing love they sang, and heav'n's whole orb with al - le -
and the bless - ed maid, her Son, the Sav - ior in a
hath re - trieved our loss, from His poor man - ger to His
on this joy - ful day a - round us all His glo - ry

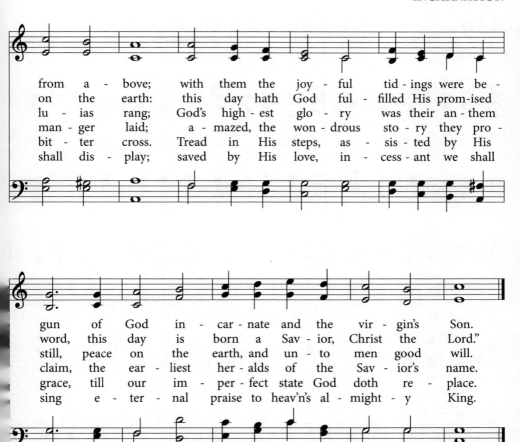

from a - bove; with them the joy - ful tid - ings were be -
on the earth: this day hath God ful - filled His prom-ised
lu - ias rang; God's high - est glo - ry was their an - them
man - ger laid; a - mazed, the won - drous sto - ry they pro -
bit - ter cross. Tread in His steps, as - sis - ted by His
shall dis - play; saved by His love, in - cess - ant we shall

gun of God in - car - nate and the vir - gin's Son.
word, this day is born a Sav - ior, Christ the Lord."
still, peace on the earth, and un - to men good will.
claim, the ear - liest her - alds of the Sav - ior's name.
grace, till our im - per - fect state God doth re - place.
sing e - ter - nal praise to heav'n's al - might - y King.

238 Good Christian Men, Rejoice

Latin carol, 14th cent.　　　　　IN DULCI JUBILO　　　　　German carol, 14th cent.
66 77 78 55

Good Chris-tian men, re-joice with heart and soul and voice!

1. Give ye heed to what we say: News! News! Je-sus Christ is born to-day.
2. Now ye hear of end-less bliss: Joy! Joy! Je-sus Christ was born for this!
3. Now ye need not fear the grave: Peace! Peace! Je-sus Christ was born to save!

Ox and ass be-fore Him bow, and He is in the man-ger now.
He has o-pened heav-en's door, and man is blest for-ev-er-more.
Calls you one and calls you all to gain His ev-er-last-ing hall.

Christ is born to-day! Christ is born to-day!
Christ was born for this! Christ was born for this!
Christ was born to save! Christ was born to save!

Silent Night

st. 1–3, Joseph Mohr, 1816
trans. John F. Young, 1863; st. 4 anonymous

STILLE NACHT
66 88 66

Franz Gruber, 1818

1. Si - lent night! Ho - ly night! All is calm, all is bright
2. Si - lent night! Ho - ly night! Shep-herds quake at the sight.
3. Si - lent night! Ho - ly night! Son of God, love's pure light
4. Si - lent night! Ho - ly night! Won-drous star, lend thy light;

'round yon vir - gin moth-er and child! Ho - ly in - fant, so ten-der and mild,
Glo - ries stream from heav-en a - far, heav'n-ly hosts sing, "Al - le - lu - ia!
ra - diant beams from Thy ho - ly face with the dawn of re-deem - ing grace,
with the an - gels let us sing "Al - le - lu - ia" to our King:

sleep in heav - en - ly peace, sleep in heav - en - ly peace.
Christ the Sav - ior is born! Christ the Sav - ior is born!"
Je - sus, Lord at Thy birth! Je - sus, Lord at Thy birth!
"Christ the Sav - ior is born! Christ the Sav - ior is born."

240 Break Forth, O Beauteous Heavenly Light

Johann Rist, st. 1, 1641
trans. John Troutbeck, 1873
st. 2, A. T. Russell, 1851

ERMUNTRE DICH
87 87 88 77

Johann Schop, 1641
harm. Johann Sebastian Bach, 173-

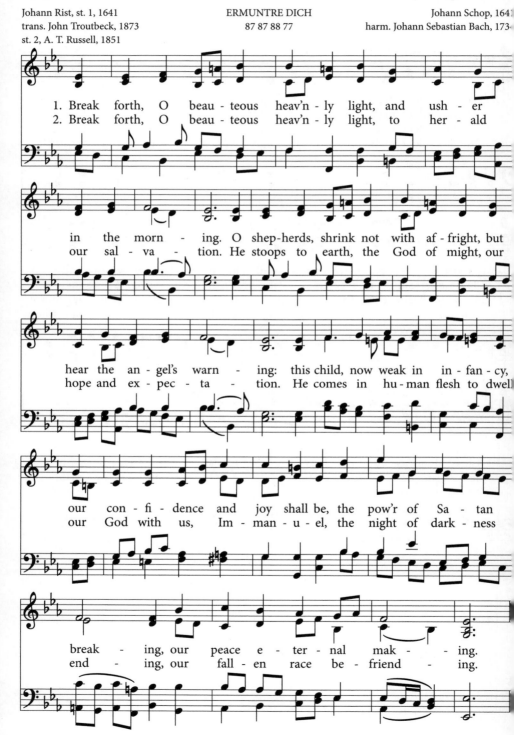

1. Break forth, O beau-teous heav'n-ly light, and ush-er in the morn - ing. O shep-herds, shrink not with af-fright, but hear the an-gel's warn - ing: this child, now weak in in-fan-cy, our con-fi-dence and joy shall be, the pow'r of Sa-tan break - ing, our peace e-ter-nal mak - ing.

2. Break forth, O beau-teous heav'n-ly light, to her-ald our sal-va - tion. He stoops to earth, the God of might, our hope and ex-pec-ta - tion. He comes in hu-man flesh to dwell, our God with us, Im-man-u-el, the night of dark-ness end - ing, our fall-en race be-friend - ing.

On Christmas Night All Christians Sing **241**

Traditional English carol

SUSSEX CAROL
88 88 88

Traditional English carol
harm. Ralph Vaughan Williams, 1912

1. On Christ-mas night all Chris-tians sing to hear the news the
2. Then why should men on earth be sad, since our Re-deem-er
3. When sin de-parts be-fore His grace, then life and health come
4. All out of dark-ness we have light, which made the an-gels

an-gels bring; on Christ-mas night all Chris-tians sing to
made us glad? Then why should men on earth be sad, since
in its place; when sin de-parts be-fore His grace, then
sing this night; all out of dark-ness we have light, which

hear the news the an-gels bring: news of great joy, news
our Re-deem-er made us glad, when from our sin He
life and health come in its place; an-gels and men with
made the an-gels sing this night: "Glo-ry to God and

of great mirth, news of our mer-ci-ful King's birth.
set us free, all for to gain our lib-er-ty?
joy may sing, all for to see the new-born King.
peace to men, now and for-ev-er-more. A-men."

242 The First Noel

Some Ancient Christmas Carols
2nd ed., 1823

THE FIRST NOWELL

Christmas Carol
Ancient and Modern, 183.

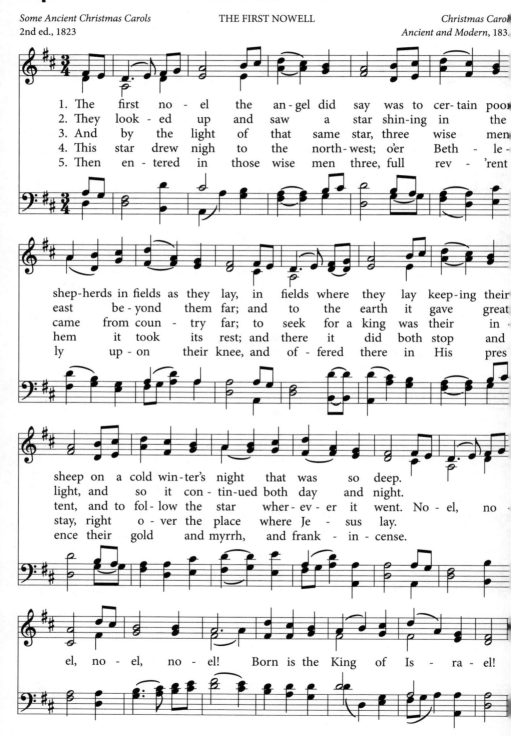

1. The first no - el the an - gel did say was to cer - tain poor shep-herds in fields as they lay, in fields where they lay keep-ing their sheep on a cold win-ter's night that was so deep.
2. They look - ed up and saw a star shin-ing in the east be - yond them far; and to the earth it gave great light, and so it con - tin-ued both day and night.
3. And by the light of that same star, three wise men came from coun - try far; to seek for a king was their in - tent, and to fol - low the star wher - ev - er it went.
4. This star drew nigh to the north-west; o'er Beth - le - hem it took its rest; and there it did both stop and stay, right o - ver the place where Je - sus lay.
5. Then en - tered in those wise men three, full rev - 'rent ly up - on their knee, and of - fered there in His pres - ence their gold and myrrh, and frank - in - cense.

No - el, no - el, no - el, no - el! Born is the King of Is - ra - el!

Infant Holy, Infant Lowly

Polish carol
trans. Edith Reed, 1920

W ZLOBIE LEZY
87 87 88 77

Polish folk melody

1. In - fant ho - ly, in - fant low - ly, for His bed a cat - tle stall;
2. Flocks were sleep-ing, shep-herds keep-ing vig - il till the morn-ing new

ox - en low - ing, lit - tle know-ing Christ, the babe, is Lord of all.
saw the glo - ry, heard the sto - ry, tid - ings of a gos - pel true.

Swift are wing - ing an - gels sing - ing, no - els ring - ing, tid-ings bring-ing:
Thus re - joic - ing, free from sor - row, prais-es voic - ing, greet the mor-row:

Christ the babe is Lord of all! Christ the babe is Lord of all!
Christ the babe was born for you; Christ the babe was born for you.

244 Lo, How a Rose E'er Blooming

German carol, 15th cent.
trans. Theodore Baker, 1894, Harriet Spaeth, 1875,
John Mattes, 1914

ES IST EIN' ROS'
76 76 676

German melody, 16th cent.
arr. Michael Praetorius, 160●

1. Lo, how a rose e'er bloom-ing from ten - der stem hath
2. I - sa - iah 'twas fore - told it, the Rose I have in
3. The shep - herds heard the sto - ry, pro - claimed by an - gels
4. This Flow'r, whose fra - grance ten - der with sweet-ness fills the
5. O Sav - ior, Child of Mar - y, who felt our hu - man

sprung, of Jes - se's lin - eage com - ing, as men of old have
mind; with Mar - y we be - hold it, the vir - gin moth - er
bright, how Christ, the Lord of glo - ry was born on earth this
air, dis - pels with glo - rious splen - dor the dark-ness eve - ry -
woe; O Sav - ior, King of glo - ry, who dost our weak - ness

sung. It came, a flow - er bright, a - mid the
kind. To show God's love a - right she bore to
night. To Beth - le - hem they sped and in the
where. True man, yet ver - y God; from sin and
know, bring us at last, we pray, to the bright

cold	of	win - ter,	when	half - spent	was		the	night.
men	a	Sav - ior,	when	half - spent	was		the	night.
man - ger	found	Him,	as	an - gel	her	-	alds	said.
death	He	saves	us	and	light - ens	eve	-	ry	load.
courts	of	heav - en	and	to Thy	end	-	less	day.

From Heaven Above to Earth I Come   245

artin Luther, 1535 — VOM HIMMEL HOCH — Martin Luther, 1535
ans. Catherine Winkworth, 1855 — LM — Valentin Schumann's *Geistliche Lieder,* 1539

1. From heav'n a - bove to earth I come, to bear good news to eve - ry home,
2. To you, this night, is born a Child of Ma - ry, cho - sen moth - er mild;
3. 'Tis Christ our God, who far on high had heard your sad and bit - ter cry;
4. Now let us all, with glad-some cheer, fol - low the shep-herds, and draw near
5. Glo - ry to God in high-est heav'n, who un - to man His Son hath giv'n,

glad ti - dings of great joy I bring, where-of I now will say and sing:
this ten - der Child of low - ly birth, shall be the joy of all the earth.
Him - self will your Sal - va - tion be, Him - self from sin will make you free.
to see this won-drous Gift of God, who hath His own dear Son be - stowed.
while an - gels sing, with pi - ous mirth, a glad New Year to all the earth.

246   In the Bleak Midwinter

Christina Georgina Rossetti, 1872   CRANHAM   Gustav Holst, 190●

1. In the bleak mid - win - ter, frost - y wind made moan,
2. Heav - en can - not hold Him, nor earth sus - tain;
3. An - gels and arch - an - gels may have gath - ered there,
4. What can I give Him, poor as I am?

earth stood hard as i - ron, wa - ter like a stone;
heav'n and earth shall flee a - way when He comes to reign;
cher - u - bim and ser - a - phim thronged the air;
If I were a shep - herd, I would bring a lamb;

snow had fall - en, snow on snow, snow on snow,
in the bleak mid - win - ter a sta - ble place suf - ficed the
but His moth - er on - ly, in her maid - en bliss,
if I were a wise man, I would do my part; yet

in the bleak mid - win - ter, long a - go.
Lord God al - might - y, Je - sus Christ.
wor - shiped the Be - lov - ed with a kiss.
what I can I give Him: give my heart.

All My Heart This Night Rejoices 247

ul Gerhardt, 1653   WARUM SOLLT' ICH MICH DENN GRÄMEN   Johann G. Ebeling, 1666
ns. Catherine Winkworth, 1858, alt.   8 336 8 336

1. All my heart this night re-joic - es as I hear far and near
2. Forth to-day the Con-qu'ror go - eth, who the foe, sin and woe,
3. Shall we still dread God's dis-pleas - ure, who, to save, free-ly gave
4. He be-comes the Lamb that tak - eth sin a-way and for aye
5. Hark! a voice from yon-der man - ger, soft and sweet, doth en-treat,

sweet-est an - gel voic - es. "Christ is born," their choirs are sing - ing
death and hell, o'er - throw-eth. God is man, man to de - liv - er;
His most cher-ished Treas - ure? To re-deem us, He hath giv - en
full a - tone-ment mak - eth. For our life His own He ten - ders;
"Flee from woe and dan - ger; breth-ren, from all ills that grieve you

till the air eve-ry-where now with joy is ring - ing.
His dear Son now is one with our blood for - ev - er.
His own Son from the throne of His might in heav - en.
and our race, by His grace, fit for glo - ry ren - ders.
you are freed; all you need I will sure - ly give you."

6. Come, then, banish all your sadness,
    one and all, great and small;
    come with songs of gladness.
    Love Him who with love is glowing;
    hail the star, near and far
    light and joy bestowing.

7. Dearest Lord, Thee will I cherish.
    Though my breath fail in death,
    yet I shall not perish,
    but with Thee abide forever
    there on high, in that joy
    which can vanish never.

248   See, amid the Winter's Snow

Edward Caswall, 1858

HUMILITY
77 77 with refrain

John Goss, 1870

1. See, a - mid the win - ter's snow, born for us on earth be - low,
2. Lo, with - in a man - ger lies He who built the star - ry skies:
3. Say, ye ho - ly shep - herds, say, what's your joy - ful news to - day?
4. "As we watched at dead of night, Lo! we saw a won - drous light;
5. Sa - cred In - fant, all di - vine, what a ten - der love was Thine,
6. Teach, O teach us, Ho - ly Child, by Thy face so meek and mild,

see the ten - der Lamb ap - pears, prom - ised from e - ter - nal years.
He who, throned in height sub - lime, sits a - mid the cher - u - bim!
Where - fore have ye left your sheep on the lone - ly moun - tain steep?
an - gels sing - ing, 'Peace on earth,' told us of the Sav - ior's birth."
thus to come from high - est bliss down to such a world as this!
teach us to re - sem - ble Thee, in Thy sweet hu - mil - i - ty.

Hail, thou ev - er bless - ed morn! Hail, re - demp - tion's hap - py dawn!

Sing through all Je - ru - sa - lem, "Christ is born in Beth - le - hem."

Angels from the Realms of Glory 249

hes Montgomery, 1816   REGENT SQUARE   Henry Smart, 1867
87 87 87

1. An - gels, from the realms of glo - ry, wing your flight o'er all the earth;
2. Shep-herds, in the fields a - bid - ing, watch-ing o'er your flocks by night,
3. Sa - ges, leave your con - tem-pla - tions; bright-er vi - sions beam a - far;
4. Saints be - fore the al - tar bend-ing, watch-ing long in hope and fear,
5. Sin - ners, wrung with true re - pen-tance, doomed for guilt to end - less pains,
6. All cre - a - tion, join in prais - ing God the Fa - ther, Spir - it, Son;

ye, who sang cre - a - tion's sto - ry, now pro-claim Mes - si - ah's birth:
God with man is now re - sid - ing; yon-der shines the in - fant light:
seek the great De - sire of na - tions; ye have seen His na - tal star:
sud - den - ly the Lord, de-scend-ing, in His tem - ple shall ap - pear:
jus - tice now re - vokes the sen - tence, mer - cy calls you; break your chains.
ev - er-more your voic - es rais - ing to th'e - ter - nal Three in One:

Come and wor-ship, come and wor-ship, wor-ship Christ, the new-born King.

250 God Rest You Merry, Gentlemen

Traditional English carol, 18th cent.   GOD REST YOU MERRY   Traditional English melody

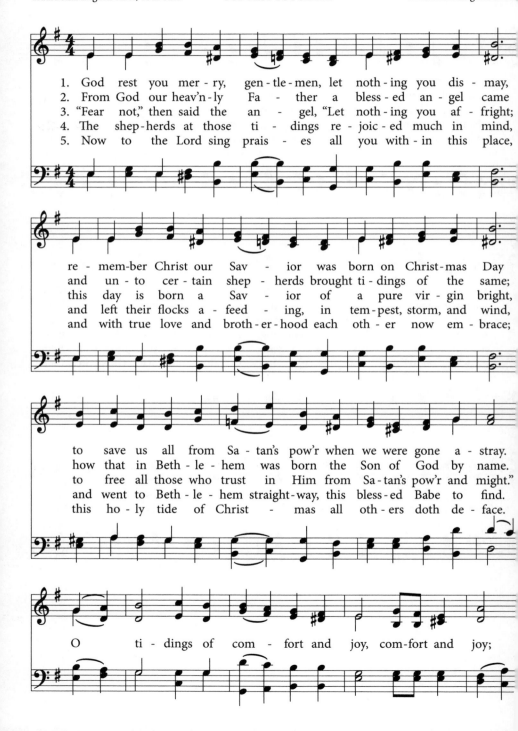

1. God rest you mer - ry, gen - tle - men, let noth - ing you dis - may,
2. From God our heav'n - ly Fa - ther a bless - ed an - gel came
3. "Fear not," then said the an - gel, "Let noth - ing you af - fright;
4. The shep - herds at those ti - dings re - joic - ed much in mind,
5. Now to the Lord sing prais - es all you with - in this place,

re - mem - ber Christ our Sav - ior was born on Christ - mas Day
and un - to cer - tain shep - herds brought ti - dings of the same;
this day is born a Sav - ior of a pure vir - gin bright,
and left their flocks a - feed - ing, in tem - pest, storm, and wind,
and with true love and broth - er - hood each oth - er now em - brace;

to save us all from Sa - tan's pow'r when we were gone a - stray.
how that in Beth - le - hem was born the Son of God by name.
to free all those who trust in Him from Sa - tan's pow'r and might."
and went to Beth - le - hem straight - way, this bless - ed Babe to find.
this ho - ly tide of Christ - mas all oth - ers doth de - face.

O ti - dings of com - fort and joy, com - fort and joy;

O ti - dings of com - fort and joy.

Behold, the Great Creator 251

homas Pestel   THIS ENDRIS NYGHT   English carol, 15th cent.
Sermons and Devotions Old and New, 1639   CM

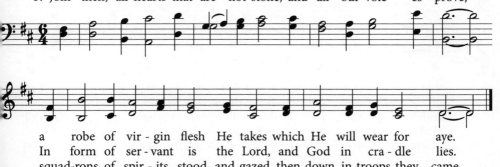

1. Be - hold, the great Cre - a - tor makes Him-self a house of clay,
2. Hark, hark, the wise e - ter - nal Word like a weak in - fant cries!
3. This won - der struck the world a - mazed, it shook the star - ry frame;
4. Glad shep - herds ran to view this sight; a choir of an - gels sings,
5. Join then, all hearts that are not stone, and all our voic - es prove,

a robe of vir - gin flesh He takes which He will wear for aye.
In form of ser - vant is the Lord, and God in cra - dle lies.
squad - rons of spir - its stood and gazed, then down in troops they came.
and east - ern sag - es with de - light a - dore this King of kings.
to cel - e - brate this ho - ly One, the God of peace and love.

252 Of the Father's Love Begotten

Marcus Aurelius C. Prudentius, 4th cent. DIVINUM MYSTERIUM Plainsong, 13th cent.
trans. John Mason Neale, 1851 87 87 87 7

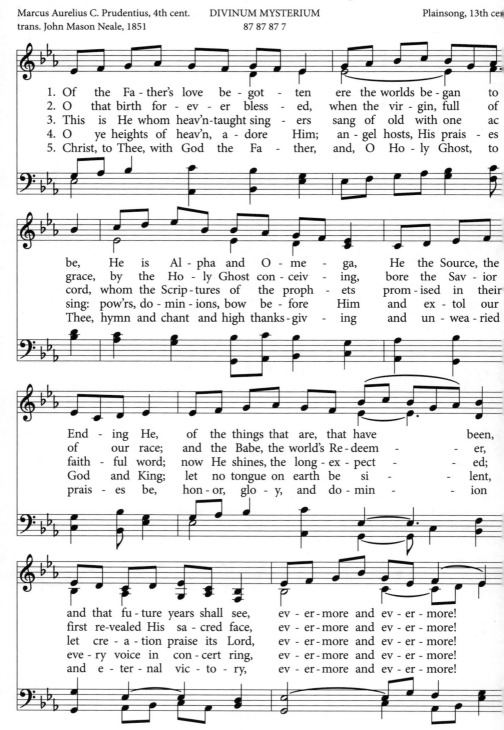

1. Of the Fa - ther's love be - got - ten ere the worlds be - gan to
2. O that birth for - ev - er bless - ed, when the vir - gin, full of
3. This is He whom heav'n-taught sing - ers sang of old with one ac -
4. O ye heights of heav'n, a - dore Him; an - gel hosts, His prais - es
5. Christ, to Thee, with God the Fa - ther, and, O Ho - ly Ghost, to

be, He is Al - pha and O - me - ga, He the Source, the
grace, by the Ho - ly Ghost con - ceiv - ing, bore the Sav - ior
cord, whom the Scrip - tures of the proph - ets prom - ised in their
sing: pow'rs, do - min - ions, bow be - fore Him and ex - tol our
Thee, hymn and chant and high thanks - giv - ing and un - wea - ried

End - ing He, of the things that are, that have been,
of our race; and the Babe, the world's Re - deem - er,
faith - ful word; now He shines, the long - ex - pect - ed;
God and King; let no tongue on earth be si - lent,
prais - es be, hon - or, glo - ry, and do - min - ion

and that fu - ture years shall see, ev - er - more and ev - er - more!
first re-vealed His sa - cred face, ev - er - more and ev - er - more!
let cre - a - tion praise its Lord, ev - er - more and ev - er - more!
eve - ry voice in con - cert ring, ev - er - more and ev - er - more!
and e - ter - nal vic - to - ry, ev - er - more and ev - er - more!

O Come, All Ye Faithful

253

ADESTE FIDELES

hn Francis Wade, ca. 1743
ns. Frederick Oakeley, 1841

John Francis Wade, ca. 1743
harm. *The English Hymnal*, 1906

1. O come, all ye faith - ful, joy - ful and tri - um- phant, O come ye,
2. God of God, Light of Light, lo, He
3. Sing, choirs of an - gels; sing in ex - ul - ta - tion; sing, all
4. Yea, Lord, we greet Thee, born this hap- py morn- ing; Je - sus,

O come ye to Beth - le - hem! Come, and be - hold Him,
ab - hors not the vir - gin's womb; ver - y God, be -
ye cit - i- zens of heav'n a - bove! Glo - ry to God, all
to Thee be all glo - ry giv'n! Word of the Fa - ther,

born the King of an - gels!
got - ten, not cre - a - ted;
glo - ry in the high - est!
now in flesh ap- pear - ing!

O come, let us a - dore Him; O come, let us

a - dore Him; O come, let us a - dore Him, Christ, the Lord!

254 While Shepherds Watched Their Flocks

Nahum Tate, 1700   WINCHESTER OLD   Este's *Psalmes*, 159
                               CM

1. While shep-herds watched their flocks by night, all seat - ed on the ground,
2. "Fear not," said he, for might - y dread had seized their trou-bled mind;
3. "To you, in Da - vid's town, this day, is born of Da - vid's line
4. "The heav - 'nly Babe you there shall find to hu - man view dis - played,
5. Thus spake the ser - aph, and forth-with ap-peared a shin - ing throng
6. "All glo - ry be to God on high, and to the earth be peace;

the an - gel of the Lord came down, and glo - ry shone a - round.
"Glad tid - ings of great joy I bring to you and all man - kind.
a Sav - ior, who is Christ the Lord; and this shall be the sign:
all mean - ly wrapped in swad-dling clothes and in a man-ger laid."
of an - gels, prais - ing God, and thus ad-dressed their joy - ful song:
good will hence-forth from heav'n to men be - gin and nev - er cease."

As with Gladness, Men of Old   255

William C. Dix, c. 1858 — DIX — 77 77 77 — Conrad Kocher, 1838 / adapt. William Henry Monk, 1861 / harm. *The English Hymnal*, 1906

1. As with glad-ness men of old did the guid-ing star be-hold;
2. As with joy-ful steps they sped to that low-ly cra-dle-bed,
3. As they of-fered gifts most rare at that cra-dle rude and bare;
4. Ho-ly Je-sus, eve-ry day keep us in the nar-row way;
5. In the heav'n-ly coun-try bright need they no cre-at-ed light;

as with joy they hailed its light, lead-ing on-ward, beam-ing bright;
there to bend the knee be-fore Him whom heav'n and earth a-dore;
so may we with ho-ly joy, pure, and free from sin's al-loy,
and, when earth-ly things are past, bring our ran-somed souls at last
Thou its Light, its Joy, its Crown, Thou its Sun which goes not down;

so, most gra-cious God, may we ev-er-more be led to Thee.
so may we with will-ing feet ev-er seek Thy mer-cy-seat.
all our cost-liest treas-ures bring, Christ, to Thee, our heav'n-ly King.
where they need no star to guide, where no clouds Thy glo-ry hide.
there for ev-er may we sing al-le-lu-ias to our King.

256 Hosanna, Loud Hosanna

Jennette Threlfall, 1873

ELLACOMBE
76 76 D

Vollstandige-Sammlung, 1827

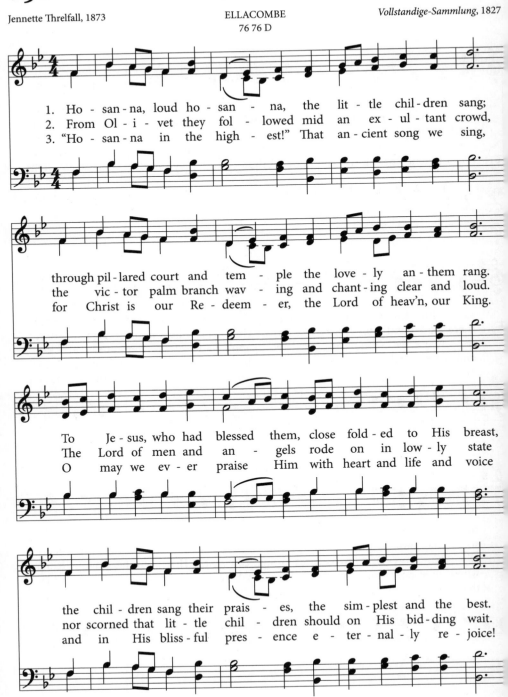

1. Ho - san - na, loud ho - san - na, the lit - tle chil - dren sang;
2. From Ol - i - vet they fol - lowed mid an ex - ul - tant crowd,
3. "Ho - san - na in the high - est!" That an - cient song we sing,

through pil - lared court and tem - ple the love - ly an - them rang.
the vic - tor palm branch wav - ing and chant - ing clear and loud.
for Christ is our Re - deem - er, the Lord of heav'n, our King.

To Je - sus, who had blessed them, close fold - ed to His breast,
The Lord of men and an - gels rode on in low - ly state
O may we ev - er praise Him with heart and life and voice

the chil - dren sang their prais - es, the sim - plest and the best.
nor scorned that lit - tle chil - dren should on His bid - ding wait.
and in His bliss - ful pres - ence e - ter - nal - ly re - joice!

All Glory, Laud, and Honor

257

Theodulph of Orleans, c. 820
trans. John Mason Neale, 1855, alt.

ST. THEODULPH
76 76 D

Melchior Teschner, 1614
harm. William Henry Monk, 1861

1. All glo - ry, laud, and hon - or to Thee, Re - deem - er, King,
2. The peo - ple of the He - brews with palms be - fore Thee went;
3. Thou didst ac - cept their prais - es; ac - cept the prayers we bring,

to whom the lips of chil - dren made sweet ho - san - nas ring!
our praise and prayer and an - thems be - fore Thee we pre - sent.
who in all good de - light - est, Thou good and gra - cious King!

Thou art the King of Is - ra - el, Thou Dav - id's roy - al Son,
To Thee, be - fore Thy pas - sion, they sang their hymns of praise;
The com - pan - y of an - gels are prais - ing Thee on high,

who in the Lord's name com - est, the King and bless - ed One.
to Thee, now high ex - alt - ed, our mel - o - dy we raise.
and we with all cre - a - tion in chor - us make re - ply.

258 O Love, How Deep

Attr. Thomas á Kempis, 15th cent.
trans. Benjamin Webb, 1854, alt.

DEO GRACIAS
LM

English melody; harm. from
Hymns Ancient and Modern, revised, 1950

1. O love, how deep, how broad, how high, how pass - ing
2. He sent no an - gel to our race, of high - er
3. For us bap - tized, for us He bore His ho - ly
4. For us to wick - ed men be - trayed, scourged, mocked, in
5. For us He rose from death a - gain, for us He
6. All glo - ry to our Lord and God for love so

thought and fan - ta - sy, that God, the Son of
or of low - er place, but wore the robe of
fast, and hun - gered sore; for us temp - ta - tions
crown of thorns ar - rayed, He bore the shame - ful
went on high to reign, for us He sent His
deep, so high, so broad— the Trin - i - ty whom

God, should take our mor - tal form for mor - tals' sake!
hu - man frame, and He Him - self to this world came.
sharp He knew, for us the temp - ter ov - er - threw.
cross and death, for us at length gave up His breath.
Spir - it here to guide, to strength - en, and to cheer.
we a - dore for - ev - er and for - ev - er - more.

Ride on, Ride on in Majesty! 259

nry Hart Milman, 1827   **TRURO**   Thomas Williams's
LM   *Psalmodia Evangelica*, 1789

1. Ride on, ride on in maj - es - ty! Hear all the tribes ho - san - na cry; O Sav - ior meek, pur - sue Your road with palms and scat - tered gar - ments strowed.
2. Ride on, ride on in maj - es - ty! In low - ly pomp ride on to die. O Christ, Your tri - umphs now be - gin o'er cap - tive death and con - quered sin.
3. Ride on, ride on in maj - es - ty! The host of an - gels in the sky look down with sad and won - d'ring eyes to see th'ap - proach - ing Sac - ri - fice.
4. Ride on, ride on in maj - es - ty! Your last and fierc - est strife is nigh. The Fa - ther on His sap - phire throne a - waits His own a - noint - ed Son.
5. Ride on, ride on in maj - es - ty! In low - ly pomp ride on to die, bow Your meek head to mor - tal pain, then take, O Christ, Your pow'r and reign.

260 My Song Is Love Unknown

Samuel Crossman, 1664   LOVE UNKNOWN   John Ireland, 19
66 66 88

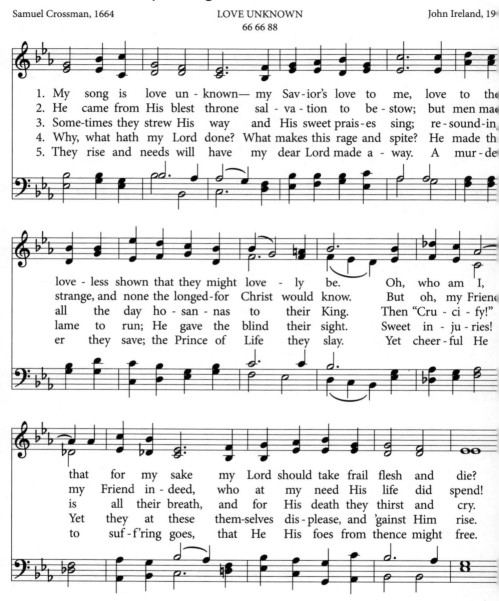

1. My song is love un-known— my Sav-ior's love to me, love to the
2. He came from His blest throne sal-va-tion to be-stow; but men ma
3. Some-times they strew His way and His sweet prais-es sing; re-sound-in
4. Why, what hath my Lord done? What makes this rage and spite? He made th
5. They rise and needs will have my dear Lord made a-way. A mur-de

love-less shown that they might love-ly be. Oh, who am I,
strange, and none the longed-for Christ would know. But oh, my Frien
all the day ho-san-nas to their King. Then "Cru-ci-fy!"
lame to run; He gave the blind their sight. Sweet in-ju-ries!
er they save; the Prince of Life they slay. Yet cheer-ful He

that for my sake my Lord should take frail flesh and die?
my Friend in-deed, who at my need His life did spend!
is all their breath, and for His death they thirst and cry.
Yet they at these them-selves dis-please, and 'gainst Him rise.
to suf-f'ring goes, that He His foes from thence might free.

6. In life, no house, no home
my Lord on earth might have;
in death, no friendly tomb
but what a stranger gave.
What may I say? Heav'n was His home;
but mine the tomb wherein He lay.

7. Here might I stay and sing—
no story so divine!
Never was love, dear King,
never was grief like Thine.
This is my Friend, in whose sweet prais
I all my days could gladly spend.

O Sacred Head, Now Wounded   **261**

tr. to Bernard of Clairvaux, 12th cent.   PASSION CHORALE   Hans Leo Hassler, 1601
German trans. Paul Gerhardt, 1656   76 76 D   harm. Johann Sebastian Bach, 1729
English trans. James Alexander, 1830

1. O   sa - cred Head, now   wound - ed, with grief and shame weighed down,
2. What Thou, my Lord, hast   suf - fered was   all   for   sin - ners' gain;
3. What lan- guage shall I   bor - row to thank Thee, dear - est Friend,
4. Be   near when I   am   dy - ing, O show Thy cross   to   me!

now scorn- ful - ly   sur - round - ed with thorns, Thine on - ly crown.
mine, mine was the trans - gres - sion, but Thine the dead - ly pain.
for   this, Thy dy - ing   sor - row, Thy pit - y   with- out end?
And, for my suc - cor   fly - ing, come, Lord, to   set me free:

O   sa - cred Head, what glo - ry, what bliss till now was Thine!
Lo, here I   fall, my   Sav - ior! 'Tis   I   de - serve Thy place;
O   make me Thine for - ev - er! And should I faint - ing be,
these eyes, new faith re - ceiv - ing, from Thee shall nev - er move;

Yet, though de - spised and   go - ry, I   joy to call Thee mine.
look on   me with Thy   fa - vor, vouch- safe to me Thy grace.
Lord, let   me nev - er,   nev - er   out - live my love for Thee.
for   he   who dies be - liev - ing, dies safe - ly in Thy love.

262 Alas, and Did My Savior Bleed?

Isaac Watts, 1707

MARTYRDOM
CM

Hugh Wilson, 18?

1. A - las, and did my Sav-ior bleed, and did my Sov-'reign die?
2. Was it for crimes that I had done He groaned up - on the tree?
3. Well might the sun in dark-ness hide and shut his glo - ries in,
4. Thus might I hide my blush-ing face while His dear cross ap - pears;
5. But drops of grief can ne'er re - pay the debt of love I owe;

Would He de - vote that sa - cred head for such a worm as I?
A - maz - ing pi - ty, grace un-known, and love be - yond de - gree!
when Christ the might-y Mak - er died for man the crea-ture's sin.
dis - solve my heart in thank-ful - ness, and melt mine eyes in tears.
here, Lord, I give my - self a - way; 'tis all that I can do.

263 Man of Sorrows, What a Name

Philip P. Bliss, 1875

MAN OF SORROWS
777 8

Philip P. Bliss, 18?

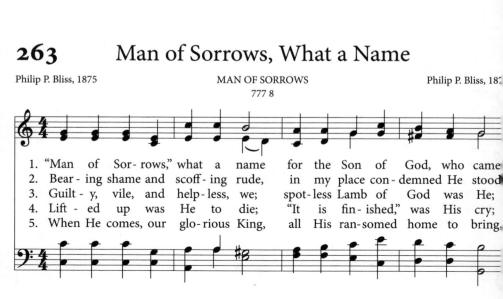

1. "Man of Sor-rows," what a name for the Son of God, who came
2. Bear - ing shame and scoff - ing rude, in my place con - demned He stood;
3. Guilt - y, vile, and help - less, we; spot-less Lamb of God was He;
4. Lift - ed up was He to die; "It is fin - ished," was His cry;
5. When He comes, our glo - rious King, all His ran-somed home to bring.

ru - ined sin - ners to re - claim!
sealed my par - don with His blood:
full a - tone - ment, can it be? Hal - le - lu - jah! What a Sav - ior!
now in heav'n ex - alt - ed high:
then a - new this song we'll sing:

Go to Dark Gethsemane 264

mes Montgomery, 1820

REDHEAD
77 77 77

Richard Redhead, 1853, alt.

1. Go to dark Geth - sem - a - ne, all who feel the tempt-er's pow'r;
2. Fol - low to the judg-ment hall; view the Lord of life ar-raigned;
3. Cal-vary's mourn-ful moun-tain climb; there, a - dor - ing at His feet,
4. Ear - ly has - ten to the tomb where they laid His breath-less clay;

your Re - deem - er's con - flict see; watch with Him one bit - ter hour;
O, the worm-wood and the gall! O, the pangs His soul sus-tained!
mark that mir - a - cle of time, God's own sac - ri - fice com - plete.
all is sol - i - tude and gloom; who has tak - en Him a - way?

turn not from His griefs a - way; learn from Je - sus Christ to pray.
Shun not suf - f'ring, shame, or loss; learn from Him to bear the cross.
"It is fin - ished!" hear Him cry; learn from Je - sus Christ to die.
Christ is ris'n! He meets our eyes: Sav - ior, teach us so to rise.

265 Throned upon the Awful Tree

John Ellerton, 1875

ARFON
77 77 77

Traditional Welsh melod
arr. Hugh Davies, c. 190

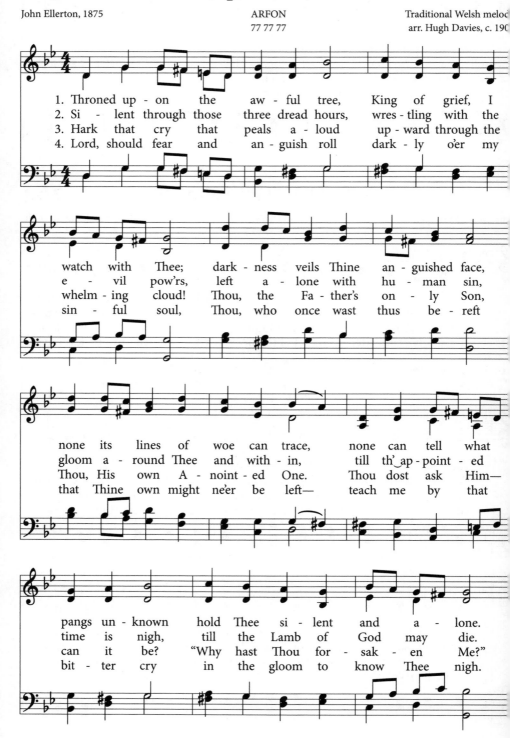

1. Throned up - on the aw - ful tree, King of grief, I
2. Si - lent through those three dread hours, wres - tling with the
3. Hark that cry that peals a - loud up - ward through the
4. Lord, should fear and an - guish roll dark - ly o'er my

watch with Thee; dark - ness veils Thine an - guished face,
e - vil pow'rs, left a - lone with hu - man sin,
whelm - ing cloud! Thou, the Fa - ther's on - ly Son,
sin - ful soul, Thou, who once wast thus be - reft

none its lines of woe can trace, none can tell what
gloom a - round Thee and with - in, till th'ap - point - ed
Thou, His own A - noint - ed One. Thou dost ask Him—
that Thine own might ne'er be left— teach me by that

pangs un - known hold Thee si - lent and a - lone.
time is nigh, till the Lamb of God may die.
can it be? "Why hast Thou for - sak - en Me?"
bit - ter cry in the gloom to know Thee nigh.

Stricken, Smitten, and Afflicted 266

Thomas Kelly, 1804, alt.   O MEIN JESU, ICH MUSS STERBEN   *Geistliche Volkslieder*, 1850
87 87 D

1. Strick-en, smit-ten, and af-flict-ed, see Him dy-ing on the tree!
2. Tell me, ye who hear Him groan-ing, was there ev-er grief like His?
3. Ye who think of sin but light-ly, nor sup-pose the e-vil great,
4. Here we have a firm foun-da-tion, here the ref-uge of the lost:

'Tis the Christ by man re-ject-ed; yes, my soul, 'tis He, 'tis He!
Friends thro' fear His cause dis-own-ing, foes in-sult-ing His dis-tress;
here may view its na-ture right-ly, here its guilt may es-ti-mate.
Christ the Rock of our sal-va-tion, His the name of which we boast.

'Tis the long-ex-pect-ed Proph-et, Da-vid's Son, yet Da-vid's Lord;
man-y hands were raised to wound Him, none would in-ter-pose to save;
Mark the Sac-ri-fice ap-point-ed; see who bears the aw-ful load;
Lamb of God, for sin-ners wound-ed, Sac-ri-fice to can-cel guilt!

by His Son God now has spo-ken; 'tis the true and faith-ful Word.
but the deep-est stroke that pierced Him was the stroke that Jus-tice gave.
'tis the Word, the Lord's A-noint-ed, Son of Man and Son of God.
None shall ev-er be con-found-ed who on Him their hope have built.

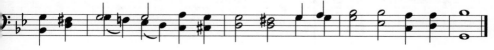

267 In the Cross of Christ I Glory

John Bowring, 1825　　　　　　　RATHBURN　　　　　　Ithamar Conkey, 184
87 87

1. In　the cross of Christ I　glo - ry, tow'r-ing o'er the wrecks of time;
2. In　the cross of Christ I　glo - ry, there for all　was grace made free,
3. When the woes of　life　o'er-take me, hopes de-ceive and fears　an - noy,
4. When the sun of　bliss　is beam-ing light and love up - on　my way,
5. Bane and bless-ing, pain and pleas-ure,　by　the cross are sanc - ti - fied;

all　the light of　sa - cred sto - ry gath - ers round its head sub - lime.
none de - serv - ing, yet　re - ceiv - ing life through death at　Cal - va - ry.
nev - er shall the cross　for - sake me. Lo!　it glows with peace and joy.
from the cross the　ra - diance stream-ing adds more lus - ter　to　the day.
peace is　there that knows　no　mea - sure, joys that through all time　a - bide.

268 His Be the Victor's Name

Samuel Whitelock Gandy, 1838　　　FESTAL SONG　　　William Henry Walter, 189
SM

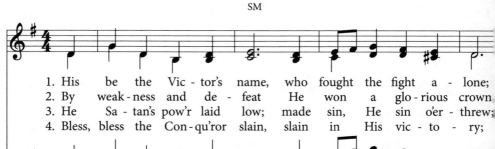

1. His　be　the Vic - tor's　name, who fought the fight a - lone;
2. By　weak - ness and de - feat　He　won　a　glo - rious crown.
3. He　Sa - tan's pow'r laid　low;　made sin, He　sin o'er - threw;
4. Bless, bless the Con - qu'ror slain, slain　in　His vic - to - ry;

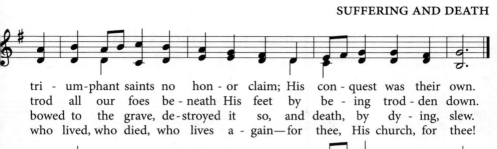

tri - um-phant saints no hon - or claim; His con - quest was their own.
trod all our foes be - neath His feet by be - ing trod - den down.
bowed to the grave, de - stroyed it so, and death, by dy - ing, slew.
who lived, who died, who lives a - gain—for thee, His church, for thee!

The Perfect Righteousness of God   269

lbert Midlane, 1861   MENDON   Traditional German melody
LM   arr. Samuel Dyer, 1828

1. The per - fect right - eous - ness of God is wit-nessed
2. God could not pass the sin - ner by; jus - tice de -
3. The judg-ment fell on Je - sus' head; 'twas in His
4. The sin - ner who be - lieves is free, can say, "The

in the Sav - ior's blood; 'tis in the cross of Christ we
mands that he should die; but in the cross of Christ we
blood sin's debt was paid; stern Jus - tice can de - mand no
Sav - ior died for me," can point to the a - ton - ing

trace His right - eous - ness, yet won - drous grace.
see how God can save, yet right - eous be.
more, and Mer - cy can dis - pense her store.
blood and say, "This made my peace with God."

270   What Wondrous Love Is This

Dupuy's *Selection of Hymns*   WONDROUS LOVE   William Walker's *Southern Harmony*, 183:
and Mead's *General Selection*, 1811   12 9 12 12 9

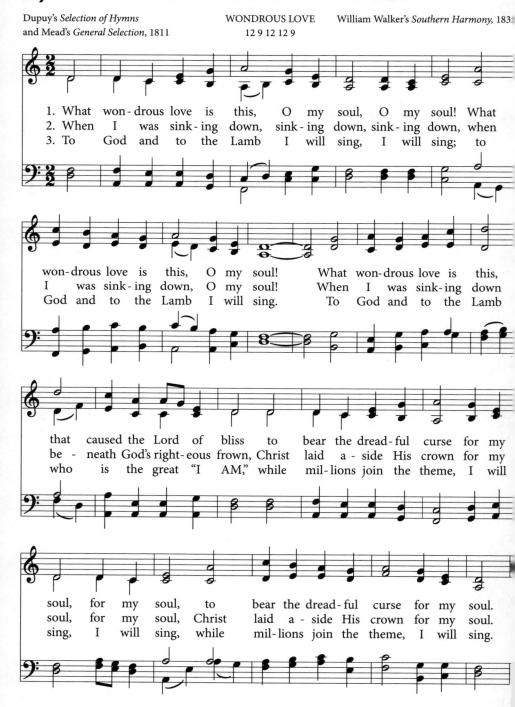

1. What won-drous love is this, O my soul, O my soul! What
2. When I was sink-ing down, sink-ing down, sink-ing down, when
3. To God and to the Lamb I will sing, I will sing; to

won-drous love is this, O my soul! What won-drous love is this,
I was sink-ing down, O my soul! When I was sink-ing down
God and to the Lamb I will sing. To God and to the Lamb

that caused the Lord of bliss to bear the dread-ful curse for my
be-neath God's right-eous frown, Christ laid a-side His crown for my
who is the great "I AM," while mil-lions join the theme, I will

soul, for my soul, to bear the dread-ful curse for my soul.
soul, for my soul, Christ laid a-side His crown for my soul.
sing, I will sing, while mil-lions join the theme, I will sing.

'Tis Finished! The Messiah Dies

271

Charles Wesley, 1762   OLIVE'S BROW   William B. Bradbury, 1853
LM

1. 'Tis fin-ished! The Mes-si-ah dies— cut off for sins, but
2. The veil is rent; in Christ a-lone the liv-ing way to
3. 'Tis fin-ished! All my guilt and pain, I want no sac-ri-
4. The reign of sin and death is o'er; all grace is now to

not His own; ac-com-plished is the sac-ri-
heav'n is seen; the mid-dle wall is bro-ken
fice be-side; for me, for me the Lamb is
sin-ners giv'n; and, lo! I plead th'a-ton-ing

fice— the great re-deem-ing work is done.
down, and all man-kind may en-ter in.
slain, 'tis fin-ished! I am jus-ti-fied.
blood, and in Thy right I claim my heav'n.

272 Ah, Holy Jesus

Johann Heermann, 1630
trans. Robert Bridges, 1897

HERZLIEBSTER JESU
11 11 11 5

Johann Crüger, 164

1. Ah, ho-ly Je-sus, how have You of-fend-ed,
   that mor-tal judg-ment has on You de-scend-ed? By foes de-
   rid-ed, by Your own re-ject-ed, O most af-flict-ed!

2. Who was the guilt-y? Who brought this up-on You?
   A-las, my trea-son, Je-sus, has un-done You! 'Twas I, Lord
   Je-sus, I it was de-nied You: I cru-ci-fied You.

3. Lo, the Good Shep-herd for the sheep is of-fered;
   the slave hath sin-ned, and the Son hath suf-fered; for our a-
   tone-ment, while we noth-ing heed-ed, God in-ter-ced-ed.

4. For me, kind Je-sus, was Your in-car-na-tion,
   Your mor-tal sor-row, and Your life's ob-la-tion; Your death of
   an-guish and Your bit-ter pas-sion, for my sal-va-tion.

5. There-fore, kind Je-sus, since I can-not pay You,
   I do a-dore You, and will ev-er pray You, think on Your
   pit-y and Your love un-swerv-ing, not my de-serv-ing.

When I Survey the Wondrous Cross   273

Isaac Watts, 1707   HAMBURG   Lowell Mason, 1824
LM

1. When I sur - vey the won - drous cross on which the
2. For - bid it, Lord, that I should boast, save in the
3. See from His head, His hands, His feet, sor - row and
4. Were the whole realm of na - ture mine, that were a

Prince of Glo - ry died, my rich - est gain I
death of Christ, my God! All the vain things that
love flow min - gled down! Did e'er such love and
pre - sent far too small; love so a - maz - ing,

count but loss, and pour con - tempt on all my pride.
charm me most, I sac - ri - fice them to His blood.
sor - row meet, or thorns com - pose so rich a crown?
so di - vine, de - mands my soul, my life, my all.

274 'Tis Midnight, and on Olive's Brow

William B. Tappan, 1822

OLIVE'S BROW
LM

William B. Bradbury, 185.

1. 'Tis mid-night, and on Ol-ive's brow the star is
dimmed that late-ly shone; 'tis mid-night; in the
gar-den now the suf-f'ring Sav-ior prays a-lone.

2. 'Tis mid-night, and, from all re-moved, Em-man-uel
wres-tles lone with fears; e'en the dis-ci-ple
that He loved heeds not His Mas-ter's grief and tears.

3. 'Tis mid-night, and, for oth-ers' guilt, the Man of
Sor-rows weeps in blood; yet He that hath in
an-guish knelt is not for-sak-en by His God.

4. 'Tis mid-night; from the heav'n-ly plains is borne the
song that an-gels know; un-heard by mor-tals
are the strains that sweet-ly soothe the Sav-ior's woe.

He Dies, the Friend of Sinners Dies! 275

aac Watts, 1709
t. Augustus Toplady, 1776

BLOCKLEY
LM

Thomas Blockley, 1861

1. He dies, the Friend of sin - ners dies! Lo! Sa - lem's
2. Here's love and grief be - yond de - gree: the Lord of
3. The ris - ing God for - sakes the tomb! The tomb in
4. Break off your tears, ye saints, and tell how high your
5. Say: "Live for - ev - er, won - drous King, born to re -

daugh - ters weep a - round. A sol - emn dark - ness
glo - ry dies for men; but lo, what sud - den
vain for - bids His rise: che - ru - bic le - gions
great De - liv - 'rer reigns. Sing how He spoiled the
deem, and strong to save!" Then ask the mon - ster:

veils the skies; a sud - den trem - bling shakes the ground.
joys we see! Je - sus, the dead, re - vives a - gain.
guard Him home, and shout Him wel - come to the skies.
hosts of hell, and led the mon - ster, Death, in chains.
"Where's thy sting? And where's thy vic - t'ry, boast - ing grave?"

276 Priest and Victim, Jesus Dies

Margaret Clarkson, 1967   RABUN   Brian Pinner © 200•
                          77 77 77

1. Priest and Vic-tim, Je - sus dies, gives Him-self in sac - ri - fice.
2. Might - y Vic-tor, see Him rise, bring-ing man to par - a - dise;
3. Lord of life, be - hold Him stand now for us at God's right hand.
4. Prince and Sav-ior, Christ shall come, soon to take His ran-somed home
5. King for - ev - er, He shall reign, Lord of death and sin and pain;

Christ, the sin - less Son of God, of - fers up for us His blood,
sin and death no more may claim those who trust His sav - ing name;
Still our hu - man frame He wears, feels our woes and heeds our prayers;
His the king-dom, His the pow'r, His the glo - ry in that hour,
pure and right-eous, strong and free, He shall rule in eq - ui - ty;

gives Him-self in sac - ri - fice, Priest and Vic-tim, Je - sus dies!
bring-ing man to par - a - dise, might - y Vic-tor, see Him rise!
now for us at God's right hand, Lord of life, be - hold Him stand!
soon to take His ran-somed home, Prince and Sav - ior, Christ shall come!
Lord of death and sin and pain, King for - ev - er, He shall reign!

It Is a Thing Most Wonderful

277

illiam Walsham How, 1883

HERONGATE
LM

English folk melody
arr. Ralph Vaughan Williams, 1906

1. It is a thing most won - der - ful, al - most too
2. And yet I know that it is true: He chose a
3. I can - not tell how He could love a child so
4. I some - times think a - bout the cross, and shut my
5. But e - ven could I see Him die, I could but
6. It is most won - der - ful to know His love for
7. And yet I want to love Thee, Lord; O light the

won - der - ful to be, that God's own Son should
poor and hum - ble lot, and wept and toiled and
weak and full of sin; His love must be most
eyes, and try to see the cru - el nails and
see a lit - tle part of that great love which,
me so free and sure; but 'tis more won - der -
flame with - in my heart, and I will love Thee

come from heav'n, and die to save a child like me.
mourned and died for love of those who loved Him not.
won - der - ful if He could die my love to win.
crown of thorns, and Je - sus cru - ci - fied for me.
like a fire, is al - ways burn - ing in His heart.
ful to see my love for Him so faint and poor.
more and more, un - til I see Thee as Thou art.

278   Christ, the Life of All the Living

Ernst C. Homburg, 1659   JESU, MEINES LEBENS LEBEN   *Das grosse Cantionale*, Darnstadt, 168
trans. Catherine Winkworth, 1863, alt.   87 87 88 77

1. Christ, the life of   all   the liv - ing, Christ, the death of   death, our foe;
2. Thou, O Christ, hast tak - en   on Thee   bit - ter strokes, a   cru - el rod;
3. Thou didst bear the smit - ing on - ly   that it might not   fall   on me;
4. Then for   all that wrought our par - don, for the sor - rows deep and sore,

who Thy - self for   us once giv - ing   to the dark - est depths of woe,
pain   and scorn were heaped up - on Thee, O Thou sin - less   Son   of God;
stood - est false - ly charged and lone - ly   that I   might be   safe   and free;
for   the an - guish   in   the gar - den,   I   will thank Thee   ev - er - more,

pa - tient - ly didst yield Thy breath   but   to save my   soul from death;
on - ly thus for   me to win,   res - cue from the bonds of   sin;
com - fort - less that   I might know   com - fort from Thy bound - less woe;
thank Thee with my   lat - est breath   for   Thy sad and   cru - el death,

praise and glo - ry   ev - er be,   bless - ed Je - sus,   un - to Thee.
praise and glo - ry   ev - er be,   bless - ed Je - sus,   un - to Thee.
praise and glo - ry   ev - er be,   bless - ed Je - sus,   un - to Thee.
for   that last and   bit - ter cry,   praise Thee ev - er - more   on high.

Sing, My Tongue, the Glorious Battle 279

Venantius Honorius Clementianus
Fortunatus, 6th cent.
trans. John Mason Neale, 19th cent.

RHUDDLAN
87 87 87

Traditional Welsh melody
harm. *The English Hymnal*, 1906

1. Sing, my tongue, the glo-rious bat-tle; sing the end-ing of the fray.
2. Tell how, when at length the full-ness of the ap-point-ed time was come,
3. Thus, with thir-ty years ac-com-plished, He went forth from Naz-a-reth,
4. Faith-ful cross, true sign of tri-umph, be for all the no-blest tree;
5. Un-to God be praise and glo-ry: to the Fa-ther and the Son,

Now a-bove the cross, the tro-phy, sound the loud tri-um-phant lay:
He, the Word, was born of wom-an, left for us His Fa-ther's home,
des-tined, ded-i-cat-ed, will-ing, did His work, and met His death;
none in fo-liage, none in blos-som, none in fruit your e-qual be;
to the e-ter-nal Spir-it hon-or now and ev-er-more be done;

tell how Christ, the world's Re-deem-er, as a vic-tim won the day.
blazed the path of true o-be-dience, shone as light a-midst the gloom.
like a lamb He hum-bly yield-ed on the cross His dy-ing breath.
sym-bol of the world's re-demp-tion, for the weight that hung on thee!
praise and glo-ry in the high-est, while the time-less ag-es run.

280 Hark! the Voice of Love and Mercy

Jonathan Evans, 1784, alt. BRYN CALFARIA William Owen, 185
87 87 444 77

1. Hark! the voice of love and mer - cy sounds a - loud from Cal - va - ry;
2. "It is fin-ished!" O what pleas-ure do these pre - cious words af - ford;
3. Fin - ished all the types and shad-ows of the ce - re - mo - nial law;
4. Tune your harps a - new, ye ser - aphs, join to sing the glo-rious them

see, it rends the rocks a - sun - der, shakes the earth, and veils the sky:
heav'n-ly bless - ings, with-out meas - ure, flow to us from Christ the Lord:
fin - ished all that God has prom-ised; death and hell no more shall awe:
all in earth, and all in heav - en, join to praise Em - man - uel's name

"It is fin - ished!" "It is fin - ished!" "It is fin - ished!" Hear the
"It is fin - ished!" "It is fin - ished!" "It is fin - ished!" Saints the
"It is fin - ished!" "It is fin - ished!" "It is fin - ished!" Saints, from
Al - le - lu - ia! Al - le - lu - ia! Al - le - lu - ia! Glo - ry

dy - ing Sav - ior cry; hear the dy - ing Sav - ior cry.
dy - ing words re - cord; saints the dy - ing words re - cord.
hence your com - fort draw; saints, from hence your com - fort draw.
to the bleed - ing Lamb! Glo - ry to the bleed - ing Lamb!

Christk the Lord Is Risen Today

281

arles Wesley, 1739   **EASTER HYMN**   *Lyra Davidica*, 1708
77 77 with alleluias

1. Christ the Lord is ris'n to - day,
2. Love's re - deem - ing work is done.
3. Lives a - gain, our glo - rious King.   Al - - le - lu - ia!
4. Soar we now where Christ has led.
5. Hail, the Lord of earth and heav'n!

Sons of men and an - gels say:
Fought the fight, the bat - tle won.
Where, O death, is now thy sting?   Al - - le - lu - ia!
Fol - l'wing our ex - alt - ed Head.
Praise to Thee by both be giv'n;

Raise your joys and tri - umphs high.
Death in vain for - bids Him rise.
Dy - ing once, He all doth save.   Al - - le - lu - ia!
Made like Him, like Him we rise.
Thee we greet tri - um - phant now;

Sing, ye heav'ns, and earth re - ply:
Christ has o - pened par - a - dise.
Where thy vic - to - ry, O grave?   Al - - le - lu - ia!
Ours the cross, the grave, the skies.
Hail, the Res - ur - rec - tion Thou!

282   Jesus Christ Is Risen Today

Latin hymn, 14th cent.
trans. *Lyra Davidica*, 1708

LLANFAIR
77 77 with alleluias

Robert Williams, 18[

1. Je - sus Christ is ris'n to - day, al - le - lu - ia!
2. Hymns of praise then let us sing, al - le - lu - ia!
3. But the pains which He en - dured, al - le - lu - ia!

our tri - um - phant ho - ly day, al - le - lu - ia!
un - to Christ, our heav'n - ly King, al - le - lu - ia!
our sal - va - tion have pro - cured; al - le - lu - ia!

who did once, up - on the cross, al - le - lu - ia!
who en - dured the cross and grave, al - le - lu - ia!
now a - bove the sky He's King, al - le - lu - ia!

suf - fer to re - deem our loss, al - le - lu - ia!
sin - ners to re - deem and save, al - le - lu - ia!
where the an - gels ev - er sing: al - le - lu - ia!

Thine Be the Glory

mond Louis Budry, 1884
ns. R. Birch Hoyle, 1923

JUDAS MACCABEUS
10 11 11 11 with refrain

George Frederick Handel, 1746

1. Thine be the glo - ry, ris - en, con - qu'ring Son;
2. Lo! Je - sus meets us, ris - en from the tomb.
3. No more we doubt Thee, glo - rious Prince of life!

Refrain: Thine be the glo - ry, ris - en, con - qu'ring Son;

End

end - less is the vic - t'ry Thou o'er death hast won.
Lov - ing - ly He greets us, scat - ters fear and gloom;
Life is naught with - out Thee; aid us in our strife;

end - less is the vic - t'ry Thou o'er death hast won!

An - gels in bright rai - ment rolled the stone a - way,
let His church with glad - ness hymns of tri - umph sing,
make us more than con - qu'rors, through Thy death - less love;

to Refrain

kept the fold - ed grave - clothes where Thy bod - y lay.
for her Lord now liv - eth; death hath lost its sting.
bring us safe through Jor - dan to Thy home a - bove.

284   Alleluia, Alleluia! Hearts to Heaven

Christopher Wordsworth, 1862   ODE TO JOY   Ludwig van Beethoven, 18
                                     87 87 D   adapt. Edward Hodges, 18

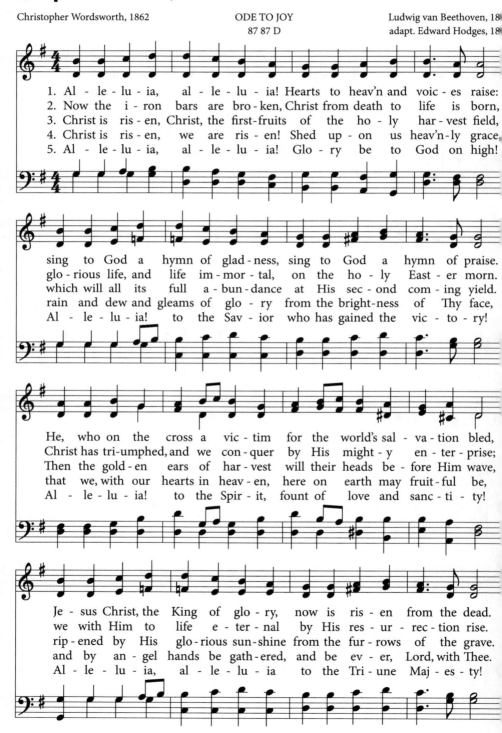

1. Al - le - lu - ia, al - le - lu - ia! Hearts to heav'n and voic - es raise:
2. Now the i - ron bars are bro - ken, Christ from death to life is born,
3. Christ is ris - en, Christ, the first-fruits of the ho - ly har - vest field,
4. Christ is ris - en, we are ris - en! Shed up - on us heav'n-ly grace,
5. Al - le - lu - ia, al - le - lu - ia! Glo - ry be to God on high!

sing to God a hymn of glad - ness, sing to God a hymn of praise.
glo - rious life, and life im - mor - tal, on the ho - ly East - er morn.
which will all its full a - bun - dance at His sec - ond com - ing yield.
rain and dew and gleams of glo - ry from the bright-ness of Thy face,
Al - le - lu - ia! to the Sav - ior who has gained the vic - to - ry!

He, who on the cross a vic - tim for the world's sal - va - tion bled,
Christ has tri-umphed, and we con - quer by His might - y en - ter - prise;
Then the gold - en ears of har - vest will their heads be - fore Him wave,
that we, with our hearts in heav - en, here on earth may fruit - ful be,
Al - le - lu - ia! to the Spir - it, fount of love and sanc - ti - ty!

Je - sus Christ, the King of glo - ry, now is ris - en from the dead.
we with Him to life e - ter - nal by His res - ur - rec - tion rise.
rip - ened by His glo - rious sun-shine from the fur - rows of the grave.
and by an - gel hands be gath-ered, and be ev - er, Lord, with Thee.
Al - le - lu - ia, al - le - lu - ia to the Tri - une Maj - es - ty!

The Day of Resurrection

285

John of Damascus, 8th cent.
trans. John Mason Neale, 1862

LANCASHIRE
76 76 D

Henry Smart, ca. 1835

1. The day of res - ur - rec - tion! Earth, tell it out a - broad,
2. Our hearts be purged from e - vil that we may see a - right
3. Now let the heav'ns be joy - ful; let earth her song be - gin!

the Pass - o - ver of glad - ness, the Pass - o - ver of God.
the Lord in rays e - ter - nal of res - ur - rec - tion light,
The world re - sound in tri - umph, and all that is there - in;

From death to life e - ter - nal, from this world to the sky,
and lis - ten - ing to His ac - cents, may hear, so calm and plain,
let all things seen and un - seen their notes in glad - ness blend,

our Christ has brought us o - ver with hymns of vic - to - ry.
His own "All hail!" and hear - ing, may raise the vic - tor strain.
for Christ the Lord is ris - en, our joy that hath no end.

286 Jesus Lives, and So Shall I

Christian F. Gellert, 1757
trans. John Dunmore Lang, 1826

ZUVERSICHT
78 78 77

Johann Crüger, 1653

1. Je - sus lives, and so shall I; Death, thy sting is
2. Je - sus lives, and reigns su - preme, and, His king - dom
3. Je - sus lives, and God ex - tends grace to each re -
4. Je - sus lives, and by His grace, vict - 'ry o'er my
5. Je - sus lives! I know full well nought from Him my
6. Je - sus lives, and death is now but my en - trance

gone for - ev - er! He who deigned for me to die
still re - main - ing, I shall al - so be with Him,
turn - ing sin - ner; re - bels He re - ceives as friends
pas - sions giv - ing, I will cleanse my heart and ways,
heart can sev - er, life nor death nor pow'rs of hell,
in - to glo - ry. Cour - age, then, my soul, for thou

lives, the bands of death to sev - er. He shall
ev - er liv - ing, ev - er reign - ing. God has
and ex - alts to high - est hon - or. God is
ev - er to His glo - ry liv - ing. Me He
joy nor grief, hence - forth for - ev - er. None of
hast a crown of life be - fore thee; thou shalt

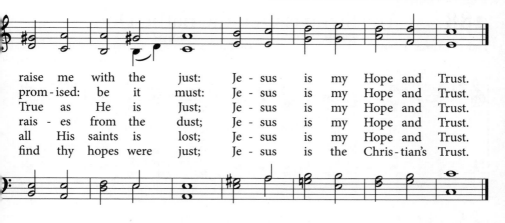

raise me with the just: Je - sus is my Hope and Trust.
prom - ised: be it must: Je - sus is my Hope and Trust.
True as He is Just; Je - sus is my Hope and Trust.
rais - es from the dust; Je - sus is my Hope and Trust.
all His saints is lost; Je - sus is my Hope and Trust.
find thy hopes were just; Je - sus is the Chris - tian's Trust.

Good Christians All, Rejoice and Sing 287

ril A. Alington, 1925   GELOBT SEI GOTT   Melchior Vulpius, 1609
                              888 with alleluias

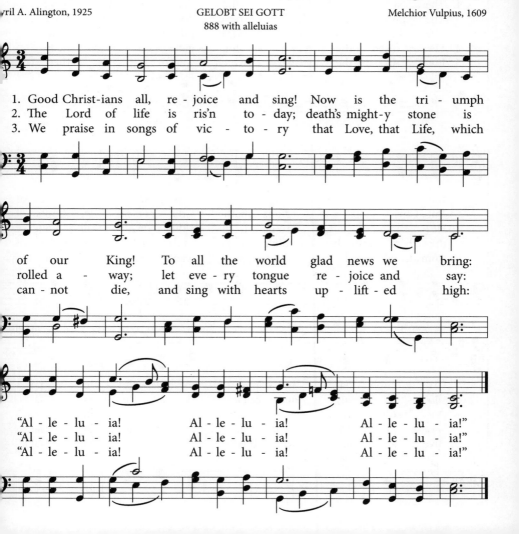

1. Good Christ-ians all, re - joice and sing! Now is the tri - umph
2. The Lord of life is ris'n to - day; death's might-y stone is
3. We praise in songs of vic - to - ry that Love, that Life, which

of our King! To all the world glad news we bring:
rolled a - way; let eve - ry tongue re - joice and say:
can - not die, and sing with hearts up - lift - ed high:

"Al - le - lu - ia! Al - le - lu - ia! Al - le - lu - ia!"
"Al - le - lu - ia! Al - le - lu - ia! Al - le - lu - ia!"
"Al - le - lu - ia! Al - le - lu - ia! Al - le - lu - ia!"

288 The Strife is O'er, the Battle Done

Latin hymn; trans. Francis Pott, 1861

VICTORY
888 4 with alleluias

Giovanni P. da Palestrina, 159
adapt. William Henry Monk, 186

Refrain

Al - le - lu - ia! Al - le - lu - ia! Al - le - lu - ia!

1. The strife is o'er, the bat - tle done;
2. The pow'rs of death have done their worst,
3. The three sad days have quick - ly sped;
4. He closed the yawn - ing gates of hell;
5. Lord, by the stripes which wound - ed Thee,

the vic - to - ry of life is won; the song of
but Christ their le - gions hath dis - persed: let shouts of
He ris - es glo - rious from the dead: all glo - ry
the bars from heav'n's high por - tals fell: let hymns of
from death's dread sting Thy ser - vants free, that we may

to Refrain

tri - umph has be - gun: al - le - lu - ia!
ho - ly joy out - burst: al - le - lu - ia!
to our ris - en Head: al - le - lu - ia!
praise His tri - umphs tell: al - le - lu - ia!
live and sing to Thee: al - le - lu - ia!

I Know That My Redeemer Lives 289

Samuel Medley, 1775

DUKE STREET
LM

John Hatton, 1793

1. I know that my Re - deem - er lives; what com - fort
2. He lives tri - um - phant from the grave, He lives e -
3. He lives to bless me with His love, He lives to
4. He lives to grant me rich sup - ply, He lives to
5. He lives to si - lence all my fears, He lives to
6. He lives, my kind, wise, heav'n - ly Friend, He lives and

this sweet sen - tence gives! He lives, He lives, who
ter - nal - ly to save, He lives all - glo - rious
plead for me a - bove, He lives my hun - gry
guide me with His eye, He lives to com - fort
wipe a - way my tears, He lives to calm my
loves me to the end; He lives, and while He

once was dead; He lives, my ev - er - last - ing Head.
in the sky, He lives ex - alt - ed there on high.
soul to feed, He lives to help in time of need.
me when faint, He lives to hear my soul's com - plaint.
trou - bled heart, He lives all bless - ings to im - part.
lives, I'll sing; He lives, my Proph - et, Priest, and King.

7. He lives and grants me daily breath;
He lives and I shall conquer death;
He lives my mansion to prepare;
He lives to bring me safely there.

8. He lives, all glory to His name!
He lives, my Jesus, still the same.
Oh, the sweet joy this sentence gives,
"I know that my Redeemer lives!"

290   This Joyful Eastertide

George Ratcliffe Woodward, 1894   VRUECHTEN   *Davids Psalmen*, Amsterdam, 16

67 67 with refrain

1. This joy-ful East-er-tide, a - way with sin and
2. Death's flood has lost its chill since Je - sus crossed the
3. My flesh in hope shall rest and for a sea - son

sor - - row! My Love, the Cru - ci - fied,
riv - - - er; Lov - er of souls, from ill
slum - - - ber till trump from east to west

has sprung to life this mor - - - row:
my pass - ing soul de - liv - - - er:
shall wake the dead in num - - - ber:

Had Christ, who once was slain, not burst His three - day pris - on,

our faith had been in vain; but now has Christ a - ris - en, a - ris - en

a - ris - en; but now has Christ a - ris - - en!

Rejoice, the Lord is King   **291**

harles Wesley, 1746, alt.

DARWALL
66 66 88

John Darwall, 1769

1. Re - joice, the Lord is King! Your Lord and King a - dore.
2. Je - sus, the Sav - ior, reigns, the God of truth and love;
3. His king - dom can - not fail, He rules o'er earth and heav'n;
4. Re - joice in glo - rious hope, for Christ the Judge shall come

Re - joice, give thanks and sing and tri - umph ev - er - more.
when He had purged our stains, He took His seat a - bove:
the keys of death and hell are to our Je - sus giv'n:
to gath - er all His saints to their e - ter - nal home:

Lift up your heart! Lift up your voice; re - joice, a - gain I say, re - joice!

292 Christ Jesus Lay in Death's Strong Bands

Martin Luther, 1524
from *Victimae Paschali*
trans. Richard Massie, 1854, alt.

CHRIST LAG IN TODESBANDEN
87 87 78 74

Latin melody, c. 11
adapt. Johann Walther, 15

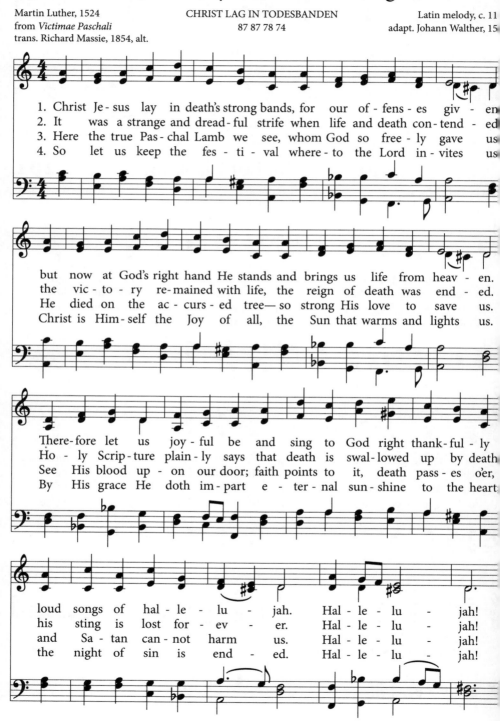

1. Christ Je-sus lay in death's strong bands, for our of-fens-es giv-en
2. It was a strange and dread-ful strife when life and death con-tend-ed
3. Here the true Pas-chal Lamb we see, whom God so free-ly gave us
4. So let us keep the fes-ti-val where-to the Lord in-vites us

but now at God's right hand He stands and brings us life from heav-en.
the vic-to-ry re-mained with life, the reign of death was end-ed.
He died on the ac-curs-ed tree— so strong His love to save us.
Christ is Him-self the Joy of all, the Sun that warms and lights us.

There-fore let us joy-ful be and sing to God right thank-ful-ly
Ho-ly Scrip-ture plain-ly says that death is swal-lowed up by death
See His blood up-on our door; faith points to it, death pass-es o'er,
By His grace He doth im-part e-ter-nal sun-shine to the heart

loud songs of hal-le-lu - jah. Hal-le-lu - jah!
his sting is lost for-ev - er. Hal-le-lu - jah!
and Sa-tan can-not harm us. Hal-le-lu - jah!
the night of sin is end - ed. Hal-le-lu - jah!

Look, Ye Saints, the Sight Is Glorious 293

Thomas Kelly, 1809 · CORONAE · 87 87 47 · William Henry Monk, 1871

1. Look, ye saints, the sight is glo - rious: see the Man of
2. Crown the Sav - ior, an - gels, crown Him; rich the tro - phies
3. Sin - ners in de - ri - sion crowned Him, mock - ing thus the
4. Hark! those bursts of ac - cla - ma - tion! Hark! those loud tri -

Sor - rows now; from the fight re - turned vic - to - rious,
Je - sus brings; in the seat of pow'r en - throne Him,
Sav - ior's claim; saints and an - gels crowd a - round Him,
um - phant chords! Je - sus takes the high - est sta - tion;

eve - ry knee to Him shall bow. Crown Him! Crown Him!
while the vault of heav - en rings. Crown Him! Crown Him!
own His ti - tle, praise His name. Crown Him! Crown Him!
O what joy the sight af - fords! Crown Him! Crown Him!

Crowns be - come the Vic - tor's brow.
Crown the Sav - ior King of kings.
Spread a - broad the Vic - tor's fame!
King of kings and Lord of lords!

294 Lamb of God, Thou Now Art Seated

James George Deck, 1841, alt. ABBOT'S LEIGH Cyril Taylor, 19
87 87 D

1. Lamb of God, Thou now art seat-ed high be-side Thy
2. Lord, in all Thy pow'r and glo-ry, still Thy thoughts and
3. Lamb of God, Thy faith-ful prom-ise says, "Be-hold, I
4. Lamb of God, when Thou in glo-ry shalt to this sad

Fa-ther's throne; all Thy gra-cious work com-plet-ed,
eyes are here; watch-ing o'er Thy ran-somed peo-ple,
quick-ly come," and our hearts, to Thine re-spon-sive,
earth re-turn, all Thy foes shall quake be-fore Thee,

all Thy might-y vic-t'ry won; eve-ry knee in heav'n
to Thy gra-cious heart so dear; Thou for them art in-
cry, "Come, Lord, and take us home." Oh, the rap-ture that
all who now de-spise Thee mourn; then shall we at Thine

is bend-ing to the Lamb for sin-ners slain; eve-ry
ter-ced-ing; ev-er-last-ing is Thy love— and a
a-waits us, when we meet Thee in the air, and with
ap-pear-ing, with Thee in Thy king-dom reign; Thine the

©1942, renewed 1970 by Hope Publishing Company. Used by permission.

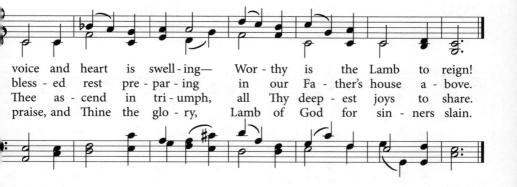

voice and heart is swell-ing— Wor - thy is the Lamb to reign!
bless - ed rest pre - par - ing in our Fa - ther's house a - bove.
Thee as - cend in tri - umph, all Thy deep - est joys to share.
praise, and Thine the glo - ry, Lamb of God for sin - ners slain.

The Head That Once Was Crowned 295

Thomas Kelly, 1820
ST. MAGNUS
CM
Jeremiah Clark, 1707

1. The head that once was crowned with thorns is crowned with glo - ry now;
2. The high - est place that heav'n af - fords is His, is His by right,
3. The joy of all who dwell a - bove, the joy of all be - low,
4. To them the cross with all its shame, with all its grace, is giv'n,
5. They suf - fer with their Lord be - low, they reign with Him a - bove,
6. The cross He bore is life and health, tho' shame and death to Him:

a roy - al di - a - dem a - dorns the might - y Vic - tor's brow.
the King of kings and Lord of lords, and heav'n's e - ter - nal Light.
to whom He man - i - fests His love, and grants His name to know.
their name, an ev - er - last - ing name, their joy, the joy of heav'n.
their prof - it and their joy to know the mys - t'ry of His love.
His peo - ple's hope, His peo - ple's wealth, their ev - er - last - ing theme.

296   Alleluia! Sing to Jesus

William C. Dix, 1867   HYFRYDOL   Rowland Prichard, 18
                               87 87 D

1. Al - le - lu - ia! Sing to Je - sus; His the scep - ter, His the thron
2. Al - le - lu - ia! Not as or - phans are we left in sor - row now
3. Al - le - lu - ia! Bread of heav - en, here on earth our food, our stay.

Al - le - lu - ia! His the tri - umph, His the vic - to - ry a - lone
Al - le - lu - ia! He is near us; faith be - lieves, nor ques - tions how
Al - le - lu - ia! Here the sin - ful flee to You from day to day.

Hark! The songs of peace - ful Zi - on thun - der like a might - y floo
Tho' the cloud from sight re - ceived Him when the for - ty days were o'er
In - ter - ces - sor, Friend of sin - ners, earth's Re - deem - er, hear our plea

"Je - sus out of eve - ry na - tion has re - deemed us by His bloo
shall our hearts for - get His prom - ise, "I am with you ev - er - more
where the songs of all the sin - less sweep a - cross the crys - tal sea.

Hail, Thou Once-Despised Jesus!   **297**

John Bakewell, 1757
alt. Augustus M. Toplady, 1776

RUSTINGTON
87 87 D

Hubert Parry, 1897

1. Hail, Thou once de - spis - ed Je - sus! Hail, Thou Gal - i - le - an king!
2. Pas - chal Lamb, by God ap - point-ed, all our sins on Thee were laid;
3. Je - sus, hail, en - throned in glo - ry, there for - ev - er to a - bide!
4. Wor - ship, hon - or, pow'r, and bless-ing Thou art wor - thy to re - ceive;

Thou didst suf - fer to re - lease us; Thou didst free sal - va - tion bring.
by al - might - y Love a - noint-ed, Thou hast full a - tone-ment made:
All the heav'n-ly host a - dore Thee, seat - ed at Thy Fa - ther's side.
high-est prais - es, with - out ceas-ing, meet it is for us to give.

Hail, Thou ag - o - niz-ing Sav - ior, bear - er of our sin and shame!
all Thy peo - ple are for - giv - en through the vir - tue of Thy blood;
There for sin - ners Thou art plead-ing; there Thou dost our place pre - pare;
Help, ye bright an - gel - ic spir - its, bring your sweet - est, no - blest lays;

By Thy mer - its we find fa - vor; life is giv - en through Thy name.
o - pened is the gate of heav - en; peace is made 'twixt man and God.
ev - er for us in - ter - ced - ing, till in glo - ry we ap - pear.
help to sing our Sav - ior's mer - its; help to chant Im - man - uel's praise!

298   Behold the Glories of the Lamb

Revelation 5:6–12; Isaac Watts, c. 1688   LYNGHAM   Thomas Jarman, c. 180
                                 CM

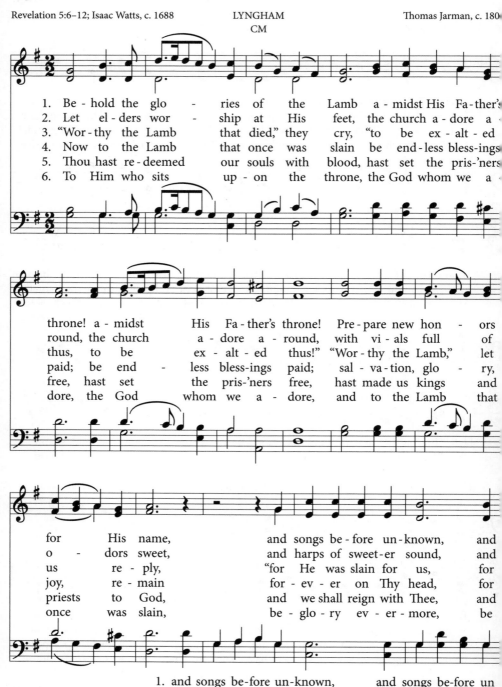

1. Be - hold the glo - ries of the Lamb a - midst His Fa - ther's
2. Let el - ders wor - ship at His feet, the church a - dore a -
3. "Wor - thy the Lamb that died," they cry, "to be ex - alt - ed
4. Now to the Lamb that once was slain be end - less bless-ings
5. Thou hast re - deemed our souls with blood, hast set the pris-'ners
6. To Him who sits up - on the throne, the God whom we a -

throne! a - midst His Fa - ther's throne! Pre - pare new hon - ors
round, the church a - dore a - round, with vi - als full of
thus, to be ex - alt - ed thus!" "Wor - thy the Lamb," let
paid; be end - less bless-ings paid; sal - va-tion, glo - ry,
free, hast set the pris-'ners free, hast made us kings and
dore, the God whom we a - dore, and to the Lamb that

for His name, and songs be - fore un - known, and
o - dors sweet, and harps of sweet-er sound, and
us re - ply, "for He was slain for us, for
joy, re - main for - ev - er on Thy head, for
priests to God, and we shall reign with Thee, and
once was slain, be - glo - ry ev - er - more, be

1. and songs be-fore un-known, and songs be-fore un

songs be - fore un - known, and songs be - fore un - known.
harps of sweet - er sound, and harps of sweet - er sound.
He was slain for us, for He was slain for us."
ev - er on Thy head, for - ev - er on Thy head.
we shall reign with Thee, and we shall reign with Thee.
glo - ry ev - er - more, be glo - ry ev - er - more.

known, and songs be-fore un-known, and songs be - fore un - known.

Jesus, in His Heavenly Glory 299

Robert C. Chapman, 1871   STUTTGART   Witt's *Psalmodia Sacra*, Gotha, 1715
87 87

1. Je - sus, in His heav'n-ly glo - ry, sits with God up - on the throne;
2. Nev - er more shall God, Je - ho - vah, smite the Shep-herd with the sword;
3. Dwell-ing in e - ter - nal sun-shine of the coun - te - nance of God,
4. On His heart our names are grav - en, on His shoul-ders we are borne;

now no more to be for - sak - en, His hu - mil - i - a - tion gone.
ne'er a - gain shall cru - el sin - ners set at nought our glo-rious Lord.
Je - sus fills all heav'n with in - cense of His rec - on - cil - ing blood.
of our God be - loved in Je - sus, we can love Him in re - turn.

300 Our Great High Priest Is Sitting

A. P. Cecil, 1841–1889   MEIRIONYDD   ascr. William Lloyd, 184(
76 76 D

1. Our great High Priest is sitting at God's right hand above,
2. Through man-i-fold temp-ta-tion, my soul holds on its course;
3. 'Twas God's most gra-cious fa-vor that gave His Son to die,

for us His hands up-lift-ing in sym-pa-thy and love;
Christ's might-y in-ter-ces-sion a-lone is my re-source;
to live our In-ter-ces-sor, to plead for us on high.

whilst here be-low, in weak-ness, we on-ward speed our way,
my gra-cious High Priest's plead-ings, who on the cross did bleed,
O Je-sus, bless-ed Sav-ior, who soon for us will come,

in sor-row oft and sick-ness, we sigh, and groan, and pray.
bring down God's grace and bless-ings and help in hour of need.
re-demp-tion's work com-plet-ed, our bat-tle fought, and won.

All Hail the Power of Jesus' Name **301**

Edward Perronet, 1779
t. John Rippon, 1787

CORONATION
CM

Oliver Holden, 1793

1. All hail the pow'r of Je - sus' name! Let an - gels pros - trate fall;
2. Ye cho - sen seed of Is - rael's race, ye ran - somed from the fall,
3. Crown Him, ye mar - tyrs of your God, who from His al - tar call;
4. Let eve - ry kin - dred, eve - ry tribe on this ter - res - trial ball
5. O that with yon - der sa - cred throng we at His feet may fall!

bring forth the roy - al di - a - dem, and crown Him Lord of all!
hail Him who saves you by His grace, and crown Him Lord of all!
ex - tol the stem of Jes - se's rod, and crown Him Lord of all!
to Him all maj - es - ty as - cribe, and crown Him Lord of all!
We'll join the ev - er - last - ing song, and crown Him Lord of all!

Bring forth the roy - al di - a - dem, and crown Him Lord of all!
Hail Him who saves you by His grace, and crown Him Lord of all!
Ex - tol the stem of Jes - se's rod, and crown Him Lord of all!
To Him all maj - es - ty as - cribe, and crown Him Lord of all!
We'll join the ev - er - last - ing song, and crown Him Lord of all!

302 All Hail the Power of Jesus' Name

Edward Perronet, 1779
and John Rippon, 1787

DIADEM
86 68 with refrain

James Ellor, 183?

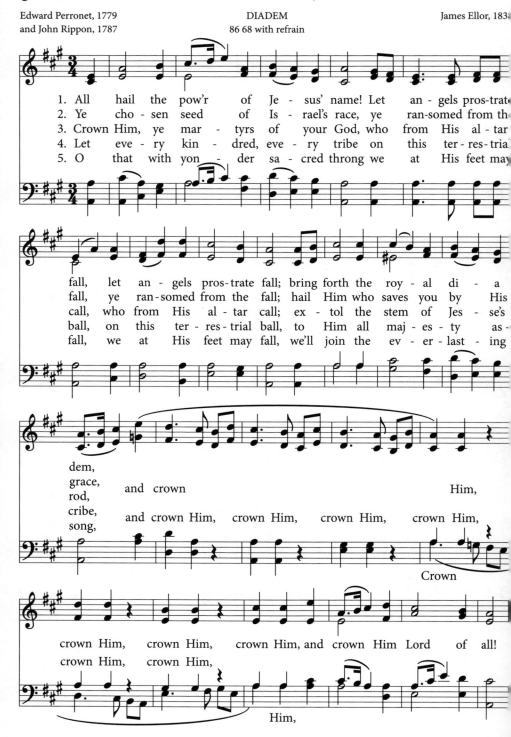

1. All hail the pow'r of Je - sus' name! Let an - gels pros-trate
2. Ye cho - sen seed of Is - rael's race, ye ran-somed from the
3. Crown Him, ye mar - tyrs of your God, who from His al - tar
4. Let eve - ry kin - dred, eve - ry tribe on this ter - res - trial
5. O that with yon - der sa - cred throng we at His feet may

fall, let an - gels pros-trate fall; bring forth the roy - al di - a
fall, ye ran-somed from the fall; hail Him who saves you by His
call, who from His al - tar call; ex - tol the stem of Jes - se's
ball, on this ter - res - trial ball, to Him all maj - es - ty as -
fall, we at His feet may fall, we'll join the ev - er - last - ing

dem,
grace,
rod,   and crown   Him,
cribe,
song,   and crown Him, crown Him, crown Him, crown Him,

Crown

crown Him, crown Him, crown Him, and crown Him Lord of all!
crown Him, crown Him,

Him,

Lord, Enthroned in Heavenly Splendor **303**

George H. Bourne, 1874   LAUDA ANIMA   John Goss, 1869
87 87 87

1. Lord, en-throned in heav'n-ly splen - dor, first - be - got - ten
2. Prince of Life, for us Thou liv - est, by Thy bod - y
3. Pas - chal Lamb! Thine off - 'ring fin - ished once for all when
4. Great High Priest of our pro - fes - sion, thro' the veil Thou
5. Life im - part - ing heav'n-ly Man - na, strick - en Rock, with

from the dead, Thou a - lone, our strong De - fend - er,
souls are healed; Prince of Peace, Thy peace Thou giv - est,
Thou wast slain, in its full - ness un - dim - in - ished
en - t'redst in; by Thy might - y in - ter - ces - sion
stream-ing side, heav'n and earth with loud ho - san - na

lift - est up Thy peo - ple's head. Hal - le - lu - jah!
by Thy blood is par - don sealed. Hal - le - lu - jah!
shall for - ev - er - more re - main. Hal - le - lu - jah!
grace and mer - cy Thou dost win. Hal - le - lu - jah!
wor - ship Thee, the Lamb who died. Hal - le - lu - jah!

Hal - le - lu - jah! Je - sus, true and liv - ing Bread!
Hal - le - lu - jah! Word of God in flesh re - vealed.
Hal - le - lu - jah! Cleans - ing souls from eve - ry stain.
Hal - le - lu - jah! On - ly sac - ri - fice for sin.
Hal - le - lu - jah! Ris'n, as - cend - ed, glo - ri - fied!

304 Jesus, the Name High over All

Charles Wesley, 1749

HIGH OVER ALL
CMD

Scottish a

1. Je - sus, the Name high o - ver all, in hell or earth or sky;
2. O that the world might taste and see the rich - es of His grace!
3. His on - ly right - eous - ness I show, His sav - ing truth pro - claim;

an - gels and mor - tals pros - trate fall, and dev - ils fear and fly.
The arms of love that com - pass me would all the world em - brace.
'tis all my busi - ness here be - low to cry, "Be - hold the Lamb!"

Je - sus, the Name to sin - ners dear, the Name to sin - ners giv'n;
Thee I shall con - stant - ly pro - claim, tho' earth and hell op - pose;
Hap - py, if with my lat - est breath I may but gasp His Name,

it scat - ters all their guilt - y fear, it turns their hell to heav'n.
bold to con - fess Thy glo - rious Name be - fore a world of foes.
preach Him to all, and cry in death, "Be - hold, be - hold the Lamb!"

Majestic Sweetness Sits Enthroned 305

Samuel Stennett, 1787   ORTONVILLE   Thomas Hastings, 1837
CM with repeat

1. Ma - jes - tic sweet - ness sits en - throned up - on the
2. No mor - tal can with Him com - pare, a - mong the
3. He saw me plunged in deep dis - tress, and flew to
4. To Him I owe my life and breath, and all the

Sav - ior's brow; His head with ra - diant glo - ries crowned,
sons of men; fair - er is He than all the fair
my re - lief; for me He bore the shame - ful cross,
joys I have; He makes me tri - umph o - ver death,

His lips with grace o'er - flow, His lips with grace o'er - flow.
who fill the heav'n - ly train, who fill the heav'n - ly train.
and car - ried all my grief, and car - ried all my grief.
and saves me from the grave, and saves me from the grave.

306 Crown Him With Many Crowns

Matthew Bridges, 1851
and Godfrey Thring, 1874

DIADEMATA
SMD

George Elvey, 1868

1. Crown Him with man - y crowns, the Lamb up - on His throne;
2. Crown Him the Lord of love; be - hold His hands and side,
3. Crown Him the Lord of life, who tri - umphed o'er the grave,
4. Crown Him the Lord of heav'n: One with the Fa - ther known,
5. Crown Him the Son of God, be - fore the worlds be - gan,

hark, how the heav'n - ly an - them drowns all mu - sic but its own!
rich wounds, yet vis - i - ble a - bove, in beau - ty glo - ri - fied.
who rose vic - to - rious in the strife for those He came to save.
One with the Spir - it through Him giv'n from yon - der glo - rious throne.
and ye who tread where He hath trod, crown Him the Son of Man.

A - wake, my soul, and sing of Him who died for thee,
No an - gel in the sky can ful - ly bear that sight,
His glo - ries now we sing, who died and rose on high,
To Thee be end - less praise, for Thou for us hast died.
All hail, Re - deem - er, hail; for Thou hast died for me;

and hail Him as thy match - less King through all e - ter - ni - ty.
but down - ward bends his won - d'ring eye at mys - ter - ies so bright.
who died e - ter - nal life to bring, and lives that death may die.
Be Thou, O Lord, through end - less days a - dored and mag - ni - fied!
Thy praise and glo - ry shall not fail through - out e - ter - ni - ty!

Come, Christians, Join to Sing

307

William E. Hickson, 1836
adapt. Christian Bateman, 1843

MADRID
66 66 D

Traditional Spanish melody, 18th cent.
arr. David Evans, 1927

1. Come, Chris-tians, join to sing, Al - le - lu - ia, A - men!
2. Come, lift your hearts on high, Al - le - lu - ia, A - men!
3. Praise yet our Christ a - gain, Al - le - lu - ia, A - men!

Loud praise to Christ our King, Al - le - lu - ia, A - men!
Let prais - es fill the sky, Al - le - lu - ia, A - men!
Life shall not end the strain, Al - le - lu - ia, A - men!

Let all, with heart and voice, be - fore His throne re - joice;
He is our Guide and Friend, to us He'll con - de - scend;
On heav - en's bliss - ful shore, His good - ness we'll a - dore,

praise is His gra-cious choice, Al - le - lu - ia, A - men!
His love shall nev - er end, Al - le - lu - ia, A - men!
sing - ing for - ev - er - more, "Al - le - lu - ia, A - men!"

308 Come Down, O Love Divine

Bianco da Siena, d. 1434
trans. Richard Frederick Littledale, Jr., 1867, alt.

DOWN AMPNEY
66 65 D

English folk tune
harm. Ralph Vaughan Williams, 1906

1. Come down, O Love di - vine, seek Thou this soul of mine,
2. O let it free - ly burn, till earth - ly pas - sions turn
3. Let ho - ly char - i - ty mine out-ward ves - ture be,
4. And so the yearn - ing strong, with which the soul will long,

and vis - it it with Thine own ar - dor glow - ing;
to dust and ash - es in its heat con - sum - ing;
and low - li - ness be - come mine in - ner cloth - ing;
shall far out - pass the pow'r of hu - man tell - ing;

O Com - fort - er, draw near, with - in my heart ap - pear,
and let Thy glo - rious light shine ev - er on my sight,
true low - li - ness of heart, which takes the hum - bler part,
no soul can guess its grace, till he be - come the place

and kin - dle it, Thy ho - ly flame be - stow - ing.
and clothe me 'round, the while my path il - lum - ing.
and o'er its own short - com - ings weeps with loath - ing.
where - in the Ho - ly Spir - it makes His dwell - ing.

Spirit of God, Descend upon My Heart **309**

George Croly, 1867, alt.

MORECAMBE
10 10 10 10

Frederick C. Arkinson, 1870

1. Spir - it of God, de - scend up - on my heart,
2. I ask no dream, no proph - et ec - sta - sies,
3. Hast Thou not bid us love Thee, God and King;
4. Teach me to feel that Thou art al - ways nigh.
5. Teach me to love Thee as Thine an - gels love,

wean it from earth, through all its puls - es move.
no sud - den rend - ing of the veil of clay,
all, all Thine own— soul, heart, and strength, and mind?
Teach me the strug - gles of the soul to bear,
one ho - ly pas - sion fill - ing all my frame;

Stoop to my weak - ness, might - y as Thou art,
no an - gel vis - i - tant, no op'n - ing skies,
I see Thy cross; there teach my heart to cling.
to check the ris - ing doubt, the reb - el sigh.
the kin - dling of the heav'n - de - scend - ed Dove,

and make me love Thee as I ought to love.
but take the dim - ness of my soul a - way.
O let me seek Thee, and O let me find!
Teach me the pa - tience of un - an - swered prayer.
my heart an al - tar, and Thy love its flame.

310   Not All the Outward Forms on Earth

Isaac Watts, 1706   VOX DILECTI   John B. Dykes, 1868
                 CMD

1. Not all the out-ward forms on earth, nor rites that God has giv'n,
2. The Spir-it, like some heav'n-ly wind, blows on the sons of flesh,

nor will of man, nor blood, nor birth, can raise a soul to heav'n.
new mod-els all the car-nal mind, and forms the man a-fresh.

The sov-'reign will of God a-lone cre-ates us heirs of grace
Our quick-ened souls a-wake, and rise from the long sleep of death;

born in the im-age of His Son, a new, pe-cu-liar race.
on heav'n-ly things we fix our eyes, and praise em-ploys our breath.

Come, Holy Spirit, Heavenly Dove

311

Isaac Watts, 1707

ST. AGNES
CM

John B. Dykes, 1866

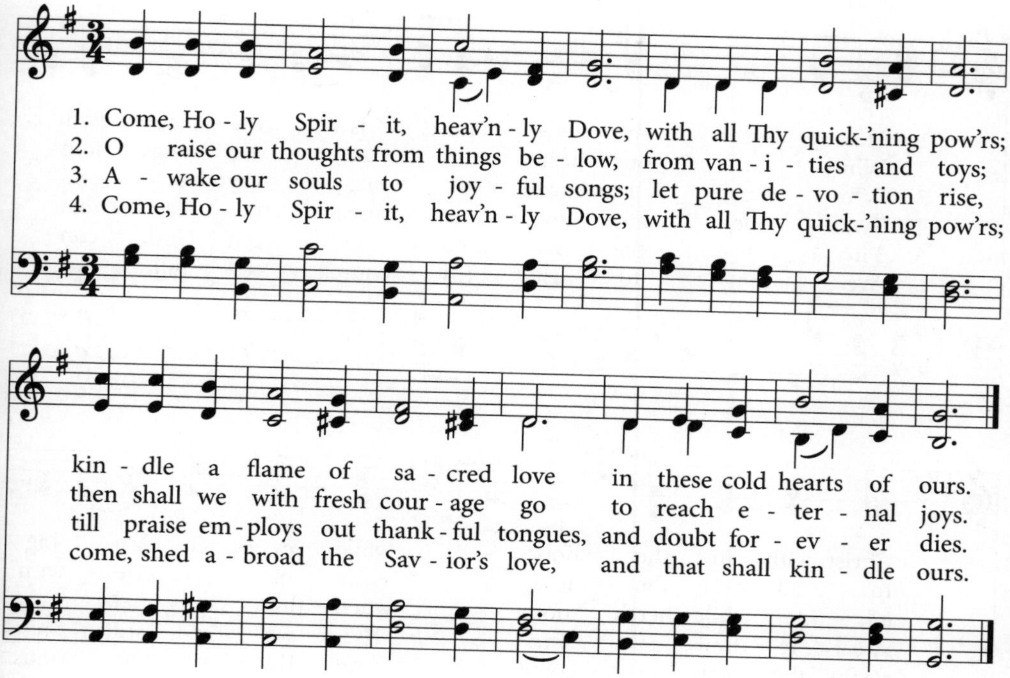

1. Come, Ho - ly Spir - it, heav'n - ly Dove, with all Thy quick-'ning pow'rs;
2. O raise our thoughts from things be - low, from van - i - ties and toys;
3. A - wake our souls to joy - ful songs; let pure de - vo - tion rise,
4. Come, Ho - ly Spir - it, heav'n - ly Dove, with all Thy quick-'ning pow'rs;

kin - dle a flame of sa - cred love in these cold hearts of ours.
then shall we with fresh cour - age go to reach e - ter - nal joys.
till praise em - ploys out thank - ful tongues, and doubt for - ev - er dies.
come, shed a - broad the Sav - ior's love, and that shall kin - dle ours.

312 How Sweet and Awful Is the Place

Isaac Watts, 1707, alt.

ST. COLUMBA
CM

Irish melody
harm. *The English Hymnal*, 1906

1. How sweet and aw - ful is the place with
2. While all our hearts and all our songs join
3. "Why was I made to hear Thy voice and
4. 'Twas the same love that spread the feast that
5. Pit - y the na - tions, O our God, con -
6. We long to see Thy church - es full, that

Christ with - in the doors, while ev - er - last - ing
to ad - mire the feast, each of us cries, with
en - ter while there's room, when thou - sands make a
sweet - ly drew us in; else we had still re -
strain the earth to come; send Thy vic - to - rious
all the chos - en race may, with one voice and

love dis - plays the choic - est of her stores.
thank - ful tongues, "Lord, why was I a guest?"
wretch - ed choice and rath - er starve than come?
fused to taste, and per - ished in our sin.
Word a - broad, and bring the stran - gers home.
heart and soul, sing Thy re - deem - ing grace.

Arise, My Soul, Arise

arles Wesley, 1742   LENOX   Lewis Edson, 1782
66 66 888

1. A - rise, my soul, a - rise,   shake off thy guilt - y fears.
2. He ev - er lives a - bove,   for me to in - ter - cede;
3. Five bleed-ing wounds He bears,   re - ceived on Cal - va - ry;
4. The Fa - ther hears Him pray,   His dear A - noint - ed One;
5. My God is rec - on - ciled,   His par-d'ning voice I hear;

The bleed - ing Sac - ri - fice   in my be - half ap - pears.
His all - re - deem - ing love,   His pre - cious blood to plead.
they pour ef - fec - tual prayers,   they strong - ly plead for me.
He can - not turn a - way   the pres - ence of His Son.
He owns me for a child,   I can no long - er fear.

Be - fore the throne my Sure - ty stands, be - fore the throne my
His blood a - toned for all our race, His blood a - toned for
"For - give him, O, for - give," they cry; "For - give him, O, for -
His Spir - it an - swers to the blood, His Spir - it an - swers
With con - fi - dence I now draw nigh, with con - fi - dence I

Sure - ty stands; my name is writ - ten on His hands.
all our race, and sprin - kles now the throne of grace.
give," they cry, "Nor let that ran - somed sin - ner die!"
to the blood, and tells me I am born of God.
now draw nigh, and, "Fa - ther, Ab - ba, Fa - ther," cry.

314 Amazing Grace! How Sweet the Sound

st. 1–5 John Newton, 1779
st. 6 anon.

NEW BRITAIN
CM

Columbian Harmony, 18

1. A - maz - ing grace! how sweet the sound that
2. 'Twas grace that taught my heart to fear, and
3. Through man - y dan - gers, toils, and snares, I
4. The Lord has prom - ised good to me, His
5. The earth shall soon dis - solve like snow; the
6. When we've been there ten thou - sand years, bright

saved a wretch like me! I once was lost, but
grace my fears re - lieved; how pre - cious did that
have al - read - y come; 'tis grace has brought me
Word my hope se - cures; He will my Shield and
sun for - bear to shine; but God, who called me
shin - ing as the sun, we've no less days to

now am found, was blind, but now I see.
grace ap - pear the hour I first be - lieved
safe thus far, and grace will lead me home
Por - tion be as long as life en - dures
here be - low, will be for - ev - er mine.
sing God's praise than when we'd first be - gun.

Here Is Love

315

1–2 William Rees, 1855
ns. William Edwards
3 attr. William Williams, 1744

CYMRAEG
87 87 D

Robert Lowry, 1876

1. Here is love, vast as the o-cean, lov-ing-kind-ness as the flood:
2. On the mount of cru-ci-fix-ion, foun-tains o-pened deep and wide;
3. In Thy truth Thou dost di-rect me by Thy Spir-it through Thy word;

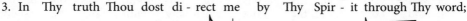

when the Prince of Life, our Ran-som, shed for us His pre-cious blood.
through the flood-gates of God's mer-cy flowed a vast and gra-cious tide.
and Thy grace my need is meet-ing as I trust in Thee, my Lord.

Who His love will not re-mem-ber? Who can cease to sing His praise?
Grace and love, like might-y riv-ers, poured in-ces-sant from a-bove,
Of Thy full-ness Thou art pour-ing Thy great love and pow'r on me

He can nev-er be for-got-ten through-out heav'ns e-ter-nal days.
and heav'n's peace and per-fect jus-tice kissed a guilt-y world in love.
with-out mea-sure, full and bound-less, draw-ing out my heart to Thee.

316   It Is Well with My Soul

Horatio G. Spafford, 1876   VILLE DU HAVRE   Philip P. Bliss, 18

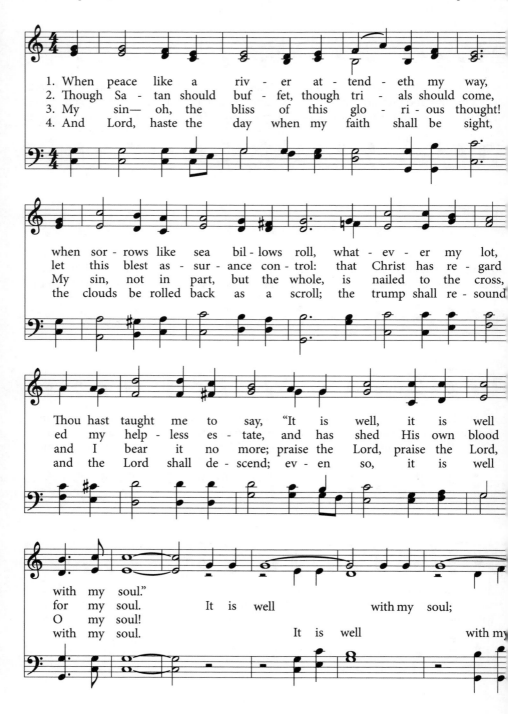

1. When peace like a riv - er at - tend - eth my way,
2. Though Sa - tan should buf - fet, though tri - als should come,
3. My sin— oh, the bliss of this glo - ri - ous thought!
4. And Lord, haste the day when my faith shall be sight,

when sor - rows like sea bil - lows roll, what - ev - er my lot,
let this blest as - sur - ance con - trol: that Christ has re - gard
My sin, not in part, but the whole, is nailed to the cross,
the clouds be rolled back as a scroll; the trump shall re - sound

Thou hast taught me to say, "It is well, it is well
ed my help - less es - tate, and has shed His own blood
and I bear it no more; praise the Lord, praise the Lord,
and the Lord shall de - scend; ev - en so, it is well

with my soul."
for my soul.   It is well   with my soul;
O my soul!
with my soul.   It is well   with my

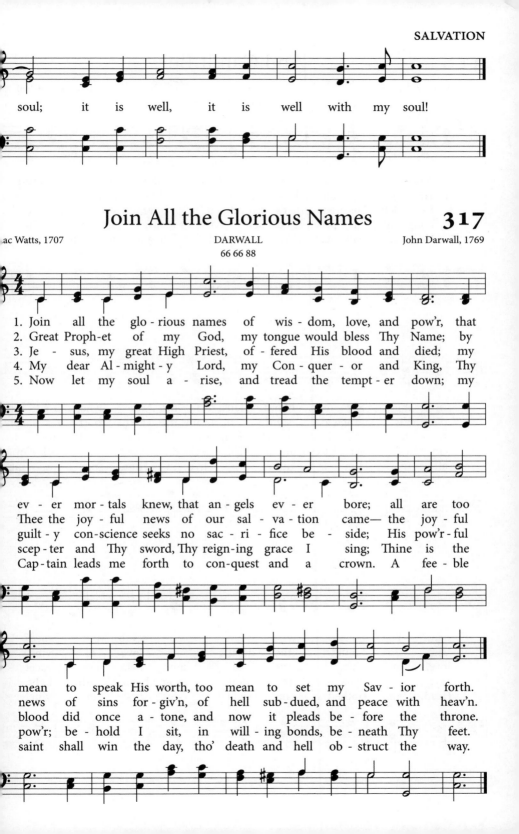

soul; it is well, it is well with my soul!

Join All the Glorious Names

317

...ac Watts, 1707

DARWALL
66 66 88

John Darwall, 1769

1. Join all the glo - rious names of wis - dom, love, and pow'r, that
2. Great Proph-et of my God, my tongue would bless Thy Name; by
3. Je - sus, my great High Priest, of - fered His blood and died; my
4. My dear Al - might - y Lord, my Con - quer - or and King, Thy
5. Now let my soul a - rise, and tread the tempt - er down; my

ev - er mor - tals knew, that an - gels ev - er bore; all are too
Thee the joy - ful news of our sal - va - tion came— the joy - ful
guilt - y con-science seeks no sac - ri - fice be - side; His pow'r-ful
scep - ter and Thy sword, Thy reign-ing grace I sing; Thine is the
Cap-tain leads me forth to con-quest and a crown. A fee - ble

mean to speak His worth, too mean to set my Sav - ior forth.
news of sins for - giv'n, of hell sub - dued, and peace with heav'n.
blood did once a - tone, and now it pleads be - fore the throne.
pow'r; be - hold I sit, in will - ing bonds, be - neath Thy feet.
saint shall win the day, tho' death and hell ob - struct the way.

318 And Can It Be

Charles Wesley, 1738, alt. SAGINA Thomas Campbell, 18

88 88 88 with refrain

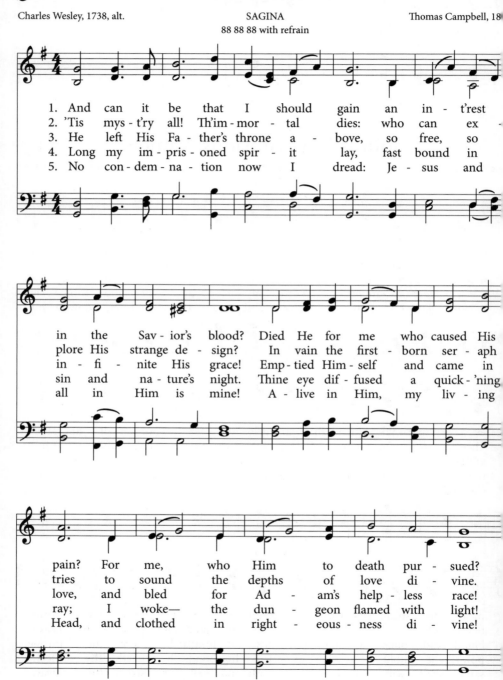

1. And can it be that I should gain an in - t'rest
2. 'Tis mys - t'ry all! Th'im - mor - tal dies: who can ex -
3. He left His Fa - ther's throne a - bove, so free, so
4. Long my im - pris - oned spir - it lay, fast bound in
5. No con - dem - na - tion now I dread: Je - sus and

in the Sav - ior's blood? Died He for me who caused His
plore His strange de - sign? In vain the first - born ser - aph
in - fi - nite His grace! Emp - tied Him - self and came in
sin and na - ture's night. Thine eye dif - fused a quick - 'ning
all in Him is mine! A - live in Him, my liv - ing

pain? For me, who Him to death pur - sued?
tries to sound the depths of love di - vine.
love, and bled for Ad - am's help - less race!
ray; I woke— the dun - geon flamed with light!
Head, and clothed in right - eous - ness di - vine!

A - maz - ing love! how can it be that Thou,
'Tis mer - cy all! Let earth a - dore, let an - -
'Tis mer - cy all, im - mense and free, O praise
My chains fell off, my heart was free; I rose,
Bold I ap - proach the e - ter - nal throne, and claim

my God, shouldst die for me?
gel minds in - quire no more.
my God, it found out me. A - maz - ing love!
went forth, and fol - lowed Thee.
the crown through Christ my own!

how can it be that Thou, my God, shouldst die for me!

319 One There Is, Above All Others

John Newton, 1779   GODESBERG   Heinrich Albert, 1643
                              87 87 77

1. One there is, a - bove all oth - ers, well de - serves the
2. Which of all our friends to save us, could or would have
3. Men, when raised to loft - y sta - tions, of - ten know their
4. When He lived on earth a - bas - ed, Friend of sin - ners
5. Could we bear from one an - oth - er, what He dai - ly
6. O for grace our hearts to soft - en! Teach us, Lord, at

name of Friend; His is love be - yond a broth - er's,
shed their blood? But our Je - sus died to have us
friends no more; slight and scorn their poor re - la - tions
was His name; now, a - bove all glo - ry rais - ed,
bears from us? Yet this glo - rious Friend and Broth - er
length to love; we, a - las! for - get too of - ten

cost - ly, free, and knows no end; they who once His
rec - on - ciled in Him to God; this was bound - less
though they val - ued them be - fore. But our Sav - ior
He re - joic - es in the same; still He calls them
loves us though we treat Him thus; though for good we
what a Friend we have a - bove; but when home our

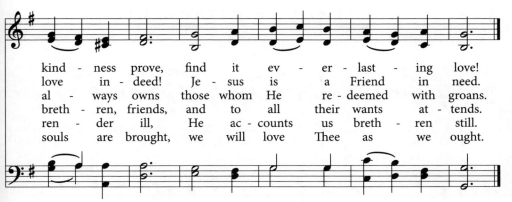

kind - ness prove, find it ev - er - last - ing love!
love in - deed! Je - sus is a Friend in need.
al - ways owns those whom He re - deemed with groans.
breth - ren, friends, and to all their wants at - tends.
ren - der ill, He ac - counts us breth - ren still.
souls are brought, we will love Thee as we ought.

Praise the Savior, Ye Who Know Him **320**

Thomas Kelly, 1806   ACCLAIM   Traditional German melody
888 5

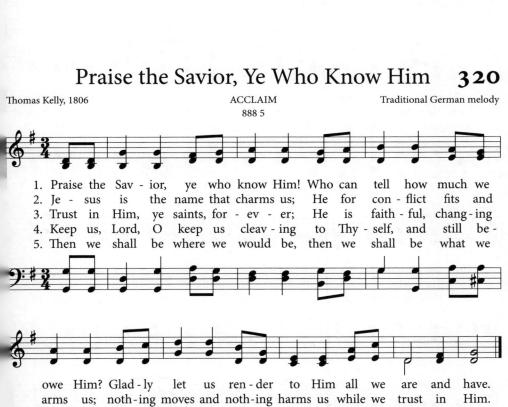

1. Praise the Sav - ior, ye who know Him! Who can tell how much we
2. Je - sus is the name that charms us; He for con - flict fits and
3. Trust in Him, ye saints, for - ev - er; He is faith - ful, chang - ing
4. Keep us, Lord, O keep us cleav - ing to Thy - self, and still be -
5. Then we shall be where we would be, then we shall be what we

owe Him? Glad - ly let us ren - der to Him all we are and have.
arms us; noth - ing moves and noth - ing harms us while we trust in Him.
nev - er; nei - ther force nor guile can sev - er those He loves from Him.
liev - ing, till the hour of our re - ceiv - ing prom - ised joys with Thee.
should be; things that are not now, nor could be, soon shall be our own.

321   O the Deep, Deep Love of Jesus

S. Trevor Francis, 1898   EBENEZER   Thomas J. Williams, 1897
                        87 87 D

1. O the deep, deep love of Je-sus, vast, un-meas-ured, bound-less, free,
2. O the deep, deep love of Je-sus, spread His praise from shore to shore!
3. O the deep, deep love of Je-sus, love of eve-ry love the best;

roll-ing as a might-y o-cean in its full-ness o-ver me.
How He lov-eth, ev-er lov-eth, chang-eth nev-er, nev-er-more!
'tis an o-cean vast of bless-ing, 'tis a ha-ven sweet of rest.

Un-der-neath me, all a-round me, is the cur-rent of Thy love;
How He watch-eth o'er His loved ones, died to call them all His own;
O the deep, deep love of Je-sus, 'tis a heav'n of heav'ns to me;

lead-ing on-ward, lead-ing home-ward, to Thy glo-rious rest a-bove.
how for them He in-ter-ced-eth, watch-eth o'er them from the throne
and it lifts me up to glo-ry, for it lifts me up to Thee.

I Sought the Lord

Jean Ingelow, 1878

PEACE
10 10 10 6

George W. Chadwick, 1893

1. I sought the Lord, and af-ter-ward I knew He moved my
2. Thou didst reach forth Thy hand and mine en-fold; I walked and
3. I find, I walk, I love, but O, the whole of love is

soul to seek Him, seek-ing me; it was not I that
sank not on the storm-vexed sea; 'twas not so much that
but my an-swer, Lord, to Thee! For Thou wert long be -

found, O Sav-ior true; no, I was found of Thee.
I on Thee took hold, as Thou, dear Lord, on me.
fore-hand with my soul, al-ways Thou lov-edst me.

323 Praises for Thy Glorious Grace

Ephesians 1:3–14
Mark Minnick © 2001

MT. CALVARY
87 87 with refrain

Joan J. Pinkston © 2001

1. God and Fa-ther of our Sav-ior, praise for glo-ries of Thy grace,
2. Cho-sen sin-ners long pre-des-tined to be ho-ly, blame-less still,
3. Thine own Son, love's dear Re-deem-er, ran-som's price His pre-cious blood;
4. Mys-t'ry of e-ter-nal wis-dom, Thy good pleas-ure now made known;
5. Thou, in-tent Thine heirs to make us, work-est all things to this will,
6. Bless Thee for Thy prom-ised Spir-it, Ho-ly Spir-it, Chris-tians' Seal,

eve-ry bless-ing pur-posed fa-vor, grant-ed in Thy Son's em-brace.
made Thy sons by love un-fath-omed. Oh, the kind-ness of Thy will!
sins for-giv-en for the treas-ure of that age-less, cleans-ing flood.
heav'n and earth's en-tire cre-a-tion bent be-neath Thy Son's bright throne.
that those hop-ing first in Je-sus might with praise the heav-ens fill.
Pledge we shall in Christ in-her-it what re-demp-tion shall re-veal!

God and Fa-ther, we would bless Thee; help us praise Thee in this place.

Hal-le-

Hal-le-lu-jah, bless-ed Fa-ther, prais-es for Thy glo-rious grace.

lu, hal-le-lu-jah,

A Good High Priest Is Come

324

John Cennick, 1744

MILLENNIUM
66 66 88

English melody
Plymouth Collection of Hymns and Tunes, 1855

1. A good High Priest is come, sup - ply - ing Aar - on's place,
2. He once temp - ta - tions knew of eve - ry sort and kind,
3. He died, but lives a - gain, and by the throne He stands,
4. I oth - er priests dis - claim, and laws and off - 'rings too;

and tak - ing up his room, dis - pens - ing life and grace;
that He might suc - cor show to eve - ry temp - ted mind;
there shows how He was slain, op - 'ning His pierc - éd hands;
none but the bleed - ing Lamb the might - y work can do;

the law by Aar - on's priest - hood came,
in eve - ry point the Lamb was tried
our Priest a - - bides and pleads the cause
He shall have all the praise: for He

but grace and truth by Je - sus' name.
like us, and then for us He died.
of us who have trans - gressed His laws.
has loved, and died, and lives for me.

325 Not What These Hands Have Done

Horatius Bonar, 1861

TERRA BEATA
SMD

English folk melody
adapt. Franklin L. Sheppard, 1915

1. Not what these hands have done can save this guilt - y soul;
2. Thy work a - lone, O Christ, can ease this weight of sin;
3. Thy grace a - lone, O God, to me can par - don speak;

not what this toil - ing flesh has borne can make my spir - it whole.
Thy blood a - lone, O Lamb of God, can give me peace with - in.
Thy pow'r a - lone, O Son of God, can this sore bon - dage break.

Not what I feel or do can give me peace with God;
Thy love to me, O God, not mine, O Lord, to Thee,
I bless the Christ of God; I rest on love di - vine;

not all my prayers and sighs and tears can bear my aw - ful load.
can rid me of this dark un - rest, and set my spir - it free.
and with un - fal - t'ring lip and heart, I call this Sav - ior mine.

Jesus, My Highest Treasure

Salomon Liscovius, 1672
Tr. Frederick William Foster, 1789

OSLO
76 76 D

Scandinavian folksong

1. Je - sus, my high - est treas - ure, in Thy com - mun - ion blest
2. O Joy, all joys ex - cel - ling, the Bread of Life Thou art,
3. O let my eyes be light - ened by sight of Thy dear face;
4. Earth's glo - ries to in - her - it is not what I de - sire;

I find un - fail - ing pleas - ure, true hap - pi - ness and rest;
Thou cam'st to make Thy dwell - ing in my un - wor - thy heart.
my life be - low be bright - ened by tast - ing of Thy grace;
to heav'n as - pires my spir - it, glow - ing with no - bler fire.

my - self a will - ing of - f'ring I give to Thee a - lone,
My spir - it's hun - gry crav - ing Thou canst for - ev - er still;
with - out Thee, might - y Sav - ior, to live is nought but pain;
Where Christ Him - self ap - pear - eth in bright - est maj - es - ty,

be - cause by death and suf - f'ring Thou didst for me a - tone.
from deep - est an - guish sav - ing, with bliss my cup canst fill.
to have Thy love and fa - vor is hap - pi - ness and gain.
for me a place pre - par - eth, there, there I long to be.

327 I Heard the Voice of Jesus Say

Horatius Bonar, 1850

KINGSFOLD
CMD

English County Songs, 189
harm. Ralph Vaughan Williams, 190

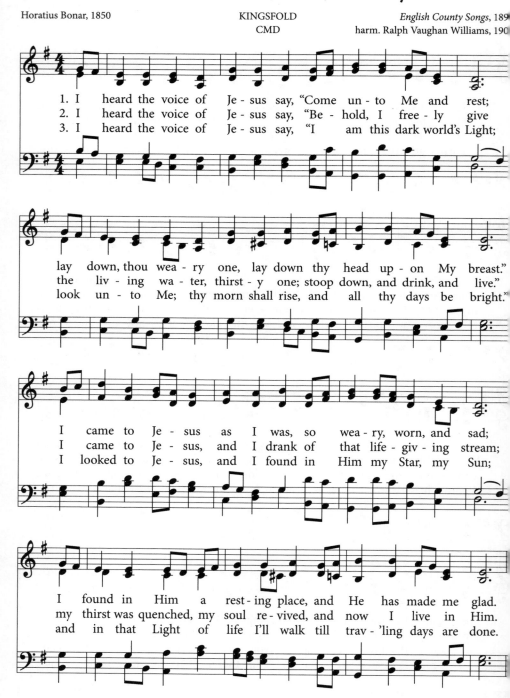

1. I heard the voice of Je - sus say, "Come un - to Me and rest;
2. I heard the voice of Je - sus say, "Be - hold, I free - ly give
3. I heard the voice of Je - sus say, "I am this dark world's Light;

lay down, thou wea - ry one, lay down thy head up - on My breast."
the liv - ing wa - ter, thirst - y one; stoop down, and drink, and live."
look un - to Me; thy morn shall rise, and all thy days be bright."

I came to Je - sus as I was, so wea - ry, worn, and sad;
I came to Je - sus, and I drank of that life - giv - ing stream;
I looked to Je - sus, and I found in Him my Star, my Sun;

I found in Him a rest - ing place, and He has made me glad;
my thirst was quenched, my soul re - vived, and now I live in Him.
and in that Light of life I'll walk till trav - 'ling days are done.

I Heard the Voice of Jesus Say

328

Horatius Bonar, 1846   THIRD MODE MELODY   Thomas Tallis, 1561
CMD

1. I heard the voice of Je-sus say, "Come un-to Me and rest;
2. I heard the voice of Je-sus say, "Be-hold, I free-ly give
3. I heard the voice of Je-sus say, "I am this dark world's Light;

lay down, thou wea-ry one, lay down thy head up-on My breast."
the liv-ing wa-ter; thirst-y one, stoop down, and drink, and live."
look un-to Me, thy morn shall rise, and all thy day be bright."

I came to Je-sus as I was, so wea-ry worn and sad;
I came to Je-sus, and I drank of that life-giv-ing stream;
I looked to Je-sus, and I found in Him my Star, my Sun;

I found in Him a rest-ing-place, and He has made me glad.
my thirst was quenched, my soul re-vived, and now I live in Him.
and in that Light of life I'll walk till trav-'ling days are done.

329 Before the Throne of God Above

Charitie Lees Smith
alternate lyrics by Vikki Cook © 1997

BEFORE THE THRONE
LMD

Vikki Cook © 1997

1. Be - fore the throne of God a - bove   I have a strong and per - fect
2. When Sa - tan tempts me to de - spair, and tells me of the guilt with-
3. Be - hold Him there, the ris - en Lamb! My per - fect, spot - less Right - eous -

plea,   a great High Priest whose name is "Love,"   who ev - er
in,   up - ward I   look   and   see Him there   who made an
ness;   the great un - change - a - ble I   AM,   the King of

lives and pleads for   me.   My name is grav - en   on His hands;
end to all   my   sin. Be - cause the sin - less   Sav - ior died,
glo - ry and of   grace! One with Him - self I   can - not die;

my name is   writ - ten   on His heart;   I know that
my sin - ful soul   is   count - ed free;   for God the
my soul is   pur - chased with His blood;   my life is

while in heav'n He stands, no tongue can bid me thence de -
Just is sat - is - fied to look on Him and par - don
hid with Christ on high, with Christ my Sav - ior and my

part; no tongue can bid me thence de - part.
me; to look on Him and par - don me.
God; with Christ my Sav - ior and my God!

Jesus, the Very Thought of Thee — 330

attr. Bernard of Clairvaux, 12th cent.
trans. Edward Caswall, 1849

ST. AGNES
CM

John B. Dykes, 1866

1. Je - sus, the ver - y thought of Thee with sweet-ness fills my breast;
2. No voice can sing, no heart can frame, nor can the mem-ory find
3. O hope of eve - ry con - trite heart, O joy of all the meek,
4. But what to those who find? Ah, this no tongue or pen can show;
5. Je - sus, our on - ly Joy be Thou, as Thou our Prize wilt be;

but sweet - er far Thy face to see, and in Thy pres - ence rest.
a sweet - er sound than Thy blest name, O Sav - ior of man - kind.
to those who fall, how kind Thou art! How good to those who seek!
the love of Je - sus, what it is, none but His loved ones know.
Je - sus, be Thou our Glo - ry now and through e - ter - ni - ty.

331 Ask Ye What Great Thing I Know

Johann Schwedler, 1741
trans. Benjamin Hall Kennedy, 1863

HENDON
77 77 7

Henri A. Malan, 1837
harm. Lowell Mason, 1841

1. Ask ye what great thing I know, that de-lights and stirs me so? What the high re-ward I win? Whose the name I glo-ry in? Je-sus Christ, the Cru-ci-fied.
2. Who de-feats my fier-cest foes? Who con-soles my sad-dest woes? Who re-vives my faint-ing heart, heal-ing all its hid-den smart? Je-sus Christ, the Cru-ci-fied.
3. Who is life in life to me? Who the death of death will be? Who will place me on His right, with the count-less hosts of light? Je-sus Christ, the Cru-ci-fied.
4. This is that great thing I know; this de-lights and stirs me so: faith in Him who died to save, Him who tri-umphed o'er the grave: Je-sus Christ, the Cru-ci-fied.

Jesus, Thy Blood and Righteousness

332

Nicolaus Ludwig von Zinzendorf, 1739
trans. John Wesley, 1740

GERMANY
LM

William Gardiner's *Sacred Melodies*, 1815

1. Je - sus, Thy blood and right - eous - ness my beau - ty
2. Bold shall I stand in Thy great day, for who aught
3. Lord, I be - lieve Thy pre - cious blood, which at the
4. Je - sus, be end - less praise to Thee, whose bound - less
5. When from the dust of death I rise to claim my
6. O let the dead now hear Thy voice; now bid Thy

are, my glo - rious dress; 'midst flam - ing worlds, in
to my charge shall lay? Ful - ly ab - solved through
mer - cy seat of God for - ev - er doth for
mer - cy hath for me, for me a full a -
man - sion in the skies, e'en then this shall be
ran - somed ones re - joice; their beau - ty this, their

these ar - rayed, with joy shall I lift up my head.
these I am, from sin and fear, from guilt and shame.
sin - ners plead, for me, e'en for my soul, was shed.
tone - ment made, an ev - er - last - ing ran - som paid.
all my plea, Je - sus hath lived, hath died, for me.
glo - rious dress, Je - sus, Thy blood and right - eous - ness.

333 I Will Sing of My Redeemer

Philip P. Bliss, 1876   HYFRYDOL   Rowland Prichard, 1844
87 87 D

1. I will sing of my Re-deem-er and His won-drous love to me.
2. I will tell the won-drous sto-ry how, my lost es-tate to save,
3. I will praise my dear Re-deem-er; His tri-um-phant pow'r I'll tell,
4. I will sing of my Re-deem-er and His heav'n-ly love to me;

On the cru-el cross He suf-fered, from the curse to set me free.
in His bound-less love and mer-cy, He the ran-som free-ly gave.
how the vic-to-ry He giv-eth o-ver sin and death and hell.
He from death to life hath brought me, Son of God, with Him to be!

Sing, O sing of my Re-deem-er, with His blood He pur-chased me.

On the cross He sealed my par - don, paid the debt and made me free.

Jesus! What a Friend for Sinners

334

J. Wilbur Chapman, 1910

HYFRYDOL
87 87 D

Rowland Prichard, 1844

1. Je - sus! what a Friend for sin - ners! Je - sus! Lov - er of my soul;
2. Je - sus! what a Strength in weak - ness! Let me hide my - self in Him;
3. Je - sus! what a Help in sor - row! While the bil - lows o'er me roll,
4. Je - sus! what a Guide and Keep - er! While the tem - pest still is high,
5. Je - sus! I do now re - ceive Him; more than all in Him I find;

friends may fail me, foes as - sail me; He, my Sav - ior, makes me whole.
tempt - ed, tried, and some-times fail - ing, He, my Strength, my vic - t'ry wins.
e - ven when my heart is break - ing, He, my Com - fort, helps my soul.
storms a - bout me, night o'er - takes me, He, my Pi - lot, hears my cry.
He hath grant - ed me for - give - ness: I am His, and He is mine!

Hal - le - lu - jah! what a Sav - ior! Hal - le - lu - jah! what a Friend!

Sav - ing, help - ing, keep - ing, lov - ing; He is with me to the end.

335 I Greet Thee, Who My Sure Redeemer Art

Strasbourg Psalter, 1545
TOULON
10 10 10 10
Genevan Psalter, 1551

1. I greet Thee, who my sure Re-deem-er art, my on-ly trust and Sav-ior of my heart, who pain didst un-der-go for my poor sake; I pray Thee from our hearts all cares to take.

2. Thou art the King of mer-cy and of grace, reign-ing om-nip-o-tent in eve-ry place: so come, O King, and our whole be-ing sway; shine on us with the light of Thy pure day.

3. Thou art the Life, by which a-lone we live, and all our sub-stance and our strength re-ceive; O com-fort us in death's ap-proach-ing hour, strong-heart-ed then to face it by Thy pow'r.

4. Thou hast the true and per-fect gen-tle-ness, no harsh-ness hast Thou and no bit-ter-ness: make us to taste the sweet grace found in Thee and ev-er stay in Thy sweet u-ni-ty.

5. Our hope is in no oth-er save in Thee; our faith is built up-on Thy prom-ise free; O grant to us such strong-er hope and sure that we can bold-ly con-quer and en-dure.

My God, I Love Thee

Attr. Francis Xavier, 16th cent.
trans. Edward Caswall, 1849, alt.

KINGSFOLD
CMD

English County Songs, 1893
harm. Ralph Vaughan Williams, 1906

1. My God, I love Thee, not be-cause I hope for heav'n there-by,
2. And griefs and tor-ments num-ber-less, and sweat of ag-o-ny,
3. Not with the hope of gain-ing aught, nor seek-ing a re-ward,

nor yet for fear that, lov-ing not, I might for-ev-er die.
e'en death it-self, and all for man who was Thine en-e-my.
but as Thy-self hast lov-ed me, O ev-er-lov-ing Lord!

But for that Thou didst all man-kind up-on the cross em-brace;
Then why, most lov-ing Je-sus Christ, should I not love Thee well?
E'en so I love Thee, and will love, and in Thy praise will sing,

for us didst bear the nails and spear, and man-i-fold dis-grace;
Not for the sake of win-ning heav'n, nor an-y fear of hell;
sole-ly be-cause Thou art my God, and my e-ter-nal King!

337 There Is a Fountain

William Cowper, 1772, alt.

CLEANSING FOUNTAIN
CM with refrain

Lowell Mason, 1831
with camp meeting refrain, ca. 1865

1. There is a foun-tain filled with blood, drawn from Im-man - uel's veins;
2. The dy - ing thief re - joiced to see that foun-tain in his day;
3. Dear dy - ing Lamb, Thy pre - cious blood shall nev - er lose its pow'r
4. E'er since by faith I saw the stream Thy flow-ing wounds sup - ply,
5. When this poor lisp-ing, stamm-'ring tongue lies si - lent in the grave,

and sin - ners plunged be - neath that flood lose all their guilt-y stains;
and there may I, though vile as he, wash all my sins a - way;
till all the ran - somed church of God be saved to sin no more;
re - deem - ing love has been my theme, and shall be till I die;
then in a no - bler, sweet - er song, I'll sing Thy pow'r to save;

lose all their guilt - y stains, lose all their guilt - y stains;
wash all my sins a - way, wash all my sins a - way;
be saved to sin no more, be saved to sin no more;
and shall be till I die, and shall be till I die;
I'll sing Thy pow'r to save, I'll sing Thy pow'r to save;

and sin - ners plunged be - neath that flood lose all their guilt-y stains.
and there may I, though vile as he, wash all my sins a - way.
till all the ran-somed church of God be saved to sin no more.
re - deem - ing love has been my theme, and shall be till I die.
then in a no - bler, sweet - er song, I'll sing Thy pow'r to save.

My Jesus, I Love Thee

William R. Featherston, 1862

GORDON
11 11 11 11

Adoniram Gordon, 1876

1. My Je - sus, I love Thee; I know Thou art mine; for Thee all the
2. I love Thee be - cause Thou hast first lov - èd me and pur - chased my
3. I'll love Thee in life, I will love Thee in death, and praise Thee as
4. In man - sions of glo - ry and end - less de - light, I'll ev - er a -

fol - lies of sin I re - sign; my gra - cious Re - deem - er, my
par - don on Cal - va - ry's tree; I love Thee for wear - ing the
long as Thou lend - est me breath; and say, when the death - dew lies
dore Thee in heav - en so bright; I'll sing with a glit - ter - ing

Sav - ior art Thou; if ev - er I loved Thee, my Je - sus, 'tis now.
thorns on Thy brow; if ev - er I loved Thee, my Je - sus, 'tis now.
cold on my brow: "If ev - er I loved Thee, my Je - sus, 'tis now."
crown on my brow: If ev - er I loved Thee, my Je - sus, 'tis now.

339 My Hope Is Built on Nothing Less

Edward Mote, 1797–1874   THE SOLID ROCK   William B. Bradbury, 1816–1868
88 88 88

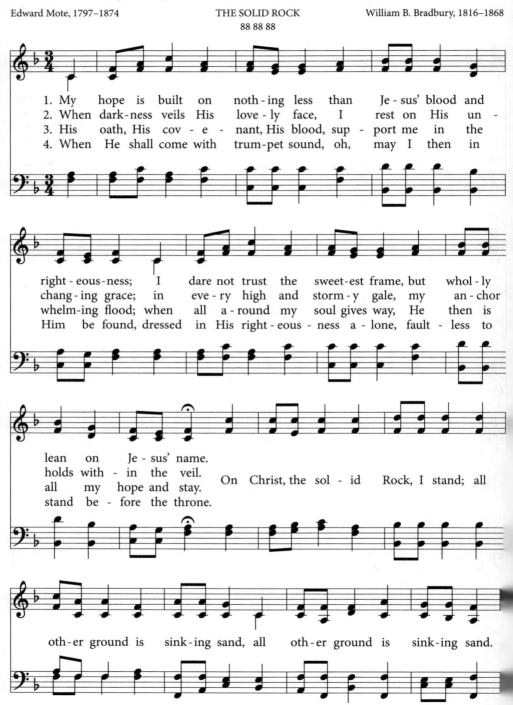

1. My hope is built on noth-ing less than Je-sus' blood and
2. When dark-ness veils His love-ly face, I rest on His un -
3. His oath, His cov-e - nant, His blood, sup - port me in the
4. When He shall come with trum-pet sound, oh, may I then in

right - eous-ness; I dare not trust the sweet-est frame, but whol-ly
chang-ing grace; in eve-ry high and storm-y gale, my an-chor
whelm-ing flood; when all a-round my soul gives way, He then is
Him be found, dressed in His right-eous-ness a-lone, fault-less to

lean on Je-sus' name.
holds with-in the veil.
all my hope and stay.   On Christ, the sol-id Rock, I stand; all
stand be-fore the throne.

oth-er ground is sink-ing sand, all oth-er ground is sink-ing sand.

How Deep the Father's Love for Us   **340**

Stuart Townend © 1995   TOWNEND   Stuart Townend © 1995

1. How deep the Fa-ther's love for us, how vast be-yond all mea - sure,
2. Be - hold the man up - on a cross, my sin up - on His shoul-ders;
3. I will not boast in an - y - thing, no gifts, no pow'r, no wis - dom;

that He should give His on - ly Son to make a wretch His treas - ure.
a - shamed, I hear my mock-ing voice call out a - mong the scoff - ers.
but I will boast in Je - sus Christ, His death and res - ur - rec - tion.

How great the pain of sear-ing loss— the Fa-ther turns His face a - way
It was my sin that held Him there un - til it was ac - com - plished;
Why should I gain from His re - ward? I can - not give an an - swer;

as wounds which mar the Cho - sen One bring man - y sons to glo - ry.
His dy - ing breath has brought me life— I know that it is fin - ished.
but this I know with all my heart— His wounds have paid my ran - som.

341 In Christ Alone

Keith Getty and Stuart Townend
© 2002 Thankyou Music

IN CHRIST ALONE

Keith Getty and Stuart Townend

1. In Christ a - lone my hope is found; He is my light, my strength, my
2. In Christ a - lone who took on flesh, full - ness of God in help - less
3. There in the ground His bod - y lay, Light of the world by dark - ness
4. No guilt in life, no fear in death: this is the pow'r of Christ in

song; this cor - ner - stone, this sol - id ground, firm through the
babe; this gift of love and right - eous - ness, scorned by the
slain. Then burst - ing forth in glo - rious day— up from the
me. From life's first cry to fi - nal breath, Je - sus com-

fierc - est drought and storm. What heights of love, what depths of
ones He came to save. Till on that cross as Je - sus
grave He rose a - gain! And as He stands in vic - to -
mands my des - ti - ny. No pow'r of hell, no scheme of

peace, when fears are stilled, when striv - ings cease! My com - for - ter,
died, the wrath of God was sat - is - fied. For ev - 'ry sin
ry, sin's curse has lost its grip on me. For I am His
man can ev - er pluck me from His hand. Till He re - turns

my all in all; here in the love of Christ I stand.
on Him was laid; here in the death of Christ I live.
and He is mine, bought with the pre-cious blood of Christ.
or calls me home, here in the pow'r of Christ I'll stand.

I Hear the Words of Love
342

Horatius Bonar, 1861

ST. MICHAEL
SM

Louis Bourgeois, 1543
adapt. William Crotch, 1836

1. I hear the words of love; I gaze up-on the blood;
2. 'Tis ev-er-last-ing peace, sure as Je-ho-vah's name;
3. The clouds may go and come, and storms may sweep my sky,
4. I change—He chang-es not; the Christ can nev-er die;
5. My love is oft-times low; my joy still ebbs and flows;

I see the might-y sac-ri-fice, and I have peace with God.
'tis sta-ble as His stead-fast throne, for-ev-er-more the same.
this blood-bought friend-ship chang-es not; the cross is ev-er nigh.
His love, not mine, the rest-ing place; His truth, not mine, the tie.
but peace with Him re-mains the same; no change Je-ho-vah knows.

343 The Power of the Cross

Stuart Townend and
Keith Getty © 2005

OH, TO SEE THE DAWN

Stuart Townend and
Keith Getty © 2005

1. Oh, to see the dawn of the dark - est day:
2. Oh, to see the pain writ - ten on Your face,
3. Now the day - light flees; now the ground be - neath
4. Oh, to see my name writ - ten in the wounds,

Christ on the road to Cal - va - ry. Tried by sin - ful
bear - ing the awe - some weight of sin. Eve - ry bit - ter
quakes as its Mak - er bows His head. Cur - tain torn in
for through Your suf - fering I am free! Death is crushed to

men, torn and beat - en, then nailed to a cross of
thought, eve - ry e - vil deed crown - ing Your blood-stained
two; dead are raised to life; "Fin - ished!" the vic - tory
death; life is mine to live, won through Your self - less

wood.
brow. 1-3. This the power of the cross:
cry. 4. This the power of the cross:
love!

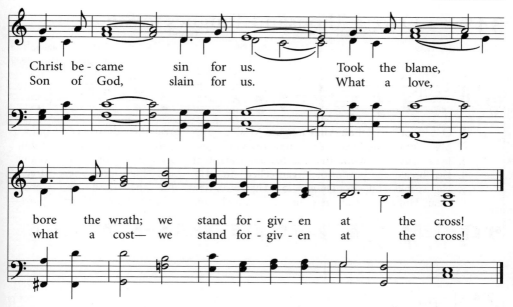

Christ be - came sin for us. Took the blame,
Son of God, slain for us. What a love,

bore the wrath; we stand for - giv - en at the cross!
what a cost— we stand for - giv - en at the cross!

Not All the Blood of Beasts 344

Isaac Watts, 1709   SOUTHWELL   William Daman, *The Psalmes of David*, 1579
SM

1. Not all the blood of beasts on Jew - ish al - tars slain
2. But Christ, the heav'n - ly Lamb, takes all our sins a - way;
3. My faith would lay her hand on that dear head of Thine,
4. My soul looks back to see the bur - den Thou didst bear
5. Be - liev - ing, we re - joice to see the curse re - move;

could give the guilt - y con - science peace or wash a - way the stain.
a Sac - ri - fice of nobl - er name and rich - er blood than they.
while like a pen - i - tent I stand, and there con - fess my sin.
when hang - ing on the curs - ed tree; I know my guilt was there.
we bless the Lamb with cheer - ful voice and sing His bleed - ing love.

345   O for a Thousand Tongues to Sing

Charles Wesley, 1739   AZMON   Carl G. Gläser, 1828
                 CM   arr. Lowell Mason, 1839

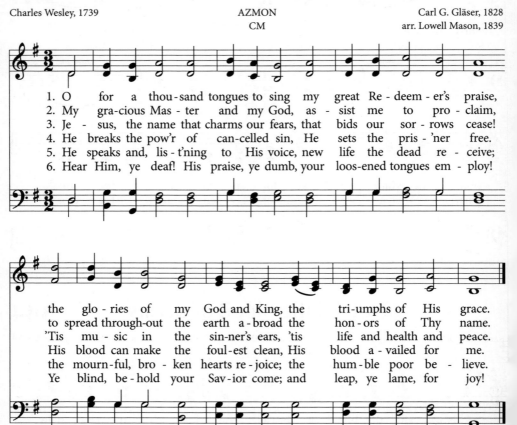

1. O   for   a   thou-sand tongues to sing   my   great Re - deem - er's   praise,
2. My   gra-cious Mas - ter   and my God, as - sist   me   to   pro - claim,
3. Je - sus, the name that charms our fears, that   bids our   sor - rows cease!
4. He breaks the pow'r of   can-celled sin, He   sets the   pris - 'ner   free.
5. He speaks and, lis - t'ning   to His voice, new   life the   dead   re - ceive;
6. Hear Him, ye deaf! His praise, ye dumb, your   loos-ened tongues em - ploy!

the   glo - ries of   my   God and King, the   tri-umphs of   His   grace.
to spread through-out   the   earth a - broad the   hon - ors of   Thy   name.
'Tis   mu - sic in   the   sin-ner's ears, 'tis   life and health and   peace.
His blood can make   the   foul-est clean, His   blood a - vailed for   me.
the mourn-ful, bro - ken hearts re - joice; the   hum - ble poor be - lieve.
Ye   blind, be - hold your   Sav-ior come; and   leap, ye lame, for   joy!

Blessed Jesus, at Thy Word

346

st. 1–3 Tobias Clausnitzer, 1663
trans. Catherine Winkworth, 1827–1878, alt.
st. 4 anon.

LIEBSTER JESU
78 78 88

Johann Rudolph Ahle, 1664
harm. Johann Sebastian Bach, 18th cent. alt.

1. Bless - ed Je - sus, at Thy Word we are gath - ered
2. All our know - ledge, sense, and sight lie in deep - est
3. Glo - rious Lord, Thy - self im - part! Light of Light, from
4. Fa - ther, Son, and Ho - ly Ghost, praise to Thee and

all to hear Thee; let our hearts and souls be stirred
dark - ness shroud - ed, till Thy Spir - it breaks our night
God pro - ceed - ing, o - pen Thou our ears and heart,
ad - o - ra - tion! Grant that we Thy Word may trust

now to seek and love and fear Thee; by Thy teach - ings
with the beams of truth un - cloud - ed; Thou a - lone to
help us by Thy Spir - it's plead - ing. Hear the cry Thy
and ob - tain true con - so - la - tion while we here be -

sweet and ho - ly, drawn from earth to love Thee sole - ly.
God canst win us; Thou must work all good with - in us.
peo - ple rais - es; hear, and bless our prayers and prais - es.
low must wan - der, till we sing Thy prais - es yon - der.

347 O Word of God Incarnate

William Walsham How, 1867

MUNICH
76 76 D

Neuvermehrtes Meiningisches Gesangbuch, 1689
adapt. Felix Mendelssohn, 1847

1. O Word of God in-car-nate, O Wis-dom from on high,
2. The church from her dear Mas-ter re-ceived the gift di-vine,
3. It float-eth like a ban-ner be-fore God's host un-furled;
4. O make Thy church, dear Sav-ior, a lamp of bur-nished gold,

O Truth un-changed, un-chang-ing, O Light of our dark sky,
and still that light she lift-eth o'er all the earth to shine.
it shin-eth like a bea-con a-bove the dark-ling world.
to bear be-fore the na-tions Thy true light as of old.

we praise Thee for the ra-diance that from the hal-lowed page,
It is the gold-en cas-ket, where gems of truth are stored;
It is the chart and com-pass that o'er life's surg-ing sea,
O teach Thy wan-d'ring pil-grims by this their path to trace,

a lan-tern to our foot-steps, shines on from age to age.
it is the heav'n-drawn pic-ture of Christ, the liv-ing Word.
'mid mists and rocks and quick-sands, still guides, O Christ, to Thee.
'til, clouds and dark-ness end-ed, they see Thee face to face.

Thy Word Is Like a Garden, Lord

348

Edwin Hodder, 1862

ELLACOMBE
CMD

Vollstandige-Sammlung, 1827
adapt. William Henry Monk, 1868

1. Thy Word is like a gar-den, Lord, with flow-ers bright and fair;
2. Thy Word is like a star-ry host: a thou-sand rays of light
3. O may I love Thy pre-cious Word, may I ex-plore the mine,

and eve-ry-one who seeks may pluck a love-ly clus-ter there.
are seen to guide the trav-el-er, and make his path-way bright.
may I its frag-rant flow-ers glean, may light up-on me shine.

Thy Word is like a deep, deep mine; and jew-els rich and rare
Thy Word is like an ar-mor-y, where sol-diers may re-pair,
O may I find my ar-mor there, Thy Word my trust-y sword;

are hid-den in its might-y depths for eve-ry search-er there.
and find, for life's long bat-tle day, all need-ful weap-ons there.
I'll learn to fight with eve-ry foe the bat-tle of the Lord.

349 How Firm a Foundation

"K" in John Rippon's *A Selection of Hymns*, 1787

FOUNDATION
11 11 11 11

A Compilation of Genuine Church Music, 1832

1. How firm a foun - da - tion, ye saints of the Lord,
2. "In eve - ry con - di - tion, in sick - ness, in health,
3. "Fear not, I am with thee, O be not dis - mayed,
4. "When through the deep wa - ters I call thee to go,
5. "When through fi - ery tri - als thy path - way shall lie,
6. "The soul that on Je - sus hath leaned for re - pose

is laid for your faith in His ex - cel - lent word!
in pov - er - ty's vale, or a - bound - ing in wealth,
for I am thy God and will still give thee aid.
the riv - ers of sor - row shall not o - ver - flow;
My grace, all - suf - fi - cient, shall be thy sup - ply.
I will not, I will not de - sert to his foes;

What more can He say than to you He has said,
at home and a - broad, on the land, on the sea,
I'll strength - en thee, help thee, and cause thee to stand,
for I will be with thee, thy trou - bles to bless,
The flame shall not hurt thee, I on - ly de - sign
that soul, though all hell should en - deav - or to shake,

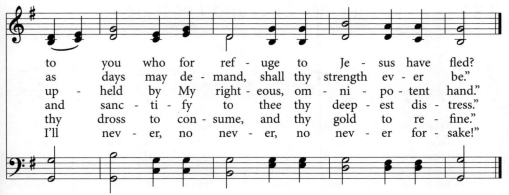

to   you   who   for   ref - uge   to   Je - sus have   fled?
as   days   may   de - mand, shall   thy   strength ev - er   be."
up - held by   My   right - eous, om - ni - po - tent hand."
and   sanc - ti - fy to   thee   thy   deep - est dis - tress."
thy   dross   to   con - sume,   and   thy   gold   to   re - fine."
I'll   nev - er, no   nev - er, no   nev - er for - sake!"

May the Mind of Christ, My Savior   **350**

Kate B. Wilkinson, 1925   ST. LEONARDS   A. Cyril Barham-Gould, 1925
                                        87 85

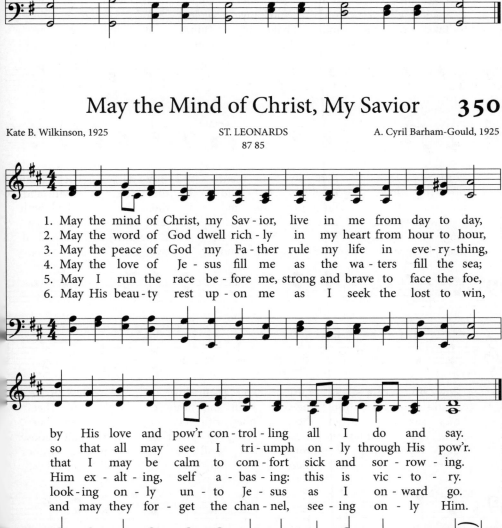

1. May the mind of Christ, my Sav - ior, live   in   me from day to day,
2. May the word of God dwell rich - ly   in   my heart from hour to hour,
3. May the peace of God my Fa - ther rule my life in eve - ry - thing,
4. May the love of Je - sus fill me   as   the wa - ters fill the sea;
5. May I   run the   race be - fore me, strong and brave to face the foe,
6. May His beau - ty rest up - on me   as   I   seek the lost to win,

by   His love and pow'r con - trol - ling   all   I   do and say.
so   that all may see   I   tri - umph   on - ly through His pow'r.
that I   may be   calm to com - fort sick and sor - row - ing.
Him ex - alt - ing, self a - bas - ing: this is   vic - to - ry.
look - ing on - ly   un - to Je - sus   as   I   on - ward go.
and may they for - get the chan - nel, see - ing on - ly Him.

351 Take My Life, and Let It Be

Frances R. Havergal, 1874   HENDON   Henri A. Malan, 1827
                                        77 77 with repeat

1. Take my life, and let it be con - se - crat - ed,
2. Take my hands and let them move at the im - pulse
3. Take my voice and let me sing al - ways, on - ly
4. Take my sil - ver and my gold; not a mite would
5. Take my will and make it Thine; it shall be no
6. Take my love— my Lord, I pour at Thy feet its

Lord, to Thee. Take my mo - ments and my days— let them
of Thy love. Take my feet and let them be swift and
for my King. Take my lips and let them be filled with
I with - hold. Take my in - tel - lect and use eve - ry
long - er mine. Take my heart— it is Thine own; it shall
treas - ure store. Take my - self, and I will be ev - er,

flow in cease - less praise, let them flow in cease - less praise.
beau - ti - ful for Thee, swift and beau - ti - ful for Thee.
mes - sag - es from Thee, filled with mes - sag - es from Thee.
pow'r as Thou shalt choose, eve - ry pow'r as Thou shalt choose.
be Thy roy - al throne, it shall be Thy roy - al throne.
on - ly, all for Thee, ev - er, on - ly, all for Thee.

Be Thou My Vision

352

Irish hymn, 8th cent.
trans. Mary Elizabeth Byrne, 1905
vers. Eleanor Hull, 1912, alt.

SLANE
10 11 11 11

Irish folk melody

1. Be Thou my Vi - sion, O Lord of my heart; be all else but
2. Be Thou my Wis - dom, be Thou my true Word; be Thou ev - er
3. Be Thou my Breast-plate, my Sword for the fight; be Thou my whole
4. Rich - es I heed not, nor man's emp - ty praise, be Thou mine in -
5. High King of heav - en, Thou heav-en's bright Sun, O grant me its

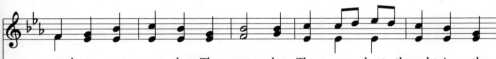

naught to me, save that Thou art; be Thou my best thought in the
with me and I with Thee, Lord; be Thou my great Fa - ther, and
Ar - mor, be Thou my true Might; be Thou my soul's Shel - ter, be
her - i - tance, now and al - ways; be Thou and Thou on - ly the
joys, af - ter vic - t'ry is won; Great Heart of my own heart, what-

day and the night, both wak-ing and sleep - ing, Thy pres-ence my light.
I Thy true son, be Thou in me dwell - ing, and I with Thee one.
Thou my strong Tow'r, O raise Thou me heav'n-ward, great Pow'r of my pow'r.
first in my heart, O High King of heav - en, my Trea-sure Thou art.
ev - er be - fall, still be Thou my Vi - sion, O Rul - er of all.

353 Credo

David Oestreich © 2014
based on The Apostles' Creed

OESTREICH
CMD

Josh Bauder © 2017

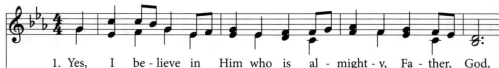

1. Yes, I be - lieve in Him who is al - might - y, Fa - ther, God,
2. Who un - der Pon - tius Pi - late's hand was scorned and suf - fered grief;
3. From there one day He will re - turn to judge the souls of men;
4. Yes, I be - lieve God does for - give the sins of those who come

who made all things in heav - en, earth, who made them ver - y good.
who then was cru - ci - fied and, dead, laid in a bor - rowed grave;
the small and great, liv - ing and dead, must all be - fore Him stand.
to Him con - fess - ing Je - sus Lord and trust - ing in His name.

Yes, I be - lieve in Je - sus Christ, God's on - ly Son, our Lord,
who from de - scent to depths of earth the third day rose a - gain,
Yes, I be - lieve the Ho - ly Ghost is ver - y God who calls
Yes, I be - lieve the right-eous dead Christ's res - ur - rec - tion share,

be - got - ten by the Spi - rit and of Vir - gin Mar - y born.
as - cend - ed in - to heav - en where He sits at God's right hand.
the pen - i - tent to His true church, where each com - munes with all.
that bless - ed life with Him for all e - ter - ni - ty is theirs.

The Apostles' Creed 354

I believe in God, the Father almighty, Creator of heaven and earth,

and in Jesus Christ, His only Son, our Lord,
  who was conceived by the Holy Spirit, born of the virgin Mary,
  suffered under Pontius Pilate, was crucified, died, and was buried;
  He descended into hell; on the third day He rose again from the dead;
  He ascended into heaven, and is seated at the right hand of God the
      Father almighty;
      from there He will come to judge the living and the dead.

I believe in the Holy Spirit, the holy catholic church,
  the communion of saints, the forgiveness of sins,
  the resurrection of the body, and life everlasting. Amen.

The Nicene Creed 355

We believe in one God, the Father, the Almighty, maker of heaven and earth, of
  all that is, seen and unseen.

We believe in one Lord, Jesus Christ, the only Son of God, eternally
  begotten of the Father, God from God, Light from Light, true God from
  true God, begotten, not made, of one being with the Father. Through Him all
  things were made.

For us and for our salvation He came down from heaven: by the power of
  the Holy Spirit He became incarnate from the virgin Mary, and was made
  man. For our sake He was crucified under Pontius Pilate; He suffered death
  and was buried. On the third day He rose again in accordance with the
  Scriptures; He ascended into heaven and is seated at the right hand of the
  Father.

He will come again in glory to judge the living and the dead, and His
  kingdom will have no end.

We believe in the Holy Spirit, the Lord, the Giver of life, who proceeds from the
  Father and the Son. With the Father and the Son He is worshiped and glorified.
  He has spoken through the prophets.

We believe in one holy catholic and apostolic church.
We acknowledge one baptism for the forgiveness of sins.
We look for the resurrection of the dead, and the life of the world to come.
Amen.

356 Come, Thou Fount

Robert Robinson, 1758

NETTLETON
87 87 D

J. Wyeth's
Repository of Sacred Music, Part II, 1813

1. Come, Thou Fount of eve-ry bless-ing; tune my heart to sing Thy grace;
2. Here I raise mine Eb-e-ne-zer: hith-er by Thy help I'm come,
3. Oh to grace how great a debt-or dai-ly I'm con-strained to be!

streams of mer-cy, nev-er ceas-ing, call for songs of loud-est praise.
and I hope by Thy good pleas-ure safe-ly to ar-rive at home.
Let Thy good-ness, like a fet-ter, bind my wan-d'ring heart to Thee;

Teach me some me-lo-dious son-net, sung by flam-ing tongues a-bove;
Je-sus sought me when a stran-ger wan-d'ring from the fold of God.
prone to wan-der, Lord, I feel it, prone to leave the God I love;

praise the mount! I'm fixed up-on it, mount of Thy re-deem-ing love.
He, to res-cue me from dan-ger, in-ter-posed His pre-cious blood.
here's my heart, O take and seal it; seal it for Thy courts a-bove!

Christian Hearts, in Love United

357

Nicholas Ludwig von Zinzendorf, 1723
trans. Frederick William Foster, 1789

CASSEL
87 87 D

Christian Gregor, *Chorale Book*, 1735

1. Christ-ian hearts, in love u-nit-ed, seek a-lone in Je-sus rest;
2. Come then, come, O flock of Je-sus, cov-e-nant with Him a-new;
3. Grant, Lord, that with Thy di-rec-tion "Love each oth-er," we com-ply.
4. O that such may be our un-ion as Thine with the Fa-ther is,

has He not your love ex-cit-ed? Then let love in-spire each breast.
un-to Him who con-quered for us, pledge we love and ser-vice true;
Aim-ing with un-feigned af-fec-tion Thy love to ex-em-pli-fy,
and not one of our com-mun-ion e'er for-sake the path of bliss;

Mem-bers on our Head de-pend-ing, lights re-flect-ing Him, our Sun,
and should our love's un-ion ho-ly firm-ly linked no more re-main,
let our mu-tual love be glow-ing, so that all will plain-ly see
may our light shine forth with bright-ness, from Thy light re-flect-ed, shine;

Chris-tians, His com-mands at-tend-ing, we in Him, our Lord, are one.
wait ye at His foot-stool low-ly, till He draw it close a-gain.
that we, as on one stem grow-ing, liv-ing branch-es are in Thee.
thus the world will bear us wit-ness, that we, Lord, are tru-ly Thine.

358 O for a Closer Walk with God

William Cowper, 1769

CAITHNESS
CM

Scottish Psalter, 1635
harm. *The English Hymnal*, 1906, alt.

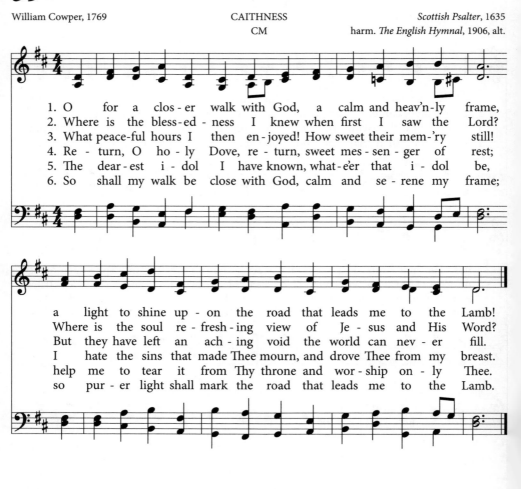

1. O for a clos-er walk with God, a calm and heav'n-ly frame,
2. Where is the bless-ed-ness I knew when first I saw the Lord?
3. What peace-ful hours I then en-joyed! How sweet their mem-'ry still!
4. Re-turn, O ho-ly Dove, re-turn, sweet mes-sen-ger of rest;
5. The dear-est i-dol I have known, what-e'er that i-dol be,
6. So shall my walk be close with God, calm and se-rene my frame;

a light to shine up-on the road that leads me to the Lamb!
Where is the soul re-fresh-ing view of Je-sus and His Word?
But they have left an ach-ing void the world can nev-er fill.
I hate the sins that made Thee mourn, and drove Thee from my breast.
help me to tear it from Thy throne and wor-ship on-ly Thee.
so pur-er light shall mark the road that leads me to the Lamb.

359 Teach Me, My God and King

George Herbert, 1633
alt. John Wesley, 1738

FESTAL SONG
SM

William Henry Walter, 1894

1. Teach me, my God and King, in all things Thee to see,
2. To scorn the sens-es' sway, while still to Thee I tend;
3. All may of Thee par-take; noth-ing so small can be,
4. If done t'o-bey Thy laws, e'en ser-vile la-bors shine;

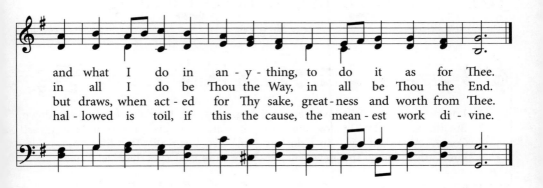

and what I do in an - y - thing, to do it as for Thee.
in all I do be Thou the Way, in all be Thou the End.
but draws, when act - ed for Thy sake, great - ness and worth from Thee.
hal - lowed is toil, if this the cause, the mean - est work di - vine.

My Soul, Be on Thy Guard

360

George Heath, 1781

BOYLSTON
SM

Lowell Mason, 1832

1. My soul, be on thy guard; ten thou-sand foes a - rise;
2. O watch, and fight, and pray; the bat - tle ne'er give o'er;
3. Ne'er think the vic - t'ry won, nor once at ease sit down;
4. Fight on, my soul, till death shall bring thee to my God;

the hosts of sin are press-ing hard to draw thee from the skies.
re - new it bold - ly eve - ry day, and help di - vine im - plore.
the ar-duous work will not be done till thou hast got the crown.
He'll take thee, at thy part-ing breath, up to His rest a - bove.

361 Love Divine, All Loves Excelling

Charles Wesley, 1747, alt.

BEECHER
87 87 D

John Zundel, 1870

1. Love di - vine, all loves ex - cell - ing, joy of heav'n to earth come down,
2. Breathe, O breathe Thy lov - ing Spir - it in - to eve - ry trou - bled breast!
3. Come, Al - might - y to de - liv - er, let us all Thy life re - ceive;
4. Fin - ish, then, Thy new cre - a - tion; pure and spot - less let us be;

fix in us Thy hum - ble dwell - ing, all Thy faith - ful mer - cies crown!
Let us all in Thee in - her - it, let us find the prom - ised rest.
sud - den - ly re - turn and nev - er, nev - er - more Thy tem - ples leave.
let us see Thy great sal - va - tion per - fect - ly re - stored in Thee.

Je - sus, Thou art all com - pas - sion, pure, un - bound - ed love Thou art;
Take a - way our love of sin - ning; Al - pha and O - me - ga be;
Thee we would be al - ways bless - ing, serve Thee as Thy hosts a - bove;
Changed from glo - ry in - to glo - ry, till in heav'n we take our place,

vis - it us with Thy sal - va - tion, en - ter eve - ry trem - bling heart.
end of faith, as its be - gin - ning, set our hearts at lib - er - ty.
pray, and praise Thee with - out ceas - ing, glo - ry in Thy per - fect love.
till we cast our crowns be - fore Thee, lost in won - der, love, and praise.

More Love to Thee

362

Elizabeth Prentiss, 1856

MORE LOVE TO THEE
64 64 66 44

William Doane, 1870

1. More love to Thee, O Christ, more love to Thee! Hear Thou the
2. Once earth-ly joy I craved, sought peace and rest; now Thee a -
3. Let sor-row do its work, come grief and pain; sweet are Thy
4. Then shall my lat - est breath whis - per Thy praise; this be the

prayer I make on bend-ed knee. This is my ear - nest plea:
lone I seek; give what is best. This all my prayer shall be:
mes - sen-gers, sweet their re - frain, when they can sing with me:
part - ing cry my heart shall raise; this still its prayer shall be:

more love, O Christ, to Thee; more love to Thee, more love to Thee!

363 Jesus Calls Us o'er the Tumult

Cecil F. Alexander, 1852 PLEADING SAVIOR Leavitt's *The Christian Lyre*, 1830
87 87 D

1. Je - sus calls us o'er the tu - mult of our life's wild, rest - less sea;
2. In our joys and in our sor-rows, days of toil and hours of ease,

day by day His sweet voice sound-eth, say - ing, "Chris-tian, fol - low me."
still He calls, in cares and pleas-ures, "Chris-tian, love me more than these."

Je - sus calls us from the wor-ship of the vain world's gold - en store,
Je - sus calls us— by Thy mer-cies, Sav - ior, may we hear Thy call;

from each i - dol that would keep us, say - ing, "Chris-tian, love me more."
give our hearts to Thine o - be - dience, serve and love Thee best of all.

O Jesus, I Have Promised

364

John E. Bode, 1868

ANGEL'S STORY
76 76 D

Arthur H. Mann, 1883

1. O Je - sus, I have prom - ised to serve Thee to the end;
2. O let me feel Thee near me, the world is ev - er near;
3. O let me hear Thee speak - ing in ac - cents clear and still,
4. O Je - sus, Thou hast prom - ised to all who fol - low Thee

be Thou for - ev - er near me, my Mas - ter and my Friend:
I see the sights that daz - zle, the tempt - ing sounds I hear;
a - bove the storms of pas - sion, the mur - murs of self - will;
that where Thou art in glo - ry there shall Thy ser - vant be;

I shall not fear the bat - tle if Thou art by my side,
my foes are ev - er near me, a - round me and with - in;
O speak to re - as - sure me, to has - ten or con - trol!
and, Je - sus, I have prom - ised to serve Thee to the end;

nor wan - der from the path - way if Thou wilt be my Guide.
but, Je - sus, draw Thou near - er, and shield my soul from sin.
O speak, and make me lis - ten, Thou Guard - ian of my soul!
O give me grace to fol - low, my Mas - ter and my Friend!

365   O Church, Arise

Keith Getty and Stuart Townend   O CHURCH ARISE   Keith Getty and Stuart Townend
© 2005 Thankyou Music

1. O church, a - rise and put your ar - mor on; hear the
2. Our call to war, to love the cap - tive soul, but to
3. Come, see the cross where love and mer - cy meet, as the
4. So Spir - it, come! Put strength in eve - ry stride, give

call of Christ our Cap - tain; for now the weak can say that
rage a - gainst the cap - tor; and with the sword that makes the
Son of God is strick - en; then see His foes lie crushed be -
grace for eve - ry hur - dle, that we may run with faith to

they are strong in the strength that God has giv - en. With shield of
wound-ed whole, we will fight with faith and val - or. When faced with
neath His feet, for the Con-quer - or has ris - en! And as the
win the prize of a ser - vant good and faith - ful. As saints of

faith and belt of truth we'll stand a-gainst the dev - il's lies, an ar - my
trials on eve - ry side, we know the out-come is se - cure, and Christ wil
stone is rolled a - way, and Christ e - merg-es from the grave, this vic - t'ry
old still line the way, re - tell-ing tri-umphs of His grace, we hear thei

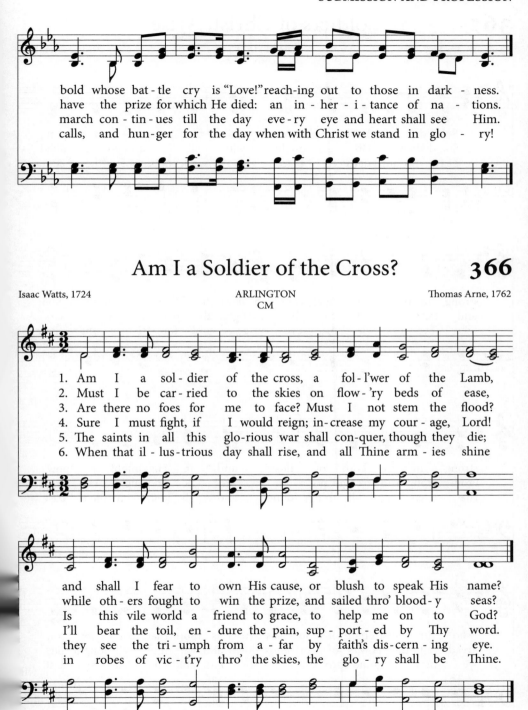

bold whose bat-tle cry is "Love!" reach-ing out to those in dark - ness.
have the prize for which He died: an in - her - i - tance of na - tions.
march con - tin - ues till the day eve-ry eye and heart shall see Him.
calls, and hun-ger for the day when with Christ we stand in glo - ry!

Am I a Soldier of the Cross? 366

Isaac Watts, 1724

ARLINGTON
CM

Thomas Arne, 1762

1. Am I a sol - dier of the cross, a fol - l'wer of the Lamb,
2. Must I be car - ried to the skies on flow - 'ry beds of ease,
3. Are there no foes for me to face? Must I not stem the flood?
4. Sure I must fight, if I would reign; in - crease my cour - age, Lord!
5. The saints in all this glo - rious war shall con - quer, though they die;
6. When that il - lus - trious day shall rise, and all Thine arm - ies shine

and shall I fear to own His cause, or blush to speak His name?
while oth - ers fought to win the prize, and sailed thro' blood-y seas?
Is this vile world a friend to grace, to help me on to God?
I'll bear the toil, en - dure the pain, sup - port - ed by Thy word.
they see the tri - umph from a - far by faith's dis - cern - ing eye.
in robes of vic - t'ry thro' the skies, the glo - ry shall be Thine.

367   Soldiers of Christ, Arise

Charles Wesley, 1747   DIADEMATA   George Elvey, 1868
SMD

1. Sol - diers of Christ, a - rise, and put your ar - mor on,
2. Stand then in His great might, with all His strength en - dued,
3. Leave no un-guard-ed place, no weak-ness of the soul;

strong, in the strength which God sup-plies thro' His e - ter-nal Son;
and take, to aid you in the fight, the pan - o - ply of God.
take eve - ry vir - tue, eve - ry grace, and for - ti - fy the whole.

strong in the Lord of hosts and in His might - y pow'r,
From strength to strength go on, wres - tle and fight and pray;
That, hav - ing all things done and all your con - flicts past,

who in the strength of Je - sus trusts is more than con - quer - or.
tread all the pow'rs of dark-ness down and win the well-fought day.
ye may o'er-come thro' Christ a - lone and stand com-plete at last.

He Who Would Valiant Be

368

John Bunyan, 1678
adapt. Percy Dearmer, 1906

ST. DUNSTAN'S
65 65 66 65

Charles Winfred Douglas, 1917

1. He who would val - iant be 'gainst all dis - as - ter, let him in
2. Who so be - set him round with dis - mal sto - ries, do but them-
3. Since, Lord, Thou dost de - fend us with Thy Spir - it, we know we

con - stan - cy fol - low the Mas - ter. There's no dis - cour - age-ment
selves con-found—his strength the more is. No foes shall stay his might,
at the end shall life in - her - it. Then, fan - cies, flee a - way!

shall make him once re - lent his first a - vowed in - tent to be a pil-grim.
though he with gi - ants fight; he will make good his right to be a pil-grim.
I'll fear not what men say, I'll la - bor night and day to be a pil-grim.

369   Guide Me, O Thou Great Jehovah

William Williams, 1745
st. 1 trans. Peter Williams, 1771

CWM RHONDDA
87 87 87 with repeat

John Hughes, 1907

1. Guide me, O Thou great Je - ho - vah, pil - grim through this
2. O - pen now the crys - tal foun - tain, whence the heal - ing
3. When I tread the verge of Jor - dan, bid my anx - ious

bar - ren land. I am weak, but Thou art might - y; hold me
stream doth flow. Let the fire and cloud - y pil - lar lead me
fears sub - side. Death of death, and hell's de - struc - tion, land me

with Thy pow'r - ful hand. Bread of heav - en, Bread of heav - en,
all my jour - ney through. Strong De - liv - 'rer, strong De - liv - 'rer,
safe on Ca - naan's side. Songs of prais - es, songs of prais - es,

feed me till I want no more; feed me till I want no more.
be Thou still my Strength and Shield; be Thou still my Strength and Shield.
I will ev - er give to Thee; I will ev - er give to Thee.

Jesus, Still Lead On

Nicolaus Ludwig von Zinzendorf, 1721
trans. Jane Borthwick, 1854

SEELENBRÄUTIGAM
55 88 55

Adam Drese, 1665

1. Je - sus, still lead on till our rest be won. And, al - though
2. If the way be drear, if the foe be near, let not faith -
3. When we seek re - lief from a long - felt grief— when op - pressed
4. Je - sus, still lead on till our rest be won; Heav'n - ly Lead -

the way be cheer - less, we will fol - low, calm and fear - less;
less fears o'er - take us, let not faith and hope for - sake us;
by new temp - ta - tions, Lord, in - crease and per - fect pa - tience.
er, still di - rect us, still sup - port, con - sole, pro - tect us,

guide us by Your hand to our Fa - ther - land.
for, thro' man - y a woe, to our home we go.
Show us that bright shore where we weep no more.
till we safe - ly stand in our Fa - ther - land.

371 My Faith Looks up to Thee

Ray Palmer, 1830   OLIVET   Lowell Mason, 1832
66 4 66 64

1. My faith looks up to Thee, Thou Lamb of Cal - va - ry,
2. May Thy rich grace im - part strength to my faint - ing heart,
3. While life's dark maze I tread, and griefs a - round me spread,
4. When ends life's tran-sient dream, when death's cold, sul - len stream

Sav - ior di - vine! Now hear me while I pray, take all my
my zeal in - spire; as Thou hast died for me, O may my
be Thou my Guide; bid dark - ness turn to day, wipe sor - row's
shall o'er me roll, blest Sav - ior, then in love, fear and dis -

guilt a - way; O let me from this day be whol - ly Thine.
love to Thee pure, warm, and change-less be, a liv - ing fire.
tears a - way, nor let me ev - er stray from Thee a - side.
trust re - move; O bear me safe a - bove, a ran - somed soul.

Savior, Like a Shepherd Lead Us

372

Dorothy A. Thrupp, 1836   JESU, BONE PASTOR   John Henry Willcox, 1827–1875

87 87 87

1. Sav - ior, like a shep-herd lead us, much we need Thy ten - der care;
2. Thou hast prom-ised to re - ceive us, poor and sin - ful though we be;
3. Ear - ly let us seek Thy fa - vor, ear - ly let us do Thy will;

in Thy pleas - ant pas-tures feed us; for our use Thy folds pre - pare.
Thou hast mer - cy to re - lieve us; grace to cleanse and pow'r to free.
do Thou, Lord, our on - ly Sav - ior, with Thy love our bos-oms fill.

Bless-ed Je - sus, bles-sed Je - sus, Thou hast bought us, Thine we are.
Bless-ed Je - sus, bles-sed Je - sus, let us ear - ly turn to Thee.
Bless-ed Je - sus, bles-sed Je - sus Thou hast loved us; love us still.

373 Approach, My Soul, the Mercy Seat

John Newton, 1779

BURFORD
CM

A. Williams's *Supplement to Psalmody*, c. 1780
harm. Edward Miller, 1790

1. Ap - proach, my soul, the mer - cy seat, where Je - sus
2. Thy prom - ise is my on - ly plea, with this I
3. Bowed down be - neath a load of sin, by Sa - tan
4. Be Thou my shield and hid - ing place, that, shel - tered
5. O won - drous love, to bleed and die, to bear the
6. "Poor tem - pest - tos - séd soul, be still, my prom - ised

1. an - swers pray'r; there hum - bly fall be -
2. ven - ture nigh; Thou call - est bur - dened
3. sore - ly pressed, by wars with - out, and
4. near Thy side, I may my fierce ac -
5. cross and shame, that guilt - y sin - ners
6. grace re - ceive"; 'tis Je - sus speaks; I

1. fore His feet, for none can per - ish there.
2. souls to Thee, and such, O Lord, am I.
3. fears with - in, I come to Thee for rest.
4. cus - er face, and tell him Thou hast died.
5. such as I, mighty plead Thy gra - cious name.
6. must, I will, I can, I do be - lieve.

What Various Hindrances We Meet 374

William Cowper, 1779   CONTRITION   Christian Knorr von Rosenroth, 1684
LM

1. What var - ious hin - dran - ces we meet in com - ing
2. Prayer makes the dark - ened clouds with-draw; prayer climbs the
3. Re - strain - ing prayer, we cease to fight; prayer makes the
4. Have you no words? Ah, think a - gain: words flow a -
5. Were half the breath thus vain - ly spent to heav'n in

to the mer - cy seat! Yet who that knows the worth of
lad - der Ja - cob saw; gives ex - er - cise to faith and
Chris - tian's ar - mor bright; and Sa - tan trem - bles when he
pace when you com - plain, and fill a fel - low - crea - ture's
sup - pli - ca - tion sent, our cheer - ful song would of - t'ner

prayer but wish - es to be of - ten there!
love; brings eve - ry bless - ing from a - bove.
sees the weak - est saint up - on his knees.
ear with the sad tale of all your care.
be, "Hear what the Lord hath done for me!"

375 Lord, Teach Us How to Pray Aright

James Montgomery, 1823   ST. AGNES   John B. Dykes, 1866
                          CM

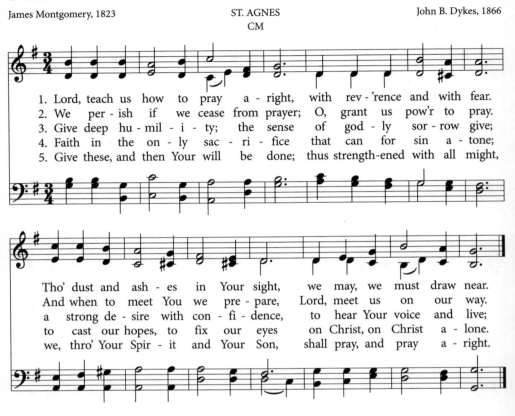

1. Lord, teach us how to pray a-right, with rev-'rence and with fear.
2. We per-ish if we cease from prayer; O, grant us pow'r to pray.
3. Give deep hu-mil-i-ty; the sense of god-ly sor-row give;
4. Faith in the on-ly sac-ri-fice that can for sin a-tone;
5. Give these, and then Your will be done; thus strength-ened with all might,

Tho' dust and ash-es in Your sight, we may, we must draw near.
And when to meet You we pre-pare, Lord, meet us on our way.
a strong de-sire with con-fi-dence, to hear Your voice and live;
to cast our hopes, to fix our eyes on Christ, on Christ a-lone.
we, thro' Your Spir-it and Your Son, shall pray, and pray a-right.

376 Come, My Soul, Thy Suit Prepare

John Newton, 1779   VIENNA   Justin H. Knecht, 1797
                          77 77

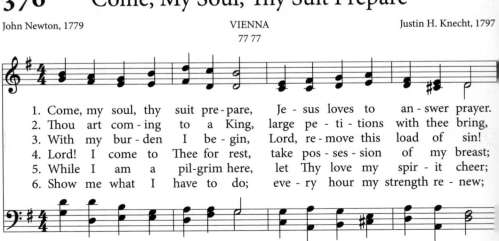

1. Come, my soul, thy suit pre-pare, Je-sus loves to an-swer prayer.
2. Thou art com-ing to a King, large pe-ti-tions with thee bring,
3. With my bur-den I be-gin, Lord, re-move this load of sin!
4. Lord! I come to Thee for rest, take pos-ses-sion of my breast;
5. While I am a pil-grim here, let Thy love my spir-it cheer;
6. Show me what I have to do; eve-ry hour my strength re-new;

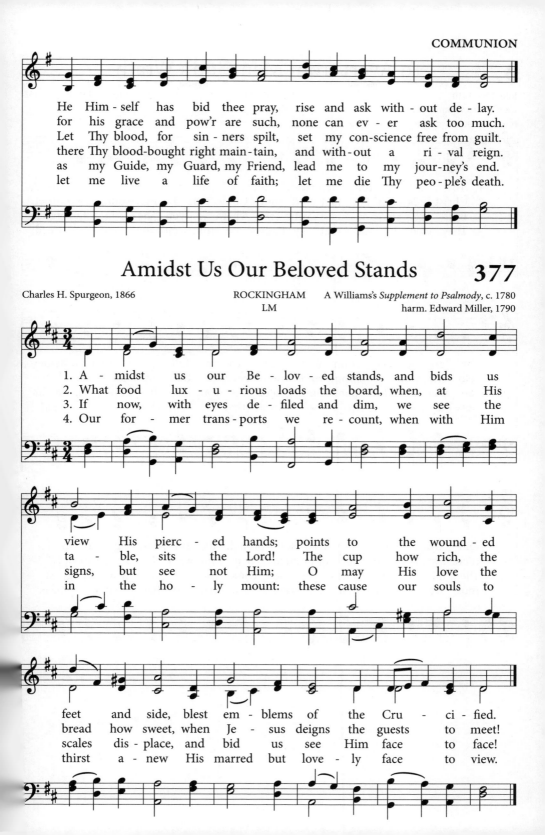

He Him-self has bid thee pray, rise and ask with-out de-lay.
for his grace and pow'r are such, none can ev-er ask too much.
Let Thy blood, for sin-ners spilt, set my con-science free from guilt.
there Thy blood-bought right main-tain, and with-out a ri-val reign.
as my Guide, my Guard, my Friend, lead me to my jour-ney's end.
let me live a life of faith; let me die Thy peo-ple's death.

Amidst Us Our Beloved Stands 377

Charles H. Spurgeon, 1866   ROCKINGHAM   A Williams's *Supplement to Psalmody*, c. 1780
                              LM   harm. Edward Miller, 1790

1. A-midst us our Be-lov-ed stands, and bids us
2. What food lux-u-rious loads the board, when, at His
3. If now, with eyes de-filed and dim, we see the
4. Our for-mer trans-ports we re-count, when with Him

view His pierc-ed hands; points to the wound-ed
ta-ble, sits the Lord! The cup how rich, the
signs, but see not Him; O may His love the
in the ho-ly mount: these cause our souls to

feet and side, blest em-blems of the Cru-ci-fied.
bread how sweet, when Je-sus deigns the guests to meet!
scales dis-place, and bid us see Him face to face!
thirst a-new His marred but love-ly face to view.

378   To Avert from Men God's Wrath

John Hus, 1410
trans. Martin Luther, 1524
trans. Christian Ignatius La Trobe, 1789

REDHEAD
77 77 77

Richard Redhead, 1853

1. To a - vert from men God's wrath, Je - sus suf - fered in our stead;
2. Christ bids each af - flict - ed soul, "Come that I may soothe your grief.
3. But ex - am - ine first your case, wheth - er you be in the faith;
4. They who Je - sus' mer - cy knows are from wrath and en - vy freed;

by an ig - no - min - ious death He a full a - tone - ment made;
No one who is strong and whole needs a doc - tor for re - lief;
do you long for pard - 'ning grace? Is your on - ly hope His death?
love un - to our neigh - bor shows that we are His flock in - deed;

and by His most pre - cious blood brought us, sin - ners, nigh to God.
there - fore have no fear, draw nigh, that your want I may sup - ply."
Then, how e'er your soul's op - pressed, come, you are a wor - thy guest.
thus we may in all our ways show forth our Re - deem - er's praise.

Thy Broken Body, Gracious Lord

379

Samuel P. Tregelles, 1838

BOURBON
LM

Hesperian Harp, 1848
harm. Louise McAllister, 1958

1. Thy broken bod - y, gra - cious Lord, is shad - owed
by this bro - ken bread; the wine which in this
cup is poured points to the blood which Thou hast shed.

2. And while we meet to - geth - er thus, we show that
we are one in Thee; Thy pre - cious blood was
shed for us, Thy death, O Lord, hast set us free!

3. Breth - ren in Thee, in un - ion sweet, for - ev - er
be Thy grace a - dored! 'Tis in Thy Name that
now we meet, and Thou art with us, gra - cious Lord.

4. We have one hope that Thou wilt come, Thee in the
air we wait to see, when Thou wilt give Thy
saints a home, and we shall ev - er reign with Thee.

380 Here, O My Lord, I See Thee Face to Face

Horatius Bonar, 1855　　　　　　　MORECAMBE　　　　　　　Frederick C. Arkinson, 1870
10 10 10 10

1. Here, O my Lord, I see Thee face to face;
2. Here would I feed upon the bread of God,
3. This is the hour of ban-quet and of song;
4. Too soon we rise, the sym-bols dis-ap-pear;
5. Feast af-ter feast thus comes, and pass-es by;

here would I touch and han-dle things un-seen;
here drink with Thee the roy-al wine of heav'n;
this is the heav'n-ly ta-ble spread for me;
the feast, though not the love, is past and done;
yet pass-ing, points to the glad feast a-bove;

here grasp with firm-er hand e-ter-nal grace
here would I lay a-side each earth-ly load,
here let me feast, and feast-ing, still pro-long
gone are the bread and wine, but Thou art here,
giv-ing sweet fore-taste of the fes-tal joy,

and all my wea-ri-ness up-on Thee lean.
here taste a-fresh the calm of sin for-giv'n.
the brief, bright hour of fel-low-ship with Thee.
near-er than ev-er, still my Shield and Sun.
the Lamb's great brid-al feast of bliss and love.

Father, We Thank Thee

Greek, from the *Didache*, ca. 110
trans. F. Bland Tucker, 1941
© Church Publishing Incorporated

RENDEZ À DIEU
98 98 D

Louis Bourgeois, 1543

1. Fa - ther, we thank Thee, who hast plant - ed Thy ho - ly name with-
2. Watch o'er Thy Church, O Lord, in mer - cy, save it from e - vil,

in our hearts. Knowl - edge, and faith, and life im - mor - tal
guard it still, per - fect it in Thy love, u - nite it,

Je - sus Thy Son to us im - parts. Thou, Lord, didst make all for Thy
cleansed and con-formed un - to Thy will. As grain, once scat - tered on the

pleas - ure, didst give man food for all his days, giv - ing in
hill - sides, was in this bro - ken bread made one, so from all

Christ the Bread e - ter - nal; Thine is the pow'r, be Thine the praise.
lands Thy Church be gath - ered in - to Thy king-dom by Thy Son.

382   At the Lamb's High Feast We Sing

Latin, 17th cent.
trans. Robert Campbell, 1849

SALZBURG
77 77 D

Jakob Hintze, 1678
harm. Johann Sebastian Bach, 18th cent.

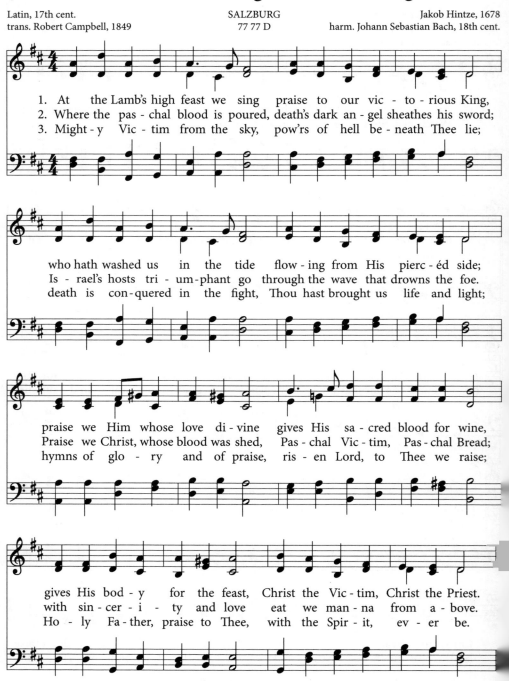

1. At the Lamb's high feast we sing praise to our vic - to - rious King,
2. Where the pas - chal blood is poured, death's dark an - gel sheathes his sword;
3. Might - y Vic - tim from the sky, pow'rs of hell be - neath Thee lie;

who hath washed us in the tide flow - ing from His pierc - éd side;
Is - rael's hosts tri - um - phant go through the wave that drowns the foe.
death is con - quered in the fight, Thou hast brought us life and light;

praise we Him whose love di - vine gives His sa - cred blood for wine,
Praise we Christ, whose blood was shed, Pas - chal Vic - tim, Pas - chal Bread;
hymns of glo - ry and of praise, ris - en Lord, to Thee we raise;

gives His bod - y for the feast, Christ the Vic - tim, Christ the Priest.
with sin - cer - i - ty and love eat we man - na from a - bove.
Ho - ly Fa - ther, praise to Thee, with the Spir - it, ev - er be.

Author of Life Divine

Charles Wesley, 1745

RHOSYMEDRE
66 66 888

John David Edwards, 1840

1. Au - thor of life di - vine, who hast a ta - ble spread,
2. Our need - y souls sus - tain with fresh sup - plies of love,

fur - nished with mys - tic wine and ev - er - last - ing bread,
till all Thy life we gain and all Thy full - ness prove,

pre - serve the life Thy - self hast giv'n, pre - serve the
and strength - ened by Thy per - fect grace, and strength - ened

life Thy - self hast giv'n, and feed and train us up for heav'n.
by Thy per - fect grace, be - hold with - out a veil Thy face.

384   Jesus, Thou Joy of Loving Hearts

attr. Bernard of Clairvaux, c. 1150   QUEBEC   Henry Baker, 1854
trans. Ray Palmer, 1858, alt.   LM

1. Je - sus, Thou joy of lov - ing hearts, Thou fount of life, Thou light of men, from the best bliss that earth im - parts, we turn un - filled to Thee a - gain.

2. Thy truth un - changed hath ev - er stood; Thou sav - est those that on Thee call; to them that seek Thee, Thou art good, to them that find Thee all in all.

3. We taste Thee, O Thou liv - ing Bread, and long to feast up - on Thee still; we drink of Thee, the Foun - tain - head, and thirst our souls from Thee to fill.

4. Our rest - less spir - its yearn for Thee, wher - e'er our change - ful lot is cast; glad when Thy gra - cious smile we see, blest when our faith can hold Thee fast.

5. O Je - sus, ev - er with us stay, make all our mo - ments calm and bright; chase the dark night of sin a - way; shed o'er the world Thy ho - ly light.

The Church's One Foundation

385

Samuel J. Stone, 1866   AURELIA   Samuel Sebastian Wesley, 1864
76 76 D

1. The church's one foun - da - tion is Je - sus Christ, her Lord;
2. E - lect from eve - ry na - tion, yet one o'er all the earth,
3. Though with a scorn - ful won - der, men see her sore op - pressed,
4. The church shall nev - er per - ish! Her dear Lord to de - fend,
5. 'Mid toil and trib - u - la - tion, and tu - mult of her war,
6. Yet she on earth hath un - ion with God the Three in One,

she is His new cre - a - tion, by wa - ter and the word.
her char - ter of sal - va - tion: one Lord, one faith, one birth.
by schis - ms rent a - sun - der, by her - e - sies dis - tressed,
to guide, sus - tain, and cher - ish, is with her to the end;
she waits the con - sum - ma - tion of peace for - ev - er - more;
and mys - tic sweet com - mun - ion with those whose rest is won;

From heav'n He came and sought her to be His ho - ly bride;
One ho - ly name she bless - es, par - takes one ho - ly food,
yet saints their watch are keep - ing, their cry goes up, "How long?"
though there be those that hate her, and false sons in her pale,
till with the vi - sion glo - rious her long - ing eyes are blest,
O hap - py ones and ho - ly! Lord give us grace that we,

with His own blood He bought her, and for her life He died.
and to one hope she press - es, with eve - ry grace en - dued.
and soon the night of weep - ing shall be the morn of song!
a - gainst the foe or trait - or she ev - er shall pre - vail.
and the great church vic - to - rious shall be the church at rest.
like them, the meek and low - ly, on high may dwell with Thee.

386 Christ Is Made the Sure Foundation

Latin, ca. 7th century
trans. John Mason Neale, 1851, alt.

WESTMINSTER ABBEY
87 87 87

Henry Purcell, 1680

1. Christ is made the sure foun-da-tion, Christ the head and cor-ner-stone, cho-sen of the Lord, and pre-cious, bind-ing all the church in one, ho-ly Zi-on's help for-ev-er, and her con-fi-dence a-lone.

2. All that ded-i-cat-ed cit-y, dear-ly loved of God on high, in ex-ult-ant ju-bi-la-tion pours per-pe-tual mel-o-dy, God the One in Three a-dor-ing in glad hymns e-ter-nal-ly.

3. To this tem-ple, where we call You, come, O Lord of Hosts, to-day; with ac-cus-tomed lov-ing-kind-ness, hear Your serv-ants as they pray; and Your full-est ben-e-dic-tion shed with-in its walls al-way.

4. Lord, here grant to all Your ser-vants what they ask of You to gain, what they gain from You, for-ev-er with the bless-ed to re-tain, and here-af-ter in Your glo-ry ev-er-more with You to reign.

5. Praise and hon-or to the Fa-ther, praise and hon-or to the Son, praise and hon-or to the Spir-it, ev-er Three, and ev-er One, one in might, and one in glo-ry, while un-end-ing a-ges run.

On Christ Salvation Rests Secure

Samuel Medley, 1785

WINCHESTER NEW
LM

Musikalisches Handbuch, 1690
harm. William Henry Monk, 1847, alt.

1. On Christ sal - va - tion rests se - cure; the Rock of
2. No oth - er hope shall in - ter - vene; to Him we
3. In Him, it is or - dained to raise a tem - ple
4. View the vast build - ing, see it rise; the work how
5. But most a - dore His pre - cious name; His glo - ry

Ag - es must en - dure; nor can that faith be
look, on Him we lean; oth - er foun - da - tions
to Je - hov - ah's praise com - posed of all the
great! the plan how wise! O won - drous fab - ric,
and His grace pro - claim; for us, con - demned, de -

o - ver - thrown which rests up - on the "Liv - ing Stone."
we dis - own and build on Christ, the "Liv - ing Stone."
saints, who own no Sav - ior but the "Liv - ing Stone."
pow'r un - known that rests it on the "Liv - ing Stone."
spised, un - done, He gave Him - self, the "Liv - ing Stone."

388 — For All the Saints

William Walsham How, 1864

SINE NOMINE
10 10 10 with alleluias

Ralph Vaughan Williams, 1906

1. For all the saints who from their la-bors rest, who Thee by
2. Thou wast their Rock, their For-tress and their Might; Thou, Lord, their
3. O blest com-mun-ion, fel-low-ship di-vine! We fee-bly
4. And when the strife is fierce, the war-fare long, steals on the
5. But then there breaks a still more glo-rious day: the saints tri-
6. From earth's wide bounds, from o-cean's far-thest coast, through gates of

faith be-fore the world con-fessed; Thy name, O Je-sus, be for-
Cap-tain in the well-fought fight; Thou, in the dark-ness drear, their
strug-gle, they in glo-ry shine; yet all are one in Thee, for
ear the dis-tant tri-umph song, and hearts are brave a-gain, and
um-phant rise in bright ar-ray; the King of glo-ry pas-ses
pearl streams in the count-less host, in praise of Fa-ther, Son, and

ev-er blest.
one true Light.
all are Thine. Al-le-lu-ia, Al-le-lu-ia!
arms are strong.
on His way.
Ho-ly Ghost.

O Give Us Homes

Barbara B. Hart © 1965

FINLANDIA
10 10 10 10 10 10

Jean Sibelius, 1899

1. O give us homes built firm up-on the Sav-ior, where Christ is Head and
2. O give us homes with god-ly fa-thers, moth-ers, who al-ways place their
3. O give us homes where Christ is Lord and Mas-ter, the Bi-ble read, the
4. O Lord, our God, our homes are Thine for-ev-er! We trust to Thee their

Coun-sel-or and Guide; where eve-ry child is taught His love and fa-vor
hope and trust in Him; whose ten-der pa-tience tur-moil nev-er both-ers;
pre-cious hymns still sung; where prayer comes first in peace or in dis-as-ter,
prob-lems, toil, and care. Their bonds of love no en-e-my can sev-er

and gives his heart to Christ, the cru-ci-fied. How sweet to know that,
whose calm and cour-age trou-ble can-not dim; a home where each finds
and praise is nat-ural speech to eve-ry tongue; where moun-tains move be -
if Thou art al-ways Lord and Mas-ter there. Be Thou the Cen-ter

tho' his foot-steps wa-ver, his faith-ful Lord is walk-ing by his side!
joy in serv-ing oth-ers, and love still shines, tho' days be dark and grim!
fore a faith that's vast-er, and Christ suf-fi-cient is for old and young.
of our least en-deav-or; be Thou our Guest, our hearts and homes to share.

390

Built on the Rock

Nicolai F. S. Grundrvig, 1837
trans. Carl Doving, 1909, alt.

KIRKEN DEN ER ET
88 88 88 8

Ludvig M. Lindeman, 1840

1. Built on the Rock, the church shall stand even when stee-ples are
2. Not in a tem-ple made with hands God the Al-might-y is
3. We are God's house of liv-ing stones, built for His own hab-i-
4. Through all the pass-ing years, O Lord, grant that, when church bells are

fall - - ing; Christ build His church in eve-ry land;
dwell - - ing; high in the heav'ns His tem-ple stands,
ta - - tion; He fills our hearts, His hum-ble thrones,
ring - - ing, man-y may come to hear God's Word

bells still are chim-ing and call - ing, call-ing the
all earth-ly tem-ples ex-cel - ling; yet He who
grant-ing us life and sal-va - tion. Yet to this
where He this prom-ise is bring - ing: "I know My

young and old to rest, call-ing the souls of
dwells in heav'n a-bove choos-es to live with
place, and earth-ly frame, we come with thanks to
own, My own know Me; you, not the world, My

those dis - tressed, long - ing for life ev - er - last - - ing.
us in love, mak - ing our bod - y His tem - - ple.
praise His name; God grants His peo - ple true bless - ing.
face shall see; My peace I leave with you. A - - men."

A Charge to Keep I Have

391

Charles Wesley, 1762, alt.

BOYLSTON
SM

Lowell Mason, 1832

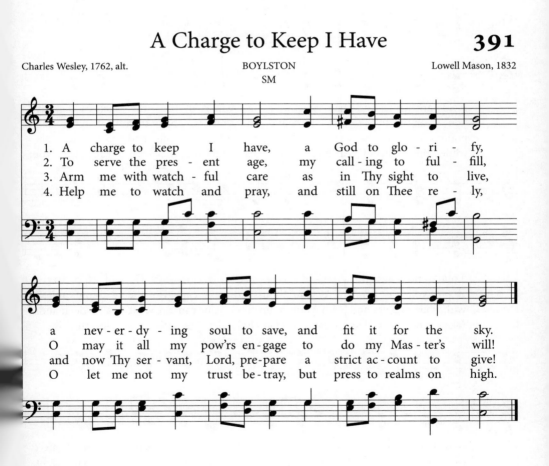

1. A charge to keep I have, a God to glo - ri - fy,
2. To serve the pres - ent age, my call - ing to ful - fill,
3. Arm me with watch - ful care as in Thy sight to live,
4. Help me to watch and pray, and still on Thee re - ly,

a nev - er - dy - ing soul to save, and fit it for the sky.
O may it all my pow'rs en - gage to do my Mas - ter's will!
and now Thy ser - vant, Lord, pre - pare a strict ac - count to give!
O let me not my trust be - tray, but press to realms on high.

392   Hark, the Voice of Jesus Calling

Daniel March, 1868, alt.   ELLESDIE   attr. Wolfgang Amadeus Mozart, 1756–1791
                        87 87 D   in Leavitt's *The Christian Lyre*, 1831
                                          arr. Hubert P. Main, 1839–1925

1. Hark, the voice of Je-sus call-ing, "Who will go and work to-day?
2. If you can-not cross the o-cean, and the dis-tant lands ex-plore,
3. If you can-not be the watch-man stand-ing high on Zi-on's wall,
4. Let none hear you i-dly say-ing, "There is noth-ing I can do,"

Fields are white, and har-vests wait-ing, who will bear the sheaves a-way?"
you can find the lost a-round you, you can help them at your door;
point-ing out the path to heav-en, off-'ring life and peace to all,
while the lost of earth are dy-ing, and the Mas-ter calls for you;

Loud and long the Mas-ter calls us, rich re-ward He of-fers free;
if you can-not give your thou-sands, you can give the wid-ow's mite;
with your prayers and with your boun-ties you can do what heav'n de-mands;
take the task He gives you glad-ly; let His work your plea-sure be;

who will an-swer, glad-ly say-ing, "Here am I, send me, send me"?
what you tru-ly give for Je-sus will be pre-cious in His sight.
you can be like faith-ful Aar-on, hold-ing up the proph-et's hands.
an-swer quick-ly when He calls you, "Here am I, send me, send me."

Christ for the World We Sing

393

Samuel Wolcott, 1869

ITALIAN HYMN
66 4 66 64

Felice de Giardini, ca. 1762

1. Christ for the world we sing; the world to Christ we bring
2. Christ for the world we sing; the world to Christ we bring
3. Christ for the world we sing; the world to Christ we bring
4. Christ for the world we sing; the world to Christ we bring

1. with lov-ing zeal: the poor and them that mourn, the faint and
2. with fer-vent pray'r: the way-ward and the lost, by rest-less
3. with one ac-cord: with us the work to share, with us re-
4. with joy-ful song: the new-born souls whose days, re-claimed from

1. o-ver-borne, sin-sick and sor-row-worn, whom Christ doth heal.
2. pas-sions tossed, re-deemed at count-less cost from dark de-spair.
3. proach to dare, with us the cross to bear, for Christ our Lord.
4. er-ror's ways, in-spired with hope and praise, to Christ be-long.

394 Come, Ye Thankful People, Come

Henry Alford, 1844   ST. GEORGE'S WINDSOR   George Elvey, 1858
77 77 D

1. Come, ye thank-ful peo-ple, come; raise the song of har-vest home.
2. All the world is God's own field, fruit un-to His praise to yield,
3. For the Lord our God shall come, and shall take His har-vest home;
4. E - ven so, Lord, quick-ly come to Thy fi - nal har-vest home.

All is safe-ly gath-ered in, ere the win-ter storms be-gin.
wheat and tares to-geth-er sown, un-to joy or sor-row grown.
from His field shall in that day all of-fens-es purge a-way;
Gath-er Thou Thy peo-ple in, free from sor-row, free from sin,

God, our Mak-er, doth pro-vide for our wants to be sup-plied;
First the blade, and then the ear, then the full corn shall ap-pear.
give His an-gels charge at last in the fire the tares to cast,
there for-ev-er pu-ri-fied, in Thy pres-ence to a-bide:

come to God's own tem-ple, come, raise the song of har-vest home.
Lord of har-vest, grant that we whole-some grain and pure may be.
but the fruit-ful ears to store in His gar-ner ev-er-more.
come, with all Thine an-gels, come; raise the glo-rious har-vest home.

Ye Servants of God, Your Master Proclaim **395**

Charles Wesley, 1744   HANOVER   William Croft, 1708
10 10 11 11

1. Ye   ser - vants of   God, your   Mas - ter   pro - claim, and   pub - lish a -
2. God   rul - eth on   high, al - might - y   to   save, and   still He   is
3. "Sal - va - tion to   God, who   sits on   the throne!" Let   all   cry a -
4. Then   let   us   a - dore, and   give Him His   right— all   glo - ry and

broad   His   won - der - ful   name;   the   name, all   vic - to - rious, of
nigh,   His   pres - ence we   have;   the   great con - gre - ga - tion His
loud,   and   hon - or   the   Son;   the   prais - es   of   Je - sus   the
pow'r,   all   wis - dom and   might,   all   hon - or   and   bless - ing, with

Je - sus   ex - tol;   His   king - dom is   glo - rious, He   rules o - ver   all.
tri - umph shall   sing,   as - crib - ing sal - va - tion   to   Je - sus, our   King.
an - gels   pro - claim, fall down on their   fac - es   and wor - ship the Lamb.
an - gels   a - bove, and thanks nev - er - ceas - ing, and   in - fi - nite   love.

396

Go, Labor On

Horatius Bonar, 1843   SONG 34   Orlando Gibbons, 1623
                          LM

1. Go, la-bor on; spend, and be spent, thy joy to
2. Go, la-bor on; 'tis not for naught; thine earth-ly
3. Go la-bor on; e-nough while here if He shall
4. Go, la-bor on while it is day: the world's dark
5. Toil on, faint not, keep watch and pray; be wise the
6. Toil on, and in thy toil re-joice; for toil comes

do the Fa-ther's will; it is the way the
loss is heav'n-ly gain; men heed thee, love thee,
praise thee, if He deign thy will-ing heart to
night is hast-'ning on. Speed, speed thy work, cast
err-ing soul to win; go forth in-to the
rest, for ex-ile home; soon shalt thou hear the

Mas-ter went; should not the ser-vant tread it still?
praise thee not; the Mas-ter prais-es— what are men?
mark and cheer; no toil for Him shall be in vain.
sloth a-way; it is not thus that souls are won.
world's high-way, com-pel the wan-d'rer to come in.
Bride-groom's voice, the mid-night peal, "Be-hold, I come."

A Mighty Fortress Is Our God

397

Martin Luther, 1529
trans. Frederick Hedge, 1852

EIN' FESTE BURG
87 87 66 66 7

Martin Luther, 1529
harm. Johann Sebastian Bach, 18th cent.

1. A might-y for-tress is our God, a bul-wark nev-er fail - ing;
2. Did we in our own strength con-fide, our striv-ing would be los - ing,
3. And tho' this world with dev - ils filled should threat-en to un-do us,
4. That word a-bove all earth-ly pow'rs, no thanks to them, a-bid - eth;

our Help-er He, a-mid the flood of mor-tal ills pre-vail - ing.
were not the right Man on our side, the Man of God's own choos - ing.
we will not fear, for God hath willed His truth to tri-umph through us.
the Spir-it and the gifts are ours through Him who with us sid - eth.

For still our an-cient foe doth seek to work us woe; his craft and pow'r are
Dost ask who that may be? Christ Je-sus, it is He; Lord Sab-a-oth His
The prince of dark-ness grim, we trem-ble not for him; his rage we can en-
Let goods and kin-dred go, this mor-tal life al - so; the bod-y they may

great, and, armed with cru-el hate; on earth is not his e - qual.
name, from age to age the same, and He must win the bat - tle.
dure, for lo, his doom is sure; one lit-tle word shall fell him.
kill: God's truth a-bid-eth still— His king-dom is for-ev - er!

398 Thou Hidden Love of God

Gerhard Tersteegen, 1729
trans. John Wesley, 1736

VATER UNSER
88 88 88

attr. Martin Luther,
Valentin Schumann's *Geistliche Lieder*, 1539

1. Thou hid - den Love of God, whose height, whose depth un - fath - omed,
2. 'Tis mer - cy all that Thou hast brought my mind to seek its
3. Is there a thing be - neath the sun that strives with Thee my
4. O hide this self from me, that I no more, but Christ in
5. O Love, Thy sov-'reign aid im - part to save me from low -
6. Each mo - ment draw from earth a - way my heart, that low - ly

no man knows, I see from far Thy beau - teous light,
peace in Thee; yet while I seek, but find Thee not,
heart to share? Ah! tear it thence, and reign a - lone,
me, may live; my vile af - fec - tions cru - ci - fy,
thought - ed care; chase this self - will from all my heart,
waits Thy call; speak to my in - most soul, and say,

and in - ly sigh for Thy re - pose; my heart is
no peace my wan - d'ring soul shall see. O when shall
the Lord of eve - ry mo - tion there; then shall my
nor let one dar - ling lust sur - vive; in all things
from all its hid - den maz - es there; make me Thy
"I am Thy love, Thy God, Thy all." To feel Thy

pained, nor can it be at rest till it finds rest in Thee.
all my wan - d'rings end, and all my steps to Thee-ward tend?
heart from earth be free, when it has found re - pose in Thee.
noth - ing may I see, noth - ing de - sire, or seek, but Thee.
dut - eous child, that I may cease-less "Ab - ba, Fa - ther," cry.
pow'r, to hear Thy voice, to taste Thy love, be all my choice!

Christ, Whose Glory Fills the Skies **399**

Charles Wesley, 1740

DIX
77 77 77

Conrad Kocher, 1838
adapt. William Henry Monk, 1861
harm. *The English Hymnal*, 1906

1. Christ, whose glo-ry fills the skies, Christ, the true and on-ly Light,
2. Dark and cheer-less is the morn un-ac-com-pa-nied by Thee;
3. Vis-it then this soul of mine, pierce the gloom of sin and grief;

Sun of right-eous-ness, a-rise, tri-umph o'er the shades of night;
joy-less is the day's re-turn, till Thy mer-cy's beams I see,
fill me, ra-dian-cy di-vine, scat-ter all my un-be-lief;

Day-spring from on high, be near; Day-star, in my heart ap-pear.
till they in-ward light im-part, glad my eyes, and warm my heart.
more and more Thy-self dis-play, shin-ing to the per-fect day.

400 Be Still, My Soul

Katharina von Schlegel, 1752
trans. Jane Borthwick, 1855

FINLANDIA
10 10 10 10 10 10

Jean Sibelius, 1899

1. Be still, my soul; the Lord is on thy side; bear pa-tient-ly the cross of grief or pain. Leave to thy God to or-der and pro-vide; in eve-ry change He faith-ful will re-main. Be still, my soul; thy best, thy heav'n-ly Friend through thorn-y ways leads to a joy-ful end.

2. Be still, my soul; thy God doth un-der-take to guide the fu-ture as He has the past. Thy hope, thy con-fi-dence let noth-ing shake; all now mys-te-rious shall be bright at last. Be still, my soul; the waves and winds still know His voice who ruled them while He dwelt be-low.

3. Be still, my soul; when dear-est friends de-part and all is dark-ened in the vale of tears, then shalt thou bet-ter know His love, His heart, who comes to soothe thy sor-rows and thy fears. Be still, my soul; thy Je-sus can re-pay from His own full-ness all He takes a-way.

4. Be still, my soul; the hour is has-t'ning on when we shall be for-ev-er with the Lord, when dis-ap-point-ment, grief, and fear are gone, sor-row for-got, love's pur-est joys re-stored. Be still, my soul; when change and tears are past, all safe and bless-ed we shall meet at last.

Sometimes a Light Surprises

401

William Cowper, 1779

BLOMSTERTID
76 76 D

Swedish *Koralbok*, 1697

1. Some-times a light sur - pris - ses the Chris-tian while he sings;
2. In ho - ly con-tem - pla - tion, we sweet-ly then pur - sue
3. "It can bring with it noth - ing, but He will bear us through;
4. Though vine nor fig tree nei - ther their wont-ed fruit should bear,

it is the Lord who ris - es with heal-ing in His wings;
the theme of God's sal - va - tion, and find it ev - er new.
who gives the lil - ies cloth - ing will clothe His peo - ple, too;
though all the field should with - er, nor flocks nor herds be there,

when com-forts are de - clin - ing, He grants the soul a - gain
Set free from pres - ent sor - row, we cheer-ful - ly can say,
be - neath the spread-ing heav - ens no crea-ture but is fed;
yet God the same a - bid - ing, His praise shall tune my voice;

a sea-son of clear shin - ing, to cheer it af - ter rain.
"E'en let the un-known mor - row bring with it what it may."
and He who feeds the ra - vens will give His chil-dren bread."
for while in Him con - fid - ing, I can-not but re - joice.

402 Children of the Heavenly Father

Carolina Sandell-Berg, 1855
trans. Ernst Olsen, 1925

TRYGGARE KAN INGEN VARA
LM

Swedish folk song

1. Chil- dren of the heav'n- ly Fa- ther safe- ly   in His bos- om gath- er;
2. God His own doth tend and nour- ish; in His ho- ly courts they flour- ish.
3. Nei- ther life nor death shall ev- er from the Lord His chil- dren sev- er;
4. Tho' He giv- eth   or   He tak- eth, God His chil- dren ne'er for- sak- eth;

nest- ling bird nor star in heav- en such a   re- fuge e'er was giv- en.
From all   e - vil things He spares them; in His might- y arms He bears them.
un - to them His grace He show- eth, and their sor- rows all He know- eth.
His the lov- ing pur- pose sole - ly   to pre- serve them pure and ho- ly.

403 Rejoice, Believer, in the Lord

John Newton, 1779

BRADFIELD
CM

J. B. Calkin, 1872

1. Re - joice, be- liev- er,   in the Lord, who makes your cause His   own;
2. Tho' man- y foes be - set your road, and fee - ble is your arm,
3. Weak as you are, you shall not faint or faint- ing shall not die!
4. Tho' some- times un- per- ceived by sense, faith sees Him al- ways near!
5. As   sure- ly as He   o - ver- came and tri- umphed once for you,

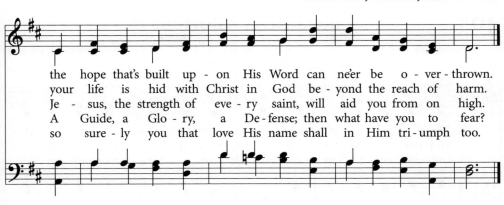

the hope that's built up - on His Word can ne'er be o - ver - thrown.
your life is hid with Christ in God be - yond the reach of harm.
Je - sus, the strength of eve - ry saint, will aid you from on high.
A Guide, a Glo - ry, a De - fense; then what have you to fear?
so sure - ly you that love His name shall in Him tri - umph too.

How Sweet the Name of Jesus Sounds **404**

John Newton, 1774, alt.   ST. PETER   Alexander Robert Reinagle, 1836
CM

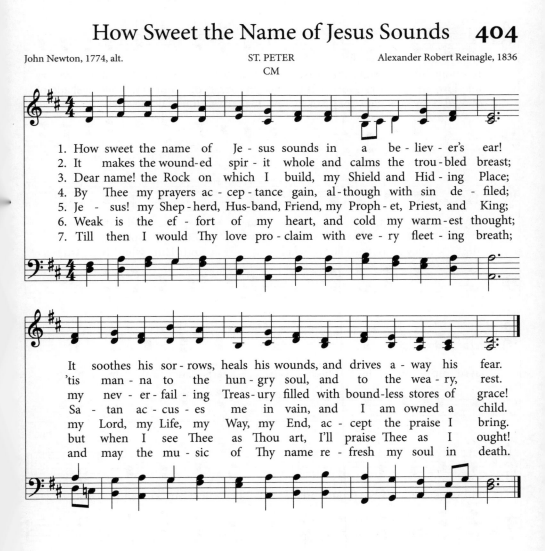

1. How sweet the name of Je - sus sounds in a be - liev - er's ear!
2. It makes the wound-ed spir - it whole and calms the trou - bled breast;
3. Dear name! the Rock on which I build, my Shield and Hid - ing Place;
4. By Thee my prayers ac - cep - tance gain, al - though with sin de - filed;
5. Je - sus! my Shep - herd, Hus - band, Friend, my Proph - et, Priest, and King;
6. Weak is the ef - fort of my heart, and cold my warm - est thought;
7. Till then I would Thy love pro - claim with eve - ry fleet - ing breath;

It soothes his sor - rows, heals his wounds, and drives a - way his fear.
'tis man - na to the hun - gry soul, and to the wea - ry, rest.
my nev - er - fail - ing Treas - ury filled with bound-less stores of grace!
Sa - tan ac - cus - es me in vain, and I am owned a child.
my Lord, my Life, my Way, my End, ac - cept the praise I bring.
but when I see Thee as Thou art, I'll praise Thee as I ought!
and may the mu - sic of Thy name re - fresh my soul in death.

405 Like a River Glorious

Frances R. Havergal, 1874

WYE VALLEY
11 11 11 11 with refrain

James Mountain, 1876

1. Like a riv-er glo-rious is God's per-fect peace, o-ver all vic-
2. Hid-den in the hol-low of His bless-ed hand, nev-er foe can
3. Eve-ry joy or tri-al fall-eth from a-bove, traced up-on our

to-rious in its bright in-crease; per-fect, yet it flow-eth full-er eve-ry
fol-low, nev-er trai-tor stand; not a surge of wor-ry, not a shade of
di-al by the Sun of Love; we may trust Him ful-ly all for us to

day; per-fect, yet it grow-eth deep-er all the way.
care, not a blast of hur-ry touch the spir-it there.
do; they who trust Him whol-ly find Him whol-ly true.

Stayed up-on Je-ho-vah, hearts are ful-ly blest;

find-ing, as He prom-ised, per-fect peace and rest.

Give to the Winds Thy Fears

406

Paul Gerhardt, 1656
trans. John Wesley, 1739

FESTAL SONG
SM

William Henry Walter, 1894

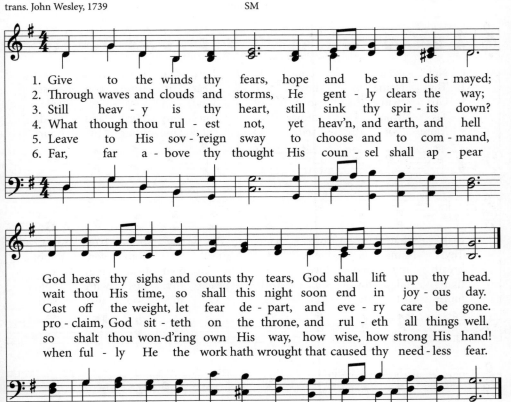

1. Give to the winds thy fears, hope and be un - dis - mayed;
2. Through waves and clouds and storms, He gent - ly clears the way;
3. Still heav - y is thy heart, still sink thy spir - its down?
4. What though thou rul - est not, yet heav'n, and earth, and hell
5. Leave to His sov - 'reign sway to choose and to com - mand,
6. Far, far a - bove thy thought His coun - sel shall ap - pear

God hears thy sighs and counts thy tears, God shall lift up thy head.
wait thou His time, so shall this night soon end in joy - ous day.
Cast off the weight, let fear de - part, and eve - ry care be gone.
pro - claim, God sit - teth on the throne, and rul - eth all things well.
so shalt thou won-d'ring own His way, how wise, how strong His hand!
when ful - ly He the work hath wrought that caused thy need - less fear.

7. Thou seest our weakness, Lord,
   our hearts are known to Thee;
   O lift Thou up the sinking heart,
   confirm the feeble knee.

8. Let us in life, in death,
   Thy steadfast truth declare,
   and publish with our latest breath
   Thy love and guardian care.

407 Not What I Am, O Lord

Horatius Bonar, 1861

LANGRAN
10 10 10 10

James Langran, 1861

1. Not what I am, O Lord, but what Thou art,
2. Thy Name is Love, I hear it from yon cross;
3. Girt with the love of God on ev-'ry side,
4. 'Tis what I know of Thee, my Lord and God,
5. More of Thyself, O show me hour by hour;

that, that a-lone can be my soul's true rest;
Thy Name is Love, I hear it from yon tomb;
breath-ing that love as heav'n's own heal-ing air,
that fills my soul with peace, my lips with song;
more of Thy glo-ry, O my God and Lord;

Thy love, not mine, bids fear and doubt de-part,
all mean-er love is per-ish-a-ble dross,
I work or wait, still fol-low-ing my Guide,
Thou art my Health, my Joy, my Staff and Rod;
more of Thy-self, in all Thy grace and pow'r;

and stills the tem-pest of my throb-bing breast.
but this shall light me through time's thick-est gloom.
brav-ing each foe, es-cap-ing ev-'ry snare.
lean-ing on Thee, in weak-ness I am strong.
more of Thy love and truth, in-car-nate Word!

Jesus, Lover of My Soul

408

Charles Wesley, 1740   ABERYSTWYTH   Joseph Parry, 1879

77 77 D

1. Je - sus, Lov - er of my soul, let me to Thy bos - om fly,
2. Oth - er ref - uge have I none, hangs my help-less soul on Thee;
3. Thou, O Christ, art all I want; more than all in Thee I find:
4. Plen-teous grace with Thee is found, grace to cov - er all my sin;

while the near - er wa - ters roll, while the tem - pest still is high:
leave, ah! leave me not a - lone, still sup - port and com - fort me!
raise the fall - en, cheer the faint, heal the sick, and lead the blind.
let the heal - ing streams a - bound; make and keep me pure with - in:

hide me, O my Sav - ior, hide, till the storm of life is past;
All my trust on Thee is stayed, all my help from Thee I bring;
Just and ho - ly is Thy name; I am all un - right-eous - ness;
Thou of life the Foun-tain art, free - ly let me take of Thee;

safe in - to the ha - ven guide, O re - ceive my soul at last!
cov - er my de-fense-less head with the shad - ow of Thy wing.
false and full of sin I am, Thou art full of truth and grace.
spring Thou up with - in my heart, rise to all e - ter - ni - ty.

409 Thou Sweet Beloved Will of God

Gerhard Tersteegen, 1729
trans. Frances Bevan, 1899

GERMANY
LM

William Gardiner's
Sacred Melodies, 1815

1. Thou sweet be - lov - ed will of God, my an - chor ground, my for - tress hill, my spir - it's si - lent fair a - bode, in Thee I hide me and am still.

2. O will, that will - est good a - lone, lead Thou the way, Thou guid - est best; a lit - tle child, I fol - low on, and trust - ing, lean up - on Thy breast.

3. God's will doth make the bit - ter sweet, and all is well when it is done; un - less His will doth hal - low it, the glo - ry of all joy is gone.

4. Self, sense, and rea - son, they may scorn that hid - den way that leads on high— still be my deep - est will up - torn, and so the pow'r of na - ture die.

5. And if in gloom I see Thee now, I lean up - on Thy love un - known— in me Thy bless - ed will is wrought, if I will noth - ing of my own.

6. O spir - it of a lit - tle child, of will be - reft, un - trou - bled, pure, I seek Thy glo - ry un - de - filed; Lord, take my will, Thy love is sure.

7. O will of God, my soul's desire,
my bread of life in want and pain;
O will of God, my guiding fire,
unite my will to Thine again.

8. O will, in me Thy work be done,
for time, and for eternity—
give joy or sorrow, all are one
to that blest soul that loveth Thee.

If Thou But Trust in God to Guide Thee **410**

Georg Neumark, 1641

NEUMARK
98 98 88

Georg Neumark, 1641
trans. Catherine Winkworth, 1864

1. If thou but trust in God to guide thee, and hope in
   Him through all thy ways, He'll give thee strength, what-e'er be-
   tide thee, and bear thee through the e - vil days; who trusts in
   God's un - chang-ing love builds on the Rock that naught can move.

2. What can these anx - ious cares a - vail thee, these nev - er -
   ceas - ing moans and sighs? What can it help, if thou be-
   wail thee o'er each dark mo - ment as it flies? Our cross and
   tri - als do but press the heav - ier for our bit - ter - ness.

3. On - ly be still, and wait His lei - sure in cheer - ful
   hope, with heart con - tent to take what-e'er thy Fa - ther's
   pleas - ure and all - dis - cern - ing love have sent; nor doubt our
   in - most wants are known to Him who chose us for His own.

4. All are a - like be - fore the High - est; 'tis eas - y
   to our God, we know, to raise thee up, though low thou
   li - est, to make the rich man poor and low; who set - teth
   still by Him are wrought who set - teth up and brings to naught.

5. Sing, pray, and keep His ways un - swerv - ing; in all thy
   la - bor faith - ful be, and trust His word; though un - de-
   serv - ing, thou yet shalt find it true for thee: God nev - er
   will for - sake in need the soul that trusts in Him in - deed.

411 What God Ordains Is Always Good

Samuel Rodigast, 1675
trans. *The Lutheran Hymnal*, 1941

WAS GOTT TUT
87 87 44 77

Severus Gastorius, 1681

1. What God or-dains is al-ways good; His will is just and ho - ly.
2. What God or-dains is al-ways good: He nev-er will de-ceive me.
3. What God or-dains is al-ways good; His lov-ing thought at-tends me;
4. What God or-dains is al-ways good; He is my Friend and Fa - ther.
5. What God or-dains is al-ways good: tho' I the cup am drink - ing
6. What God or-dains is al-ways good: this truth re-mains un-shak - en.

As He di - rects my life for me, I fol-low meek and low - ly.
He leads me in His right-eous way, and nev-er will He leave me.
no poi - son can be in the cup that my Phy - si - cian sends me.
He suf-fers naught to do me harm tho' man - y storms may gath - er.
which sav-ors now of bit - ter-ness, I take it with-out shrink - ing.
Tho' sor-row, need, or death be mine, I shall not be for - sak - en.

My God in - deed in eve - ry need knows well how He will
I take, con - tent, what He has sent; His hand that sends me
My God is true; each morn - ing new I trust His grace un -
Now I may know both joy and woe; some day I shall see
For af - ter grief God gives re - lief, my heart with com - fort
I fear no harm, for with His arm He shall em - brace and

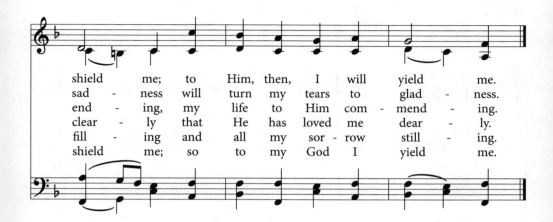

shield	me;	to	Him,	then,	I	will	yield	me.
sad -	ness	will	turn	my	tears	to	glad -	ness.
end -	ing,	my	life	to	Him	com -	mend -	ing.
clear -	ly	that	He	has	loved	me	dear -	ly.
fill -	ing	and	all	my	sor -	row	still -	ing.
shield	me;	so	to	my	God	I	yield	me.

God Moves in a Mysterious Way **412**

William Cowper, 1774 **DUNDEE** *Scottish Psalter*, 1615
CM

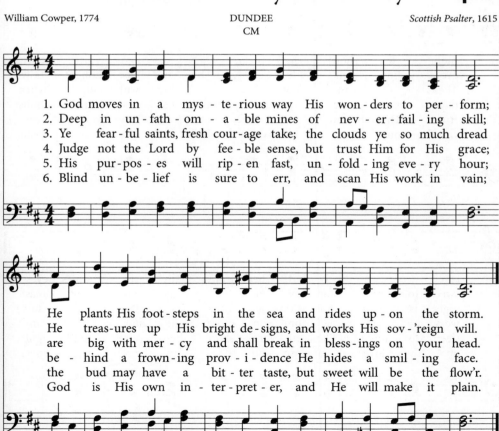

1. God moves in a mys - te - rious way His won - ders to per - form;
2. Deep in un - fath - om - a - ble mines of nev - er - fail - ing skill;
3. Ye fear - ful saints, fresh cour - age take; the clouds ye so much dread
4. Judge not the Lord by fee - ble sense, but trust Him for His grace;
5. His pur - pos - es will rip - en fast, un - fold - ing eve - ry hour;
6. Blind un - be - lief is sure to err, and scan His work in vain;

He plants His foot - steps in the sea and rides up - on the storm.
He treas - ures up His bright de - signs, and works His sov - 'reign will.
are big with mer - cy and shall break in bless - ings on your head.
be - hind a frown - ing prov - i - dence He hides a smil - ing face.
the bud may have a bit - ter taste, but sweet will be the flow'r.
God is His own in - ter - pret - er, and He will make it plain.

413   Sun of My Soul, Thou Savior Dear

John Keble, 1820   HURSLEY   *Katholisches Gesangbuch,*
                                 LM   Vienna, ca. 1774

1. Sun of my soul, Thou Savior dear, it is not
2. When the soft dews of kindly sleep my weary
3. Abide with me from morn till eve, for without
4. If some poor wand'ring child of Thine has spurned to-
5. Watch by the sick; enrich the poor with blessings
6. Come near and bless us when we wake, ere through the

night if Thou be near; O may no earth-born
eyelids gently steep, be my last thought how
Thee I cannot live; abide with me when
day the voice divine, now, Lord, the gracious
from Thy boundless store; be every mourner's
world our way we take, till in the ocean

cloud arise to hide Thee from Thy servant's eyes.
sweet to rest for ever on my Savior's breast.
night is nigh, for without Thee I dare not die.
work begin; let him no more lie down in sin.
sleep tonight like infant's slumbers, pure and light.
of Thy love we lose ourselves in heav'n above.

O Thou, in Whose Presence

414

Joseph Swain, 1791   DAVIS   Freeman Lewis, 1813
           11 8 11 8

1. O Thou, in whose pres - ence my soul takes de - light, on
2. Where dost Thou, dear Shep - herd, re - sort with Thy sheep, to
3. O why should I wan - der an al - ien from Thee, or
4. He looks, and ten thou - sand of an - gels re - joice, and
5. Dear Shep - herd! I hear, and will fol - low Thy call; I

whom in af - flic - tion I call; my com - fort by day, and my
feed them in pas - tures of love? Say, why in the val - ley of
cry in the de - sert for bread? Thy foes will re - joice, when my
myr - i - ads wait for His word; He speaks and e - ter - ni - ty,
know the sweet sound of Thy voice; re - store and de - fend me, for

song in the night, my hope, my sal - va - tion, my all.
death should I weep, or a - lone in this wil - der - ness rove?
sor - rows they see, and smile at the tears I have shed.
filled with His voice, re - ech - oes the praise of the Lord.
Thou art my All, and in Thee I will ev - er re - joice.

415 Abide with Me

Henry Lyte, 1847   EVENTIDE   William Henry Monk, 1861
10 10 10 10

1. A - bide with me: fast falls the e - ven - tide;
2. Swift to its close ebbs out life's lit - tle day;
3. I need Thy pres - ence eve - ry pass - ing hour;
4. I fear no foe, with Thee at hand to bless;
5. Hold Thou Thy cross be - fore my clos - ing eyes;

the dark - ness deep - ens; Lord, with me a - bide.
earth's joys grow dim; its glo - ries pass a - way.
what but Thy grace can foil the tempt - er's pow'r?
ills have no weight and tears no bit - ter - ness.
shine through the gloom and point me to the skies.

When oth - er help - ers fail and com - forts flee,
Change and de - cay in all a - round I see.
Who like Thy - self my guide and stay can be?
Where is death's sting? Where, grave, thy vic - to - ry?
Heav'n's morn - ing breaks, and earth's vain shad - ows flee.

Help of the help - less, O a - bide with me.
O Thou who chang - est not, a - bide with me.
Through cloud and sun - shine, O a - bide with me.
I tri - umph still if Thou a - bide with me.
In life, in death, O Lord, a - bide with me.

Glorious Things of Thee Are Spoken   **416**

John Newton, 1779   AUSTRIAN HYMN   Franz Joseph Haydn, 1797
                      87 87 D

1. Glo - rious things of thee are spo - ken, Zi - on, cit - y of our God.
2. See, the streams of liv - ing wa - ters, spring-ing from e - ter - nal love,
3. 'Round each hab - i - ta - tion hov-'ring, see the cloud and fire ap - pear
4. Sav - ior, if of Zi - on's cit - y I through grace a mem-ber am,

He whose word can - not be bro - ken formed thee for His own a - bode.
well sup - ply thy sons and daugh-ters and all fear of want re - move.
for a glo - ry and a cov - 'ring, show - ing that the Lord is near.
let the world de - ride or pit - y, I will glo - ry in Thy name.

On the Rock of A - ges found - ed, what can shake thy sure re - pose?
Who can faint while such a riv - er ev - er flows their thirst to as-suage?
Thus de - riv - ing from their ban - ner light by night and shade by day,
Fad - ing is the world-ling's pleas - ure, all his boast - ed pomp and show;

With sal - va-tion's walls sur-round-ed, thou may'st smile at all thy foes.
Grace, which like the Lord, the Giv - er, nev - er fails from age to age.
safe they feed up - on the man - na which He gives them on their way.
sol - id joys and last-ing treas-ures none but Zi - on's chil - dren know.

417   Jesus, Priceless Treasure

Johann Franck, 1653   JESU, MEINE FREUDE   Johann Crüger, 1653
trans. Catherine Winkworth, 1869, alt.   66 5 66 5 78 6   harm. Johann Sebastian Bach, 1723

1. Je - sus, price-less Treas - ure, source of pur - est pleas - ure, tru - est
2. In Thine arms I rest me, foes who would op - press me can - not
3. Sa - tan, I de - fy thee; death, I need not fly thee; fear, I
4. Wealth, I will not heed thee; where-fore should I need thee? Je - sus
5. Fare - well, thou who choos - est earth, and heav'n re - fus - est, thou wilt
6. Hence, all thoughts of sad - ness, for the Lord of glad - ness, Je - sus,

Friend to me; Long my heart hath pant - ed till it well nigh
reach me here; though the earth be shak - ing, eve - ry heart be
bid thee cease! Rage, O world, thy nois - es can - not drown our
is my joy; hon - ors, ye may glis - ten, but I will not
tempt in vain; hence, ye sins, nor blind me, get ye far be -
en - ters in; those who love the Fa - ther, tho' the storms may

faint - ed, thirst - ing af - ter Thee. Thine I am, O spot-less Lamb,
quak - ing, Je - sus calms my fear; sin and hell in con - flict fell
voic - es sing - ing still of peace; for God's pow'r guards eve - ry hour;
lis - ten, ye the soul de - stroy; want or loss or shame or cross
hind me, come not forth a - gain: past your hour, O pomp and pow'r;
gath - er, still have peace with - in; yea, what - e'er I here must bear,

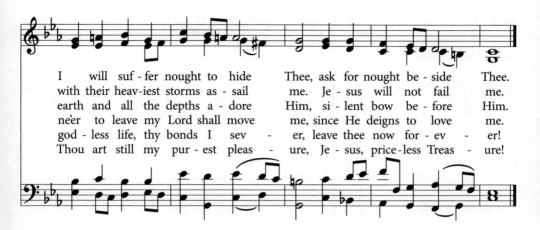

I will suf - fer nought to hide Thee, ask for nought be - side Thee.
with their heav-iest storms as - sail me. Je - sus will not fail me.
earth and all the depths a - dore Him, si - lent bow be - fore Him.
ne'er to leave my Lord shall move me, since He deigns to love me.
god - less life, thy bonds I sev - er, leave thee now for - ev - er!
Thou art still my pur - est pleas - ure, Je - sus, price-less Treas - ure!

We Walk by Faith and Not by Sight 418

Henry Alford, 1844

ST. BOTOLPH
CM

Gordon Slater, 1929

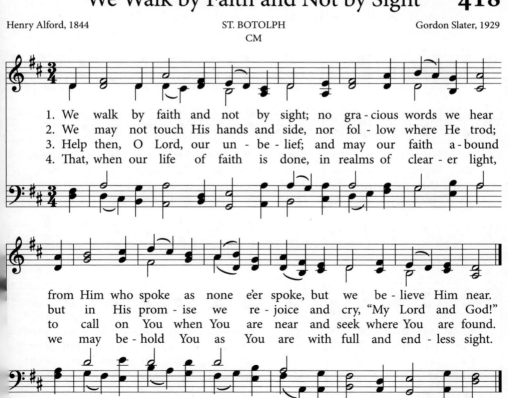

1. We walk by faith and not by sight; no gra - cious words we hear
2. We may not touch His hands and side, nor fol - low where He trod;
3. Help then, O Lord, our un - be - lief; and may our faith a - bound
4. That, when our life of faith is done, in realms of clear - er light,

from Him who spoke as none e'er spoke, but we be - lieve Him near.
but in His prom - ise we re - joice and cry, "My Lord and God!"
to call on You when You are near and seek where You are found.
we may be - hold You as You are with full and end - less sight.

419 Jerusalem the Golden

Bernard of Cluny, 12th cent.
trans. John Mason Neale, 1851

EWING
76 76 D

Alexander Ewing, 1853

1. Je - ru - sal - em the gold - en, with milk and hon - ey blest,
2. They stand, those halls of Zi - on, all ju - bi - lant with song,
3. There is the throne of Da - vid, and there, from care re - leased,
4. O sweet and bless - ed coun - try, the home of God's e - lect!

be - neath your con - tem - pla - tion sink heart and mind op - pressed;
and bright with man - y an an - gel, and all the mar - tyr throng;
the shout of those who tri - umph, the song of those who feast;
O sweet and bless - ed coun - try, that ea - ger hearts ex - pect!

I know not, O I know not what joys a - wait me there,
the Prince is ev - er in them; the day - light is se - rene;
and they, who with their Lead - er have con - quered in the fight,
In mer - cy, Je - sus, bring us to that dear land of rest,

what ra - dian - cy of glo - ry, what bliss be - yond com - pare!
the pas - tures of the bless - ed are decked in glo - rious sheen.
for - ev - er and for - ev - er are clad in robes of white.
who are, with God the Fa - ther, and Spir - it, ev - er blessed.

Jerusalem, My Happy Home

420

F. B. P., 16th cent.
based on Augustine of Hippo, 5th cent.

LAND OF REST
CM

Traditional American melody
arr. Annabel M. Buchanan, 1938

1. Je - ru - sa - lem, my hap - py home, when shall I come to thee? When will my sor - rows have an end? Thy joys, when shall I see?
2. O hap - py har - bor of the saints, O sweet and pleas - ant soil! In thee no sor - row may be found, no grief, no care, no toil.
3. Thy saints are crowned with glo - ry great; they see God face to face; they tri - umph still, they still re - joice; most hap - py is their case.
4. Je - ru - sa - lem, Je - ru - sa - lem, God grant that I may see thine end - less joy, and of the same par - tak - er ev - er be!

421 The Sands of Time Are Sinking

Anne R. Cousin, 1857
from Samuel Rutherford, 1600–1661

RUTHERFORD
76 76 76 75

Chrétien Urhan, 1834

1. The sands of time are sink - ing; the dawn of heav - en breaks;
2. The King there in His beau - ty with - out a veil is seen;
3. O Christ, He is the foun - tain, the deep, sweet well of love!
4. The bride eyes not her gar - ment, but her dear bride-groom's face;

the sum - mer morn I've sighed for, the fair sweet morn a - wakes;
it were a well - spent jour - ney, though tri - als lay be - tween:
The streams on earth I've tast - ed more deep I'll drink a - bove:
I will not gaze at glo - ry, but on my King of grace;

dark, dark has been the mid - night, but day - spring is at hand,
the Lamb with His fair ar - my on Zi - on's moun - tain stands,
there to an o - cean full - ness His mer - cy will ex - pand,
not at the crown He giv - eth, but on His pierc - éd hands:

and glo - ry, glo - ry dwell - eth in Em - man - uel's land.
and glo - ry, glo - ry dwell - eth in Em - man - uel's land.
and glo - ry, glo - ry dwell - eth in Em - man - uel's land.
the Lamb is all the glo - ry of Em - man - uel's land.

Oh, What Their Joy and Glory Must Be 422

Peter Abelard, 12th cent.
trans. John Mason Neale, 1854

O QUANTA QUALIA
10 10 10 10

Paris Antiphoner, 1681

1. Oh, what their joy and their glo-ry must be,
2. In new Je-ru-sa-lem joy shall be found,
3. We, where no trou-bles dis-trac-tion can bring,
4. Now let us wor-ship our Lord and our King,

those end-less Sab-baths the bless-ed ones see!
bless-ings of peace shall for-ev-er a-bound;
safe-ly the an-thems of Zi-on shall sing;
joy-ful-ly rais-ing our voic-es to sing:

Crowns for the val-iant, to wea-ry ones rest;
wish and ful-fill-ment are not sev-ered there,
while for Your grace, Lord, their voic-es of praise
Praise to the Fa-ther, and praise to the Son,

God shall be all, and in all, ev-er blest.
nor the things prayed for come short of the pray'r.
Your bless-ed peo-ple shall ev-er-more raise.
praise to the Spir-it, to God, Three in One.

423 God, That Madest Earth and Heaven

Reginald Heber, 1820   AR HYD Y NOS   Welsh melody, *Musical and Poetical*
                     84 84 888 4   *Relicks of the Welsh Bards, 1784*

1. God, that mad-est earth and heav-en, dark-ness and light;
2. And, when morn a-gain shall call us, to run life's way,
3. Guard us wak-ing, guard us sleep-ing, and when we die,

who the day for toil hast giv-en, for rest, the night;
may we still what-e'er be-fall us, Thy will o-bey.
may we in Thy might-y keep-ing all peace-ful lie:

may Thine an-gel guards de-fend us, slum-ber sweet Thy mer-cy
From the pow'r of e-vil hide us; in the nar-row path-way
when the last dread call shall wake us, do not Thou our God for-

send us, ho-ly dreams and hopes at-tend us, this live-long night.
guide us, nor Thy smile be e'er de-nied us, the live-long day.
sake us, but to reign in glo-ry take us with Thee on high.

In God, My Faithful God

424

Sigismund Weingärtner, 1607
trans. Catherine Winkworth, 1863, alt.

AUF MEINEN LIEBEN GOTT
66 77 77

Deutsche Lieder, Nürnberg, 1574

1. In God, my faith-ful God, I trust when dark my road;
2. My sins as-sail me sore, but I de-spair no more.
3. If death my por-tion be, then death is gain to me
4. O Je-sus Christ, my Lord, so meek in deed and word,
5. "So be it," then I say with all my heart each day.

though man-y woes o'er-take me, yet He will not for-sake me.
I build on Christ, who loves me; from this Rock noth-ing moves me.
and Christ my Life for-ev-er, from whom death can-not sev-er.
Thou once didst die to save us be-cause Thy love would have us
We, too, dear Lord, a-dore Thee, we sing with joy be-fore Thee.

His love it is doth send them and, when 'tis best, will end them.
To Him I all sur-ren-der, to Him, my soul's De-fend-er.
Come when it may, He'll shield me, to Him I whol-ly yield me.
be heirs of heav'n-ly glad-ness when ends this life of sad-ness.
Guide us while here we wan-der un-til we praise Thee yon-der.

425 Dear Refuge of My Weary Soul

Anne Steele, 1760   DEAR REFUGE   Matt Merker © 2014

1. Dear Ref - uge of my wea - ry soul, on Thee, when sor - rows rise,
2. But oh! When gloom-y doubts pre-vail, I fear to call Thee mine;
3. Hast Thou not bid me seek Thy face? And shall I seek in vain?
4. Thy mer - cy seat is o - pen still, here let my soul re - treat;

on Thee, when waves of trou - ble roll, my faint-ing hope re - lies.
the springs of com - fort seem to fail, and all my hopes de - cline.
And can the ear of sov-'reign grace be deaf when I com-plain?
with hum - ble hope at - tend Thy will, and wait be - neath Thy feet.

To Thee I tell each ris - ing grief, for Thou a - lone canst heal;
Yet gra-cious God, where shall I flee? Thou art my on - ly trust;
No, still the ear of sov-'reign grace at - tends the mourn - er's prayer;
Dear Ref - uge of my wea - ry soul, on Thee, when sor - rows rise,

Thy word can bring a sweet re - lief for eve - ry pain I feel.
and still my soul would cleave to Thee, though pros-trate in the dust.
O may I ev - er find a place to breathe my sor - rows there.
on Thee, when waves of trou - ble roll, my faint - ing hope re - lies.

Thou Hidden Source of Calm Repose **426**

Charles Wesley, 1749 — STELLA — 88 88 88 — Henri Friedrich Hemy, 1851

1. Thou hid-den source of calm re-pose, Thou all-suf-fi-cient love di-vine, my help and ref-uge from my foes, se-cure I am, if Thou art mine; and lo! from sin and grief and shame I hide me, Je-sus in Thy Name.

2. Thy might-y name sal-va-tion is, and keeps my hap-py soul a-bove; com-fort it brings, and pow'r and peace, and joy and ev-er-last-ing love; to me, with Thy dear name, are giv'n par-don and ho-li-ness and heav'n.

3. Je-sus, my all in all Thou art; my rest in toil, my ease in pain, the med-icine of my bro-ken heart, in war my peace, in loss my gain, my smile be-neath the ty-rant's frown, in shame my glo-ry and my crown.

4. In want my plen-ti-ful sup-ply, in weak-ness my al-might-y pow'r, in bonds my per-fect lib-er-ty, my light in Sa-tan's dark-est hour, my help and stay when-e'er I call, my life in death, my heav'n, my all.

427 I Asked the Lord That I Might Grow

John Newton, 1791   O WALY WALY   *Folk Songs from Somerset*, 1906

LM   arr. Dan Kreider © 2018

1. I asked the Lord that I might grow in faith and love and eve-ry grace; might more of His sal-va-tion know, and seek more ear-nest-ly His face.

2. 'Twas He who taught me thus to pray, and He, I trust, has an-swered prayer, but it has been in such a way as al-most drove me to de-spair.

3. I hoped that in some fa-vored hour at once He's an-swer my re-quest, and by His love's con-strain-ing pow'r sub-due my sins and give me rest.

4. In-stead of this He made me feel the hid-den e-vils of my heart, and let the an-gry pow'rs of hell as-sault my soul in eve-ry part.

5. Yea more, with His own hand He seemed in-tent to ag-gra-vate me woe, crossed all the fair de-signs I schemed, hum-bled my heart, and laid me low.

6. "Lord, why is this?" I trem-bling cried, "Wilt Thou pur-sue Thy worm to death?" "Tis in this way," the Lord re-plied, "I an-swer prayer for grace and faith.

7. "These in-ward tri-als I em-ploy from self and pride to set thee free, and break thy schemes of earth-ly joy that thou may'st find Thy all in Me."

Nearer, Still Nearer

428

Lelia N. Morris, 1862–1929

MORRIS
9 10 9 10 with repeat

Lelia N. Morris, 1862–1929

1. Near - er, still near - er— close to Thy heart, draw me, my
2. Near - er, still near - er— noth - ing I bring, naught as an
3. Near - er, still near - er— Lord, to be Thine, sin with its
4. Near - er, still near - er— while life shall last, till safe in

Sav - ior, so pre - cious Thou art; fold me, O fold me
of - f'ring to Je - sus my King— on - ly my sin - ful,
fol - lies I glad - ly re - sign— all of its pleas - ures,
glo - ry my an - chor is cast; through end - less a - ges,

close to Thy breast; shel - ter me safe in that Ha - ven of
now con - trite heart; grant me the cleans - ing Thy blood doth im -
pomp and its pride; give me but Je - sus, my Lord cru - ci -
ev - er to be near - er, my Sav - ior, still near - er to

Rest, shel - ter me safe in that Ha - ven of Rest.
part, grant me the cleans - ing Thy blood doth im - part.
fied, give me but Je - sus, my Lord cru - ci - fied.
Thee, near - er, my Sav - ior, still near - er to Thee.

429 The Son of God Goes Forth to War

Reginald Heber, 1827 — GREYOAKS CMD — Gregory D. Wilbur © 1994

1. The Son of God goes forth to war, a king - ly crown to gain; His blood - red ban - ner streams a - far! Who fol - lows in His train? Who best can drink His cup of woe, tri - um - phant o - ver pain, who pa - tient

2. The mar - tyr first, whose ea - gle eye could pierce be - yond the grave; who saw his Mas - ter in the sky and called on Him to save. Like Him, with par - don on His tongue, in midst of mor - tal pain, he prayed for

3. A glo - rious band, the cho - sen few on whom the Spir - it came, twelve val - iant saints, their hope they knew, and mocked the cross and flame. They met the ty - rant's bran - dished steel, the li - on's gor - y mane; they bowed their

4. A no - ble ar - my, men and boys, the ma - tron and the maid, a - round the Sav - ior's throne re - joice in robes of light ar - rayed. They climbed the steep as - cent of heav'n, through per - il, toil and pain; O God, to

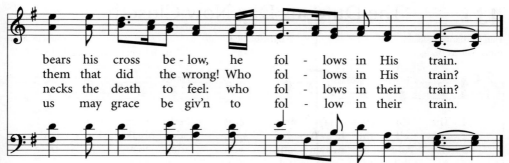

bears his cross be-low, he fol - lows in His train.
them that did the wrong! Who fol - lows in His train?
necks the death to feel: who fol - lows in their train?
us may grace be giv'n to fol - low in their train.

O Gladsome Light

430

Greek, *Phos Hilaron,* 3rd cent.
trans. Robert Bridges, 1899

NUNC DIMITTIS
66 76 67

Louis Bourgeois, 1551
arr. Claude Goudimel, 1565

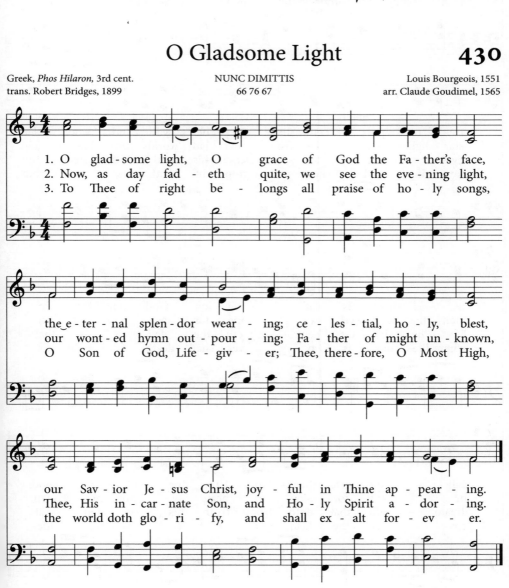

1. O glad - some light, O grace of God the Fa - ther's face,
2. Now, as day fad - eth quite, we see the eve - ning light,
3. To Thee of right be - longs all praise of ho - ly songs,

the e - ter - nal splen - dor wear - ing; ce - les - tial, ho - ly, blest,
our wont - ed hymn out - pour - ing; Fa - ther of might un - known,
O Son of God, Life - giv - er; Thee, there - fore, O Most High,

our Sav - ior Je - sus Christ, joy - ful in Thine ap - pear - ing.
Thee, His in - car - nate Son, and Ho - ly Spirit a - dor - ing.
the world doth glo - ri - fy, and shall ex - alt for - ev - er.

431 The Duteous Day Now Closeth

Paul Gerhardt, 1648
trans. Robert Bridges

INNSBRUCK
77 67 78

German melody
arr. Johann Sebastian Bach, 1685–1750

1. The du-teous day now clos-eth; each flow'r and tree re-pos-eth; shade creeps o'er wild and wood; let us, as night is fall-ing, on God our Mak-er call-ing, give thanks to Him, the Giv-er good.

2. Now all the heav'n-ly splen-dor breaks forth in star-light ten-der from myr-iad worlds un-known; and man, the mar-vel see-ing, for-gets his self-ish be-ing for joy of beau-ty not his own.

3. His care he drown-eth yon-der, lost in th' a-byss of won-der; to heav'n his soul doth steal; this life he dis-est-eem-eth, the day it is that dream-eth, that doth from truth his vi-sion seal.

4. A-while his mor-tal blind-ness may miss God's lov-ing-kind-ness, and grope in faith-less strife; but when life's day is o-ver shall death's fair night dis-cov-er the fields of ev-er-last-ing life.

May the Grace of Christ Our Savior 432

John Newton, 1799   BEACH SPRING   Traditional American melody
87 87 D   *The Sacred Harp*, 1844

May the grace of Christ our Sav - ior and the Fa - ther's bound-less love,

with the Ho - ly Spir - it's fa - vor, rest up - on us from a - bove.

Thus may we a - bide in un - ion with each oth - er and the Lord,

and pos - sess in sweet com - mun - ion joys which earth can - not af - ford.

TABLE OF COPYRIGHT HOLDERS

Church Publishing, Inc.
https://www.churchpublishing.org/
381

Crown and Covenant Publications
7408 Penn Avenue
Pittsburgh, PA 15208-2531
info@crownandcovenant.com
Taken from *The Book of Psalms for Worship* and *The Book of Psalms for Singing*.
3, 5, 6, 13, 14, 21, 22, 26, 40, 44, 46A, 47, 56, 64, 66B,
67B, 76, 84, 119I, 138, 144, 148A

Hope Publishing Company
https://www.hopepublishing.com/
65, 276

Matt Merker Music (BMI). Administrated by
Integrated Rights, www.integratedmusicrights.com.
425

Oxford University Press
https://global.oup.com/
199

Singspiration Music (ASCAP), admin. by Brentwood-
Benson Music Publishing, Inc.
389

Sovereign Grace Worship (ASCAP). Administrated by
Integrated Rights, www.integratedmusicrights.com.
329, 425

Thankyou Music (PRS), adm. worldwide at
CapitolCMGPublishing.com excluding Europe which
is adm. by Integritymusic.com.
340, 341, 343, 365

Timothy and Julie Tennent
psalms.seedbed.com
7, 10, 15, 19B, 25, 28, 34, 35A, 42B, 43, 59, 74, 78, 124,
135, 141, 143, 148B

Trinity Psalter Hymnal Joint Venture of the
Committee on Christian Education of the Orthodox
Presbyterian Church and the Board of Directors of the
United Reformed Churches in North America
607 N. Easton Rd. Building E
Willow Grove, PA 19090-2539
copyrights@trinitypsalterhymnal.org
4, 63B, 77, 86B, 93, 223

INDEX OF AUTHORS, COMPOSERS, AND SOURCES

PSALM CLASSIFICATIONS

The following is a classification of each psalm based on its function in what we might call a "gospel-shaped liturgy," that is, how individual psalms function in a service that helps us to reenact our covenant relationship with God through Christ.

For more, see Scott Aniol, *Musing on God's Music: Forming Hearts of Praise with the Psalms* (G3 Press, 2023).

Revelation
8, 24, 29, 30, 33, 45, 47, 48, 50, 65, 66, 67, 68, 76, 81, 84, 87, 95, 96, 98, 100, 108, 114, 122, 134, 145

Adoration
92, 93, 97, 99, 103, 104, 105, 106, 111, 112, 113, 115, 116, 117, 135, 146, 147, 148, 149, 150

Confession & Propitiation
6, 14, 15, 25, 32, 38, 39, 40, 41, 51, 102, 130, 143

Thanksgiving
9, 16, 18, 20, 21, 34, 75, 107, 118, 124, 136, 138, 144

Instruction
1, 2, 19, 37, 49, 73, 78, 119, 125, 127, 128, 133

Dedication
23, 46, 62, 63, 91, 101, 110, 131

Supplication
3, 4, 5, 7, 10, 11, 12, 13, 17, 22, 26, 27, 28, 31, 35, 36, 42, 43, 44, 52, 53, 54, 55, 56, 57, 58, 59, 60, 61, 64, 69, 70, 71, 72, 74, 77, 79, 80, 82, 83, 85, 86, 88, 89, 90, 94, 109, 120, 121, 123, 126, 129, 132, 137, 139, 140, 141, 142

METRICAL INDEX OF TUNES

ALPHABETICAL INDEX OF TUNES

ALPHABETICAL INDEX OF TITLES AND FIRST LINES